D0555521

BEST LOVED
AMERICAN FOLK SONGS

Books by JOHN A. LOMAX

Songs of the Cow Camp and Cattle Trail

Adventures of a Ballad Hunter

Books by JOHN A. and ALAN LOMAX

Cowboy Songs

Our Singing Country

Negro Songs as Sung by Lead Belly

BEST LOVED AMERICAN FOLK SONGS

[FOLK SONG: U. S. A.]

COLLECTED, ADAPTED AND ARRANGED BY

John A. Lomax & Alan Lomax

MUSIC ARRANGEMENTS BY

Charles Seeger & Ruth Crawford Seeger

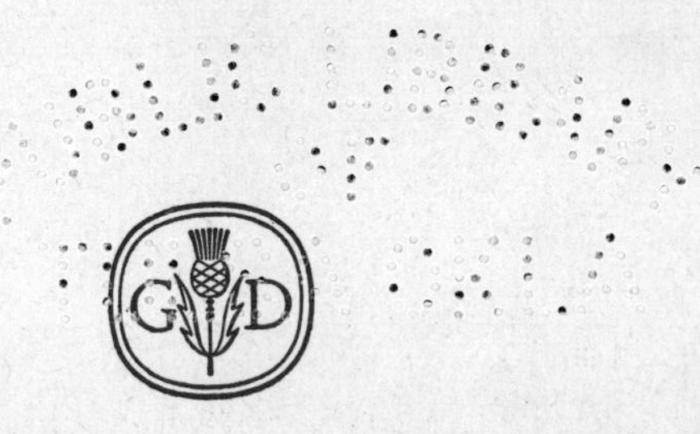

Publishers GROSSET & DUNLAP *New York*

Fourth Edition

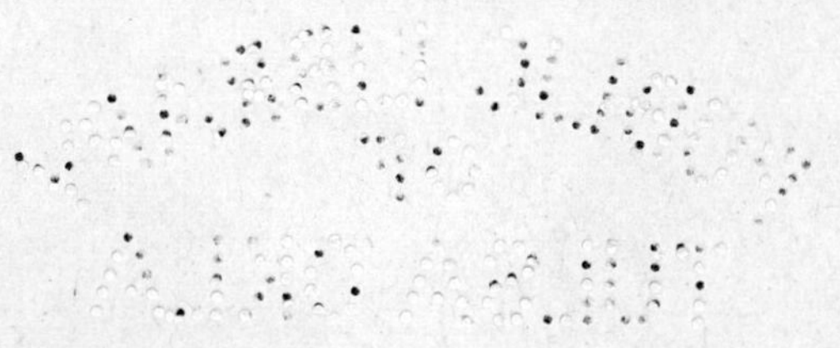

PRINTED IN THE UNITED STATES OF AMERICA

To ballad-makers, long-dead and nameless; to the jokey boys whose smiles are dust; to the singers of the lumber-woods, the cattle trail, the chain gang, the kitchen; to fiddlers in buckskin; to banjo-pickers; to guitar-frammers; to lonesome harmonica blowers; and to the horny-handed, hospitable, generous, honest, and inspired folk-artists who carved these songs out of the rock of their lives, we dedicate this, their own book.

Preface

SO MANY are the folk songs, so various are the themes, tunes, types, and styles of folk music found in the United States that one may well say . . .

These forty-eight states came singing out the wilderness
Many long years ago. . . .

A people made a three-thousand-mile march between the eastern and western oceans. Songs traveled with them; songs were born along the way. Every hamlet produced its crop of local ballads of murders, disasters, and scandals. Every occupation had its specialized poesy. Every fiddler put his own twists on the tunes he learned from his pappy. Every child had its own skipping jingle, a little different from the next child. . . . Songs flowered up out of the lives of the people as liberally as wildflowers on the West Texas plains in April, and most of them vanished as quickly, sowing the land with seed for the next springtime crop of songs. Those songs that lived to walk the long, lonesome road with the people have been largely written down by folklorists during the past fifty years. The "best" of these, the "most representative"—our favorites after years of collecting and singing—we have chosen for *Folk Song: U.S.A.* For beauty, variety, strength, and singability these 111 songs will, we believe, stand alongside any songs from any nation or level of culture.

You may not like them all at first. Folk song, as all art of serious intent, improves on acquaintance. Sing your way through this book. It was designed to be crooned and lilted, moaned and shouted through, not contemplated. Join your sin-ridden forefather as he bellows and thrashes all over the camp-meeting ground. Stomp and yell the lines of the hell-for-leather breakdown tunes. Raise up your head and howl with the cowboy over the lonesomeness and wonder of the Big West. Rock your own child to sleep with a tune that has lulled babies in log cabins and shanties. Only then will you feel how close these songs lie to your own and your country's marrow. Only then will you feel the surging life and the violent passions that lie hidden at times beneath the surface of these poker-faced songs. Only then will you feel the invigorating strength of this powerful folk art, the quality that sets it apart from popular song with its surface emotion and its cloying sweetness.

This is a sampling of America's folk songs—homemade hand-me-downs in words and music, songs accepted by whole communities, songs voted good by generations of singers and passed on by word of mouth to succeeding generations, a tradition quite distinct from popular song (made to sell and sell quickly) and cultivated art (made, so much of it, to conform to prestige patterns). If these songs had composers at first, they have been largely forgotten, and rightly so, since folk composers are adapters of old material rather than creators of original set pieces. The folk ballad-maker prefers to change an old song slightly to fit a new situation, making use of a tried tune and a well-loved plot formula and thus assuring himself of the favor of his audience. Every singer may then make his own emendations, to be accepted and passed on or rejected and forgotten by *his* audiences. So the *mass* of a people participate in folk song's growth, forever reweaving old materials to create new versions, much as an old lady creates a new quilt out of an old by adding, year by year, new scraps and patches. So folk song grows in small steps, with every slight change tested for audience reaction, thereby achieving a permanence in man's affection matched only by the greatest art. This art lives upon the lips of the multitude and is transmitted by the grapevine, surviving sometimes for centuries because it reflects so well the deepest emotional convictions of the common man. This is a truly democratic art, painting a portrait of the people, unmatched for honesty and validity in any other record.

Examine the American record. This is not calendar art, not escape literature (although there is much fantasy), or yet propaganda put out by some boost-America group advertising ours as the best of all possible lands and our people as generous and gay, well fed and genteel. Folk song, like any serious art, deals with realities—with poor boys a long way from home, with workers killed on the job, with bloody-handed murderers, with children dancing and fighting in the back yards, and with the dreams of all of these folk. There are deep shadows on this landscape, the shadows of poverty and graceless toil. There are bitter hard lines in these faces, lines of violence and cruelty. . . . What lies in the minds of the gentle grandmothers we have heard, hour upon hour, chanting as their "favorite love songs" the old ballads in which love so often leads to bloodshed? What of the continual brooding over death in the spirituals?

O lovely appearance of death,
No sight upon earth is so fair,
Not all the gay pageants that breathe
Can with a dead body compare. . . .

Yet, like Lincoln's, the somber face of the people suddenly splits with a sunburst of laughter . . .

Old Dan Tucker was a fine old man,
Washed his face in a frying pan.
Combed his head with a wagon wheel
And died with a toothache in his heel . . .

This awkward and melancholic American could kick up his heels and hooraw the world. . . .

What'll we do with the baby-o,
Take him to his mammy-o,
Wrap him up in a tablecloth,
Throw him up in the old hay loft . . .

The common man always has held the center of the stage in our balladry. From Paul Bunyan to Jesse James, the folklore heroes are brave, free-hearted, and handy on the job. A good hand was welcome and respected at the campfire, no matter what his race or religion, while a gent with "high-toned" airs was headed for certain trouble. Long before Whitman, American folk singers rhapsodized the common man in all his dazzling variety, putting him first in all the ballads, describing him at work and play, and making his passions and problems their main concern. This is the big theme of American folk song, running through all the songs—the theme stated by Burns' ". . . A man's a man for a' that." and even more powerfully in the Negro ballad, "John Henry."

A man ain't nothin' but a man. . . .

The amazing popularity of "John Henry," "Frankie," and other Negro ballads among white singers, the tremendous enthusiasm of all Americans, no matter what their prejudices, for Negro folk music, and the profound influence of this music on American culture—all this denies the effect of Jim Crow at this level of human communication. From the beginning, Negroes and whites have swapped tunes, tales, dances, and religious ideas. And in the even more basic areas of speech and motor behavior this meeting of minds between the two groups is clearer still.

White Americans, perhaps at first attracted by the exotic rhythms and earthy poesy of Negro song, have been deeply stirred by the poignant sorrow, the biting irony, and the noble yearning for a better world implicit there. And with every passing year American music becomes more definitely an Anglo-African blend. In American folk song, indeed—*A man ain't nothin' but a man. . . .*

Certainly this is what the folklorist has to say to *his* audience. He goes where book-learning is not. He lives with the underprivileged. He brings back the proof in their songs and stories and dances that these folks are expressive and concerned about the beautiful and the good. In doing so, he continually denies the validity of caste lines and class barriers. Malinowski says of the anthropologist, "He also has the duty to speak as the native's advocate." Just so, the folklorist has the duty to speak as the advocate of the common man.

When my father collected and published the songs of the cowboy and the other pioneers of the great West, he became their advocate, just as a half century earlier Major Higginson had championed the Negro slave in publishing the spirituals and declaring them beautiful. In the final analysis, it is our identification with the common man that has carried my father and myself on our ballad hunt across this continent—into work camps and honky-tonks, into a thousand small houses, into the little churches, up back-country roads, and through the still horror of a score of penitentiaries. It is this enthusiasm that laid the basis for the Archive of American Folk Song in the Library of Congress, where we added the voice of the common man to the written record of America.

Our work and that of all other American folklorists now begins to bear fruit. When the people of this country, under the impact of the war against fascism, looked about them for songs which reflected their equalitarian and democratic political principles, there came a sudden rise in popularity of American folk music. Every passing day indicates that this quickening of interest in homemade songs is no temporary fad, but the advance ground swell of an important cultural movement.

This treasury is the first attempt to set up a canon for American folk song, defining this world of people's music in terms of examples, and placing the songs in their historical, social, and psychological backgrounds. Alongside the songs themselves, we have set down our impressions of various types of singers and song-making communities. This continuity, with its illustrative folk-tales and anecdotes will, we hope, serve to make the American folk singer more real and understandable to those who have not been privileged to know him. When you come to know him, you will be well prepared to meet his kinfolk in Russia, China, Spain, Ireland, or wherever oral song lives, for in song and folklore one encounters ancient bonds that link the races and the nations into the big family of humanity.

We have confined our selection to songs in the English tongue, because we felt the rich field of songs in other languages was not yet sufficiently explored for a fair picture to be presented. The field of children's games and songs requires a book of its own and these, too we left aside. Such British ballads as "Barbara Allen" were not included, since our object was to show what American singers had created, not what they had preserved. (See item 19, Appendix II, for an excellent and inexpensive collection of these popular songs.) The topical and progressive song-making of recent years, a newly emerging urban folk music, is well covered in a recent volume. (See item 123, Appendix II.)

For the rest, the songs included are, in our judgment, the best and most representative American folk songs, chosen on the basis of our personal experience. The selection will certainly be caviled at, for many fine songs have been passed over. In this volume we have created our own versions of the songs, combining all the best stanzas we could find, in some cases creating portmanteau melodies and, in every instance, singing the songs smooth of stylistic features difficult to reproduce in print. For serious singers we have provided a list of records (Appendix III). The best way to learn folk-song style is by example. The piano accompaniments of the Seegers, in our estimation the finest that have ever been done, should prove a help rather than a hindrance in singing.

For months the whole Lomax family—Bess and Butch Hawes, Shirley Mansell, John and Margaret Lomax, Elizabeth Lomax, Ruby Terrill Lomax—fought over the selection of songs. Peter Seeger lent his remarkable talent and good taste in transcribing many tunes. Ben Botkin made useful suggestions for background material. Hally Wood helped mightily in putting the book into presentable shape. Elizabeth Lomax made invaluable rewrite suggestions. Acknowledgments to fellow folklorists who generously allowed us to reprint material from their collections is given at length in Appendices I and II, where the student will find ample bibliographical aids for further study of American folk music.

We feel most deeply indebted, however, to the hundreds of Americans who took us in out of the cold and sang for us when he went visiting around the country. We found them "common" in the folk sense, that is, generous and hospitable. We knew that, in allowing a pair of strangers to record their ballads, these singers were giving us their dearest possessions; for to them the songs are not part of the public domain, but treasured family heirlooms, mementos of adventures in the big world or tales of dearly bought experience. Typical of the attitudes of the many singers we met along the road is this statement of a Virginia mountain ballad singer.

This old house where we lived had big wide planks for a floor. There wasn't any carpet and you could look down and see the chickens walking underneath the house, and in the wintertime the snow would blow up through the cracks. We had a fireplace, but there were so many of us kids and we had so many cousins to visit us, we used to wonder how we were all gonna get near it. That's why we all tried to learn songs just as perfect as we could, because when you was the one doin' the singin' you'd get to stand close to the fire and warm.

Father would usually suggest singin' hymns and all us children would join in. Then he'd pick up his banjo and play "Boats a-Whistlin' " or "Sourwood Mountain" or "John Henry." By the time I was four or five, I was trying to mock him. I'd grab hold of our old fire shovel and pick it for a banjo. When they'd ask me what I was playin', I'd tell 'em "Sour Colic". . . .

Then there was an old colored man used to come in of an evening with his fiddle. Seem like to me my hair would raise right up on my head when he'd be fiddlin', just settin' there as close to that fire as he could get. When it would begin to sort of scorch him, he wouldn't move, he'd just rare back in his chair and keep on fiddlin'.

Then my momma, a-singin' all those beautiful old love songs like "Barbara Allen" and "Fair Ellender" and "Careless Love," she taught me all the best songs I know—and how to sing. She had a knack of puttin' little twists and quavers into a note that would send cold chills runnin' through you. I can see her right now, settin' across the fire place from my dad and us children crowdin' in as close as we could get, with her head throwed back and her eyes closed, singin' like a mocking bird.

May these songs bring you closer to the fire that burns on the hearth of the people. May you keep on "fiddlin' " with these tunes until, when you sing them, you can "raise the hair right up on the heads" of your listeners.

—Alan Lomax

New York City

Musical Foreword

THE MUSIC EDITORS WANT TO MAKE CLEAR their belief that arrangement of folk song for piano (or, for that matter, for any instruments not usually employed by oral tradition) is of the nature of translation—translation from a predominantly unwritten, rural art to a predominantly written, urban art. In such translation the original material loses some characteristics and gains others. People react variously. The folk artist who is comparatively unacquainted with concert (fine-art) music may regard it as perversion. The composer of concert music may consider it beneath notice, or at best unnecessary and banal. The arrangements in this book are presented to neither of these extremes of taste, but to the average person who accepts piano arrangement of folk stuff without question as a normal procedure. To him, the Music Editors want to say a few words to square things with "the folk," on the one hand, and with their own artistic consciences, on the other.

To begin with, these arrangements are settings, not accompaniments, the one exception being "Po' Laz'us," which is given an approximation of a blues accompaniment because that is what the piano is actually used for in so much blues playing. The difference between a setting and an accompaniment lies in the fact that in the former the original melody is played by the instrument, whereas in the latter, the original melody is given to a voice or to another instrument. The problem of the piano setting, as contrasted with that of the piano accompaniment, is that it places in the piano two functions of the original folk production, one of which may not have been present in the sources known to the arrangers.

The Anglo-American folk song is perhaps more widely current without than with accompaniment. Occasional accompaniment by banjo, fiddle, or dulcimer may have been traditional for a century or so. The guitar, now probably the most used, is a comparatively recent favorite. All of these, however, traditionally play rhythmic-harmonic accompaniment, only occasionally approaching the character of a setting (i.e., playing the tune itself in addition to the accompaniment).

But not all songs are equally susceptible even to folk-instrumental setting or accompaniment. We have, therefore, adopted the policy of approximating traditional accompaniment where it might normally be used, but treating in a freer manner those melodies where no traditional type of accompaniment seems fitting.

Examples in this volume of the approximation of folk accompaniment are in the majority. One, "Rock about My Saro Jane," is a fairly close transcription of the actual banjo-playing heard on a record. The footnote to "Sourwood Mountain" describes how that setting may be made more closely to approximate the sound of the dulcimer. For the most part, however, the simple guitar bass-and-chord pattern has been used as a model. This is also easier for the pianist, and involves least distortion of folk practice.

Examples of departure from folk tradition can be found, among others, in the "Dink Song" and "Another Man Done Gone," for which no models are known. Another example is "Sit Down, Servant," where a setting in a conventional concert style has been made, partly because no folk model was available, and partly because, concert convention being what it is, this particular kind of license is almost of itself a tradition! Songs as much in the popular as in a folk idiom as for example, "Home on the Range," are given a conventional, community song-book setting.

In cases where choral arrangement is indicated, as in some hymns, spirituals, and work-songs, three- or four-voice writing has been employed, with the idea in mind that some readers would like to try choral performance. Settings such as "Take This Hammer," while not strictly part-writing, can be readily adapted to choral rendition, even though the original singers are said never to have sung in parts.

Some songs present problems for which no very satisfactory solution could be found within the frame of the present volume. An example is "Come All You Fair and Tender Ladies." This tune, one of the most widespread in Anglo-American tradition, is more susceptible than most to varied treatment. As an antidote to the one printed on page 58, perhaps the following may serve, if only to illustrate a type of treatment *not* considered appropriate for this book:

Come All You Fair and Tender Ladies

The Music Editors agree that "one can do anything one wants with a folk song," but we feel any change not in keeping with tradition must be musically worth changing. Chromatic upholstery, overrichness of harmonic texture, modulations, and, above all, "cuteness," are to be avoided, as well in the playing as in the arranging.

Perhaps one of the most extreme departures from folk idiom to be found in a book of this sort is the employment of a single written tune and setting for all stanzas of a song. Folk-singers customarily vary their tune, not only in separate renditions of a song but in the various stanzas of a single rendition of it. Thus the tune of stanza 1 may be varied in stanza 2, and so on. The instrumental rendition or accompaniment may also vary from stanza to stanza. This is not to say that the individual folk performer approximates the conventional "theme and variations" or development section of a sonata. But it is to say that the subtle variation given by a particular singer possesses an artistic quality lost in the printed single melody and arrangement.

Obviously, also, the single tune and setting does not represent the song, but only one particular singer's variant of a song. For over the vast areas of space and time in which a folk song has its life, development of the music materials by the succession of singers through whose experience it passes does indeed approximate the kind of treatment that a skilled composer gives the subject of a fugue or the thematic nucleus of a symphony. It is for this reason that folklorists say that a folk song does not exist in any one of its variants, but rather in the aggregate of its variants. One should, perhaps, never say he "knows" a folk song. At best one can know a variant or variants of it, and may have a concept of the versions or tune-types which may be inferred from the variants that are known.

One of the losses most to be deplored in the conventional setting of a folk song is that of the instrumental interlude which often fills the gaps between stanzas of the accompanied song, taking the melody, sometimes varying it, while the voice remains silent. Users of the present book are urged to try, if they feel like it, to approximate this practice.

Twin losses of the original value of the song are found in the smoothing out of metrical irregularity and in the vague notating or omission of "blue" notes, slides, and other graces peculiar to nearly all singers in the oral tradition. Much of the reality of Anglo-American folk song lies in departure from four-square metrical structure and from the equal-tempered system of notation. A singer will, for instance, introduce into a regular 2/4 pattern a 3/4 measure (either through prolongation of a tone or insertion of a rest)—most often at ends of alternate phrases, but occasionally at high points within the phrase itself. Inversely, he will shorten a 4/4 or a 3/4 by one or two counts. And he will approach a tone, or leave it, by slides of a half-step or more—an effect which can be felt to be an inherent quality of the tune itself, and gives a sense of subtle balance between major and minor. Some of these irregularities are quite strange to the ears of trained musicians and educated amateurs. Even to attempt to represent them makes the notations practically unreadable except to a patient student. In addition, slides when played on the piano are likely to be played too slowly and to sound too labored, precise, and definite. A few attempts have been made—but only at the earnest solicitation of the Lomaxes—to give the impression of "blue" notes, as, for example, in "Po' Laz'us," "Darlin' Corey," and some others, by means of grace notes and by simultaneous clashes of major and minor seconds or thirds.

A closing word or two should be said about the harmonic treatment of Anglo-American folk song. Traditionally, few chords are required to accompany any one song. Many places where the scholarly musician would introduce a subdominant, the tonic is continued by the traditional player. Or else, a dominant may take its place, as in the eighth measure of "Cindy," which here follows the playing of many of the dance bands heard in western North Carolina and Virginia. Secondary triads and sevenths are rarely heard, and their use should not be risked by amateurs unfamiliar with folk practice, if any connection with the original spirit of the song is to be maintained. Even though an original guitar or banjo accompaniment may have plenty of thirds in the triads, it is wise, in a piano setting, to avoid too many, for they appear to be more cloying on that instrument than on the fretted ones. Contrapuntal use of fourths and fifths, even in parallel motion, is a tradition of Anglo-American folk music that has to be known first-hand to be appreciated.

The aim has been to make most of the settings fairly easy from a piano-technical viewpoint. Some more difficult settings have been made, partly because it is hoped that competent pianists may take pleasure in them, and partly because traditional folk accompaniment would be misrepresented if the impression were given that it is always simple. To the contrary, it may often be a marvel of complexity—especially on the 5-string banjo, where the short, highest string is next to the long, lowest string, and where harmonic structure in the usual sense is often lacking, the instrument making a background of sonority rather than a sequence of chords.

Pianists who find any setting too difficult are urged to simplify the notations or to "chord" for themselves, using the capital letters above the staff ("guitar chords") as a basis for a simplified version of their own. Marks for tempo, dynamics (loud and soft), phrasing, changes of tempo, and so on, have been reduced to a minimum, and should be taken as suggestions rather than as detailed prescriptions. As a rule—and as a very strict rule—the musically literate, urban admirer of folk song should realize that the tempo, dynamics, and nuances employed by the best traditional singers are just as essential elements of folk song as the pitch sequences. The best tradition, as far as we are aware, *holds strictly to a tempo*, once it is started. Meters may be cut or added to, but usually the beat is kept steady. Ritardandi and accelerandi are almost never found. Crescendi and diminuendi are equally not traditional in Anglo-American folk song. When any are heard, one can suspect influence of the radio or the concert platform, the schoolroom, or the "literary society."

Charles and Ruth Seeger

Contents

BEST LOVED
AMERICAN
FOLK SONGS

CHAPTER I

Critters and Chillun'

THE LIFE OF A FOLK SONG DEPENDS NOT upon print, but upon its appeal to children. If the young ones don't like what they hear their old folks singing, those songs will be forgotten. In this sense all folk song is made for children and that is why, since the facts of childhood are pretty much the same everywhere in our culture, folk song has a permanence not shared by any other kind of music. The songs especially created with children in mind, therefore, possess incomparable vitality and staying power. Since they must please the most critical and candid of audiences, they have unmatched charm, subtlety, strength, and, above all, fancy.

Possum up a gum stump,
Coony in the holler,
Wake, snake, june-bug
Stole a half a dollar.

In their long march across this great continent the people have tossed off thousands of such rhymes, creating for their children an American Mother Goose that includes riddles, rib-ticklers, knee-bouncers, tongue-twisters, finger plays, rocking songs, and every other sort of silly trick and fancy for the imagination of kids to feed upon. These are the songs you remember until the day you die. These are the songs by means of which you learned to sing. These are the songs from which you learned to understand and enjoy rhyme and rhythm and melody. These are the songs that gave you the feeling that the animals and the other strange things that made up the big world beyond your mother's lap were friendly and familiar and part of the family. In the long run, some of these songs may outwear even our favorite composed tunes, such as "Swanee River" and "Old Black Joe," just as the English nursery song, "Frog Went A-Courtin'," has established a more enduring place in the Anglo-American repertoire than, perhaps, any other song.

June bugs, possums, coons, roosters, geese, hound dogs, mocking birds, rattlesnakes, billy goats, razor-back hogs, liver-lipped mules—these are the profoundest subjects for American folk-song makers, since out of them emerge the bright patterns of youthful fancy. In this chapter we can do no more than give a sample of the songs Americans have made for their children, but of all the songs in this book, these are certainly the most lovable.

1. BUCKEYE JIM

HERE is a lullaby from the Southern Appalachians, a bright pattern of color out of the ragbag of the past, to be sung softly and with tenderness. The melody has the simple and unfathomable loveliness of a green branch swaying in the summer wind; but, like other things that grow up out of the soil, surely and unconsciously beautiful, this song is a mystery. Certainly it is a cousin to such other "way over yander" ditties as,

Look away, look away over yander,
The old grey goose a-smilin' at the gander.

The folk-stuff of all lands is peopled with charming animals that dance and dine and are otherwise animated with human and superhuman qualities. American animal songs, however, are ordinarily either broadly comic or deeply pathetic. In "Buckeye Jim" there is a feeling of other-worldliness, the sense of things seen through the mirror of fantasy. Hum "Buckeye Jim" and then sing "The Grey Goose," "Frog Went a-Courtin'," "Mister Rabbit," "The Boll Weevil," "Old Blue," "The Ground Hog," and other American songs about animals. Then it will be clear that "Buckeye Jim" has a special unearthly quality, a child's imagining wrapped round with the haze of sweet blue hills. Everybody wonders about the birthplace and condition of "Buckeye Jim," but not a trace has been found, not even far up the deepest hollow or across the highest hill of the Southern mountain country.

Fletcher Collins, who lives in Elon, North Carolina, caught this song from a friend in the hills. Burl Ives, raised to sing ballads by his Kentucky-bred mother, caught it from Fletcher Collins. And we caught it from Burl.

2. *ALL THE PRETTY LITTLE HORSES*

This song has been treasured by many a Southern family, Negro and white; it is the classic of Southern lullabies. It is sung in a thousand different ways by as many singers; the "pretty little horses" may be "blacks and bays" or "dapples and grays," but, whatever their color, they have carried almost every Southern child off to sleep at one time or another. Here is what Shirley Lomax Mansell says about the way the song was sung in our family:

"All the Pretty Little Horses" is a family song. There is not a time when I do not remember it. I am sure it was Grandmother Brown's song; and from our mother it now belongs to her four children. Grandmother was a hymn singer, and on Sunday afternoons alone in her room, when she rocked back and forth in her little straight, cane-bottomed rocker, she sang all the slow, sad ones—"Abide With Me," "Rock of Ages," and "Yield Not to Temptation." Grandmother did not believe that on Sunday people should do anything but attend Sunday School, then Church, then read the Bible until time to go to evening services. Her disapproval of our Sunday afternoon walks, when the children from all the neighborhood gathered to explore the woods, caused her to shut herself into her room and rock and sing, and, I am sure, pray for forgiveness for us all. Her lips would shut into a thin line and her eyes fill with tears.

But Grandmother Brown loved babies, and she sang to us all, and rocked us, hours and hours, in that same little chair. "All the Pretty Little Horses" is her wonderful lullaby. She would put in a line or two of hums at the end, drift the baby off to sleep, floating with the little horses, the song blending with the squeak of the rocker and the pat of the foot on the rug. I still sing the song to my girls when they are ill.

3. *AUNT NANCY*

Time out of mind, American children of every state have been rocked, joggled, and sung to sleep with these sweet-sour lines, the story of Aunt Nancy (Aunt Sally or Aunt Rhody) who lost her feather-bed when her best goose was drowned in the millpond. In fact, this ditty is possibly the best-known American folk song. There's irony here, pathos, humor, and, if you like, history—a reminder of the days when a goosefeather bed was the very prime in sleeping, because it cradled you and cuddled you and almost covered you at the same time.

Of course, the people have endowed all the common farm animals with personality and speech and a point of view. There are tales beyond tales about geese. Here is one that belongs with Aunt Nancy's old goose, because it's out of the same barnyard. Mose Platt, from Taylor Texas, told it this way:

One time I went to town huntin' a job, up to a little ol' town they call Rogers, and so I went up to a lady's house there and asked her for some work. She says, "Can you cut yards?" I told her I could. She says, "Well, all right, go look under the house and find a lawnmow' an' go to cuttin'."

Out back cuttin' grass—and this lady, she had some geese out in a vacant lot and under a tree there lied a goat. And so these ol' geese, in the heat of the day, raise up and says, "We're havin' a ha—ard time!"

Goat says, "Mm-mmp."

And so the geese kep' a-pickin'. Then raised up agin, says, "We're havin' a ha—ard time!"

Goat says, "Mm-mmp!"

Well, these geese raise up *agin*, says, "We're havin' a ha-ARD *time!*"

Goat says, "Ba-a-a-ad ma-anagin'!"

Keep this story firmly in mind when you sing "Aunt Nancy."

4. *LEATHERWING BAT*

The weavers of folklore have never held with our sharp distinction between animals and human beings—a recent view. Like all people who live and work close to animals and depend directly upon them for food and for helpful work, the folk endow them with human characteristics, including the power of speech. Every branch of the human family has told tales about talking animals. Like our own great tale-teller, Mark Twain, they feel sure that "Animals talk to each other. There can be no question about that; but I suppose there are very few people who can understand them."

Zeke, the ancient ex-slave, was one of those few. He used to hear the barnyard fowls discussing their affairs and when he was questioned about this, he replied with some asperity:

Sure the fowls can talk. They talk just like we do, but 'tain't everybody can understand 'em. One day I heered a turkey hen kinder sing: "We're poor—we're poor—poor." Old turkey gobbles right back at her, said, "Who in heck can help it? Who in heck can help it?"

The Yankees runned all the fowls off the plantation they couldn't catch and, just 'fore they left, the old rooster flewed up on the fence and crow—

"Is the Yankees go—o—o—one?"

The dove ask him,

"Who is you? Who is you? Who is you?"

The guinea hen settin' on the lot fence reply,

"Not yit, not yit, not yit."

And the old drake sittin' under the house, he say,

"Hush-h, hush-h, hush-h."

If barnyard fowls can discuss the Civil War, there is no reason to believe that the pretty birds of the woods cannot chatter about love. As a matter of fact, the whole idea of "Leatherwing Bat" is very possibly derived from Chaucer's *Parliment of Foules.* As Chaucer tells it (and in this work he utilized an ancient folk-tale theme), Dame Nature summons the fowls together in convention on St. Valentine's Day to contest in compliments for the favors of a charming young lady eagle. The falcon and the other predatory birds behave like knights and make courtly speeches, but the commoners of the barnyard express coarse and cynical sentiments. The goose advises the falcon in lines most reminiscent of our Southern-white song:

I say, I rede him, though he were my brother,
But she wol love him, lat him love another. . . .
Ye quek: yit quod the doke, ful well and faire,
There be mo sterres, god wot, than a paire!

That "there are more pretty girls than one" has been said in every language, but nowhere more merrily and more fitly than by the leatherwing bat and his friends.

5. *THE GREY GOOSE*

The goose keeps turning up in American folklore as a representative of humanity. In this tale from the Brazos bottoms, it takes the bitter role of the Negro faced with white man's justice:

Ole sis goose wus er sailin' on de lake, and ole brer fox wus hid in de weeds. By um by ole sis goose swum up close to der bank and ole brer fox lept out and cotched her.

"O yes, ole sis goose, I'se got yer now, you'se been er sailin' on mer lake er long time, en I'se got yer now. I'se gwine to break yer neck en pick yer bones."

"Hole on der', brer fox, hole on, I'se got jest as much right to swim in der lake as you has ter lie in der weeds. Hit's des as much my lake as hit is yours, and we is gwine to take dis matter to der cotehouse and see if you has any right to break my neck and pick my bones."

And so dey went to cote, and when dey got dere, de sheriff, he wus er fox, en de judge, he wus er fox, and der tourneys, dey wus foxes, en all de jurrymen, dey was foxes, too.

And dey tried ole sis goose, en dey 'victed her and dey 'scuted her, and dey picked her bones.

Now my chilluns, listen to me, when all de folks in de cotehouse is foxes, and you is jes er common goose, der ain't gwine to be much jestice for you pore nigger.

Out of the Brazos bottoms, too, comes the ballad of a heroic goose. They shot him, plucked him, and parboiled him, but still he was too tough to eat. Then they threw him into the hogpen and he broke the sow's teeth out; they took him to the sawmill and he tore the teeth out of the circular saw. In the end he floats away on one pin-feather, a string of little goslings in his train, honking derision at these foolish attempts to destroy him. This is the song of a subject people that feels itself stronger and more enduring than its oppressors. Like Brer Rabbit, who skips away from Brer Fox saying, "Bred and born in the briar patch," you could try everything that you wanted on the Old Grey Goose and you could try everything you wanted to on the old Negro, but they'd both end up with a house full of children, laughing at you.

The ballad, which from stylistic and other indications, seems to have been produced in the days of slavery, has been kept alive by the Negro convicts in the Texas State Penitentiary. This is where we first heard it, sung as a gang work song by James Baker (alias Iron Head). Iron Head,* a remarkable singer, had learned all of his ballads (he knew several fine versions of British ballads) from an older prisoner who had spent his "natural life" in the penitentiary and had died there. Iron Head, in typical African work-song leader style, sang the story lines of the song, while the gang replied with "Lawd, Lawd, Lawd" after every line. As the song went on and the tale of the grey goose grew taller and taller, the men grinned and shouted their astonishment louder and louder in the refrain. You could see that this simple and charming ballad of a mighty goose sustained and encouraged these men, helped them to better endure what they could not escape, made them feel strong and sound and full of hope in spite of the black bars and the guns that held them.

6. *MISTER RABBIT*

Brer Rabbit, big-eyed, timid, depending on nimbleness and motherwit for survival, was the universal hero in the animal stories of the American Negro slave; for in the character of the rabbit the folk Negro could see the qualities which would best enable him to survive under slavery. In Brer Rabbit's triumphs over Brer Fox he could symbolize his own imaginary victories over his masters.

The folk tale most suitable to our song has to do with Brer Rabbit's reliance on his speed and his "suscautiousness." It comes from Florida by way of Zora Neale Hurston's fine book of Negro folklore, *Mules and Men.*

* For a portrait of Iron Head, see the song, "Shorty George."

De dog is sho hot after him. Run dem doggone rabbits so that they sent word to de dogs dat they want peace. So they had a convention. De rabbit took de floor and said they was tired of runnin', and dodgin' all de time, and they asted de dogs to please leave rabbits alone and run somethin' else. So de dogs put it to a vote and 'greed to leave off runnin' rabbits.

So after de big meetin' Brer Dog invites de rabbit over to his house to have dinner wid him. He started on thru the woods wid Brer Dog but every now and then he'd stop and scratch his ear and listen. He stop right in his tracks. Dog say:

"Aw, come on Brer Rabbit, you too suscautious. Come on."

Kep dat up till they come to de branch just 'fore they got to Brer Dog's house. Just as Brer Rabbit started to step out on de footlog, he heard some dogs barkin' way down de creek. He heard de old hound say, "How o-l-d is he?" and de young dogs answer him: "Twenty-one or two!" So Brer Rabbit say, "Excuse me, but Ah don't reckon Ah better go home wid you today, Brer Dog."

"Aw, come on, Brer Rabbit, you always gittin' scared for nothin'. Come on."

"Ah hears dogs barkin', Brer Dog."

"Naw, you don't, Brer Rabbit."

"Yes, Ah do. Ah know dat's dogs barkin'."

"S'posin' it is, it don't make no difference. Ain't we done held a convention and passed a law dogs run no mo' rabbits? Don't pay no 'tention to every li'l bit of barkin' you hear."

Rabbit scratch his ear and say,

"Yeah, but all de dogs ain't been to no convention, and anyhow some o' dese fool dogs ain't got no better sense than to run all over dat law and break it up. De rabbits didn't go to school much and he didn't learn but three letter, and that's trust no mistake. Run every time de bush shake."

"Mister Rabbit" is a gay and tender little buck-dancing tune, that should be sung quietly and with intense syncopation. Looked at another way, it is a complete portrait of a human being, giving his most important characteristics and revealing his dream—the dream of all men—of shining like a star.

7. *OLD BLUE*

Americans in buckskin, linsey-woolsey, and blue jeans have forever loved and lied about their dogs. Kick an old flop-eared Southern hound (even though it looks like it hadn't been fed in a month) and you've made an enemy of his master. You may even get shot. There've been plenty of killings and quite a few feuds that started up over dogs. The ballad of Old Blue, certainly the best song about a dog to come out of this country, we have heard in Mississippi and Texas. It is a quiet song, very serious, intensely and genuinely sentimental, in complete contrast to the hundreds of lies we have told about hunting dogs. Sit down with a countryman anywhere and ask him about hunting dogs and this is the sort of thing you'll hear:

> You take old Blood. There was a fox hound. He started a fox around a hill and the first time they came around the fox was fifty yards in the lead. The next time around old Blood was yelling every jump and just twenty-five yards behind. The next time around old Blood and the fox was running even, stride for stride. And the *next* time old Blood was fifty yards ahead of the fox and just a-hellin'!

R. C. Whitlock of New York took his pointer to town with him one day and noticed him pointing at something in the street. Couldn't figure it out at first, then he noticed the dog was pointing at a sign. The sign read—A. Partridge, Attorney at Law. . . . Then Paul Spidell of Cumberland, Maryland, has a good hound, too. In fact, he claims that his one hound will make an assorted pack of hunting dogs. From 7 A.M. to 9 A.M. he's a fine rabbit dog; from 9 A.M. to 3 P.M. a pointer or a setter, whichever one you want; from 3 P.M. to 9 P.M. you can't beat him in a fox chase; and from then on he just runs coons. . . .

Maybe, though, the smartest dog anyone ever heard of was a pointer named Buck. Buck went through Signal Corps training with his master and, on a hunt one day, after they got home, they noticed him 'way up on the side of a hill, pointing and moving his tail in a funny way. "I believe that dog's wig-waggin'," said his master.

They watched a while more and sure enough it was true. This is the message that faithful old hound was sending:

Joe — have — you — got — any — buckshot — stop.
If — you — ain't — git — the — hell — out — of — here — stop.
There's — a — big — black — bear — up — here — and — he's — coming — your — way.

Larkin Snow in North Carolina had a fox hound named Flyin' Jib that beat the pack down around Skull Cap Mountain:

Flyin' Jib were about a half a mile ahead of 'um all, goin' fast as the report of a rifle gun. Passin' through a meader whar thar were a mowin' scythe with a blade standin' up, Flyin' Jib run chug against it with sich force that it split him wide open from the end of his nose to the tip of his tail. Thar he lay and never whimpered, tryin' to run right on.

I streaked it to him, snatched up both sides of him, slapped 'um together, but were in sich a hurry that I put two feet down and two up. But away he went after that fox, scootin' jest in that fix. You see, when he got tired runnin' on two feet on one side, he'd whirl over, quick as lightnin', on t'other, and it seemed ruther to increased his velocity. He kotch that fox a mile ahead of the whole kit of 'um. When them other fellers come up, I jist kervorted, and told 'um that were the way fur a dog to run fast and long, fust one side up, then t'other—it rested him.

8. *GROUND HOG*

The Ground Hog ballad was born and still lives way back in the coves of the Appalachians where the valleys "are so narrow you have to pour in daylight." Some long-shanked mountaineer will grab up his five-string banjo and play this rattling square-dance tune at runaway speed. Then he'll lean back his head and holler the words out of his long, red neck, so the folks in the next valley can understand every word he's singing. The louder he sings the clearer he can see himself catchin' and eatin' that hog. Every time he comes to the word "groundhog," everybody on the front steps will holler it out with him. When you tell the story, sing it that way yourself, so everybody on your block will know how you love a bait of groundhog.

Catching the ground hog varies with the region. Apparently the Northeastern breed is a sluggish and a peaceable animal which can be shot or cornered out of hand. But in the South it takes a pack of good dogs to run a ground hog to his hole. According to Professor Josiah Coombs, who collected this song in eastern Kentucky, along with a good deal of ground-hog information, "It takes a virtuoso to twist the woodchuck out of his hole with a slender green branch about five or six feet long as thick as your finger and forked at the end. The idea is to twist the end of that long switch into the hog's hide and pull him out!"

A ground hog (more commonly known as a woodchuck) makes a fine pile of meat. You take and you skin him and put him to soak overnight in salt water with soda and vinegar added. Then you boil him a while till he's tenderized. Then you put him on to roast (or if he's young, cut him up and fry him), and the good smell will tickle the nostrils of your neighbors a half a mile away. Put your teeth in him when he's done and you'll find his meat sweet. The little children will cry for more. . . .

So say the people who've tried it.

9. *SPRINGFIELD MOUNTAIN*

The most cussed and discussed American animal by far is the rattlesnake. Travelers have lied about the size, ferocity, numbers, and the deadliness of this reptile from the days of the

Puritans down to our own time. Perhaps that explains why "Springfield Mountain" is one of the best-loved (as well as the silliest) American ballads, for it tells the story of the encounter of a young man with a "pizen sarpent." Timothy Myrick of Springfield Mountain (now Wilbraham), Massachusetts, died of rattlesnake bite in Farmington, Connecticut, August 7, 1761. At the time he was engaged to marry a Miss Curtis, known in the ballad as Sally or Molly. Some local poet of serious intent made a doleful ballad upon this sad accident which ran in part as follows:

On Springfield Mountain there did dwell
a likely youth 'twas known full well
Left't Merrick's only Son
A likely youth near twenty one

One Friday Morning he did go
down to the Meadow for to mow
He mowed around and he did feel
a poisoning Serpent at his heel

When he received this deadly wound
he dropped his Scythe upon the ground
and straight for Home was his intent
calling aloud Still as he went. . . .

'twas the Seventh of August year 61
this fatal accident was done
may this a warning be to all
to be prepared when God shall call

This ballad achieved some currency in New England, where you can still hear the serious version among rural singers. This was a period, however, when the drawling *Yankee* was the popular comic figure on the stage and in humorous anecdotes, occupying the clown's position that was later given to the Irishman, the German, the Negro, and the hillbilly. A waggish, barnstorming actor by the name of Spear was tickled by the simplicity of Timothy Myrick's tragedy and composed a comic piece called "Love and Pizen." Its character is indicated by the final moralizing stanza:

And mind when you're in love don't pass
Too near to patches of high grass,
Ri-tu-ri-nu, ri-tu-di-na,
Ri-tu-ri-nu, ri-tu-di-na.

Apparently a great many other ballad-makers, to judge from the numerous forms the song has assumed, tried their hands at the same material. You find many refrains. In Missouri . . .

With a bumble, bumble, dick-a-ri-dum
Able-de-dinctum-day.

In Texas . . .

To my rattle, to my ru-ra-ree.

In Michigan . . .

Ri-too-di-od-dy-i, ri-too-di-od-dy-i,
ri-too-di-od-dy,
Oo-di-od-dy, oo-di-od-dy-i.

In Mississippi . . .

Fling-dan-de, fling-dang-de,
Fling-dang didilum didilum de.

At the moment our favorite refrain, which we bid you sing, comes from Canton, Ohio, and a singer named Albert Dull. The stanzas, woven together from a score of variants make this a cross-country ballad, which indeed it has been in the estimation of Americans.

10. *TEN THOUSAND YEARS AGO*

The animals came in one by one,
The monkey chewing a caraway bun.

The animals came in two by two,
The elephant and the kangaroo.

In such irreverent language did the people describe the entrance of the animals into Noah's Ark. This streak of irreverence, backed up by our national fondness for durn-foolishness, for the wild and crazy in humor, is responsible for such songs as this one. For college students, for kids, who grew up in an atmosphere of stuffiness in regard to religion and education, this song provided a way to poke innocent fun at the Bible, at the preacher, at the old-maid schoolteacher, all of whom were one's oppressors and natural enemies. The impudent spirit of "there ain't nothin' in this world that I don't know" has deep roots in the American character. A hundred years ago the American frontier produced a man whose main quality was a delightful and irrepressible impudence. This was Davy Crockett, master liar, bear-hunter, congressman, and hero of the Alamo. His story of his visit to the "office of sunrise" is the most delightful tall tale produced on this continent:

One January morning it was so all screwen up cold that the forest trees war so stiff that they couldn't shake, and the very daybreak froze fast as it war tryin' to dawn. The tinder box in my cabin would no more ketch fire than a sunk raft at the bottom o' the sea. Seein' that daybreak war so far behind time, I thought creation war in a fair way of freezin' fast.

"So," thinks I, "I must strike a leetle fire from my fingers, light my pipe and travel out a few leagues and see about it."

So out I walked and endeavored to keep myself unfriz by goin' at a hop, step and jump gait and whistlin' the tune "fire on the mountains!" as I went along in three double quick time. Well, arter I had walked about twenty-five miles up the peak of daybreak hill, I soon discovered what war the matter. The airth had actually friz fast on her axis and couldn't turn round; the sun had got jammed between two cakes o' ice under the wheels, an' thar he had bin shinin' and workin' to get loose, till he friz fast in his cold sweat.

"Creation!" thought I, "This is the toughest sort of suspension and it mustn't be endured—somethin' must be done, or human creation is done for."

I took a fresh twenty-pound bear steak off o' my back that I'd picked up on the road, an' beat the animal agin the ice till the hot ile began to walk out of it at all sides. I then took an' held him over the airth's axes, an' squeezed him till I'd drawed 'em loose, poured about a ton on it over the airth's face, gave the airth's cogwheel one kick backward till I got the sun loose—whistled, "Push along, keep movin'!", an in about fifteen seconds the airth gin a grunt, and begun movin'—the sun walked up beautiful, salutin' me with sich a wind of gratitude that it made me sneeze. I lit my pipe in the blaze of his top knot, shouldered my bear, an' walked home, introducin' the people to fresh daylight with a piece of sunrise in my pocket, with which I cooked my bear steaks an' enjoyed one o' the best breakfasts I had tasted for some time. If I didn't, jist wake up some mornin' and go with me to the office of sunrise!

This Crockett yarn is separated from the darn-fool ditty that follows by a half-century of time and a considerable cultural gulf; the one is the product of the rampaging frontier, while the other probably was composed by undergraduates at an Eastern college. Yet a spirit of fresh impudence and irreverence makes them kin.

1.

Buckeye Jim

Piano arrangement by
Charles and Ruth Seeger

1. 'Way up yonder above the sky,
A bluebird lived in a jay-bird's eye.
REFRAIN: Buckeye Jim, you can't go,
Go weave and spin, you can't go, Buckeye Jim.

2. 'Way up yonder above the moon,
A blue-jay nests in a silver spoon,
REFRAIN: Buckeye Jim, you can't go,
Go weave and spin, you can't go, Buckeye Jim.

3. 'Way down yonder in a wooden trough,
An old *wo* -man died of the whoopin' cough.
REFRAIN: Buckeye Jim, you can't go,
Go weave and spin, you can't go, Buckeye Jim.

4. 'Way down yonder on a hollow log,
A red bird danced with a green bullfrog.
REFRAIN: Buckeye Jim, you can't go,
Go weave and spin, you can't go, Buckeye Jim.

2.

All the Pretty Little Horses

Words and melody adapted and arranged by
John A. and Alan Lomax

Piano arrangement by
Charles and Ruth Seeger

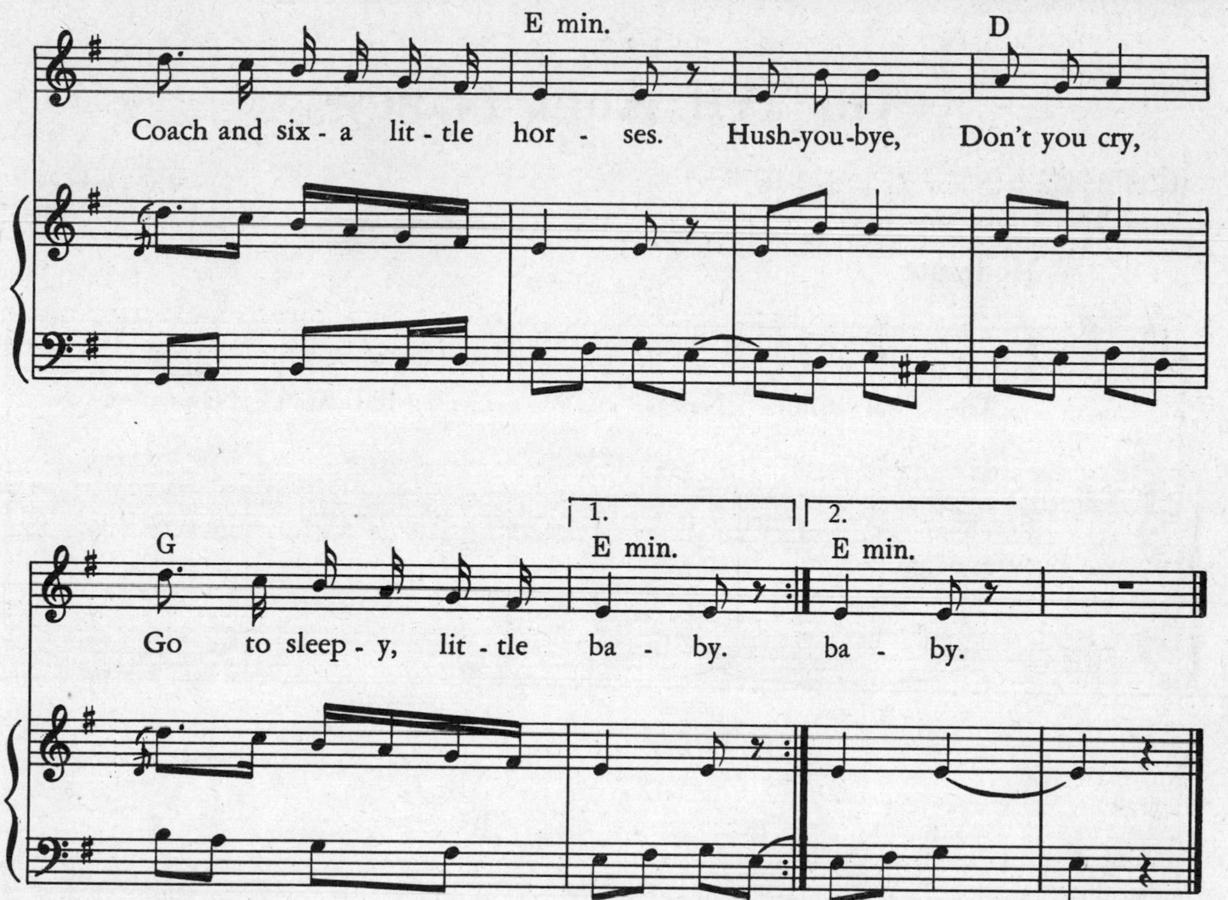

1. Hush-you-bye,
Don't you cry,
Go to sleepy, little baby.
When you wake,
You shall have
All the pretty little horses —
Blacks and bays,
Dapples and grays,
Coach and six-a little horses.
Hush-you-bye,
Don't you cry,
Go to sleepy, little baby.

2. Hush-you-bye,
Don't you cry,
Go to sleepy, little baby.
Way down yonder
In de medder
Lies a po' lil' lambie;
De bees an' de butterflies
Peckin' out its eyes,
De po' lil' thing cried, "Mammy!"
Hush-you-bye,
Don't you cry,
Go to sleepy, little baby.

3.
Go Tell Aunt Nancy

Words and melody adapted and arranged by
John A. and Alan Lomax

Piano arrangement by
Charles and Ruth Seeger

Moderate

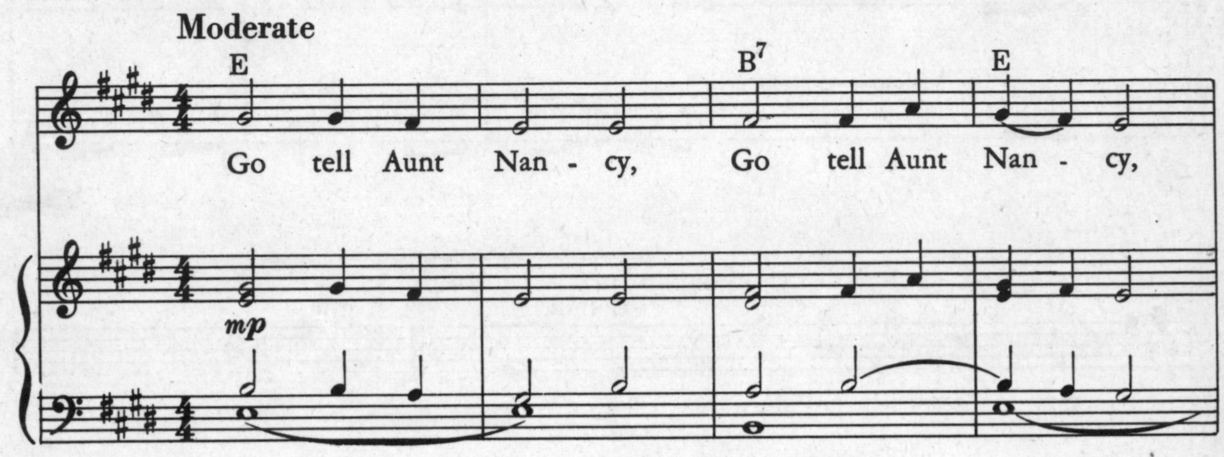

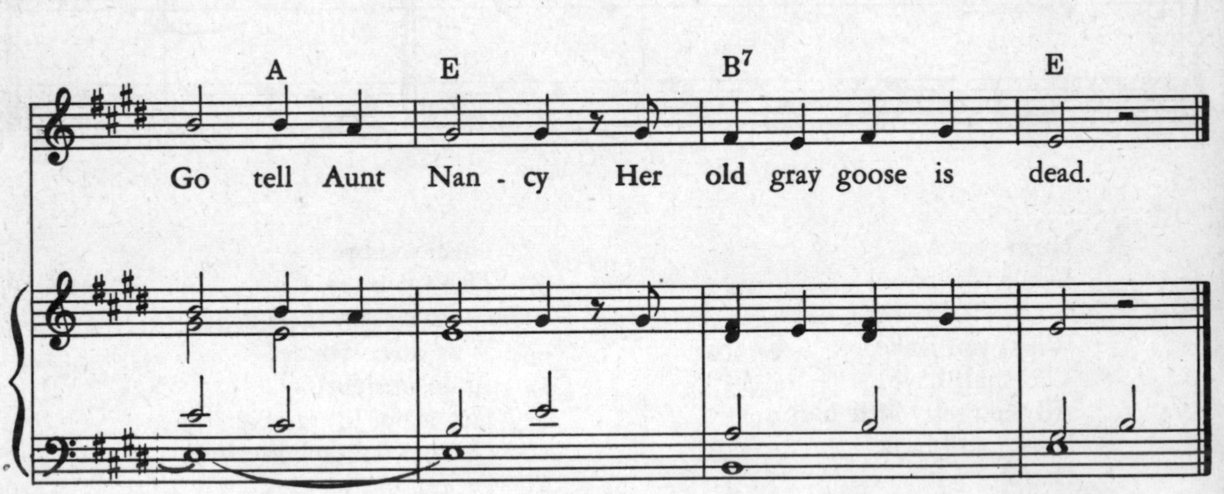

1. Go tell Aunt Nancy,
Go tell Aunt Nancy,
Go tell Aunt Nancy
Her old gray goose is dead.

2. The one she's been savin',
The one she's been savin',
The one she's been savin'
To make her feather bed.

3. She drownded in the millpond,
She drownded in the millpond,
She drownded in the millpond
Standing on her head.

4. Old gander's weepin',
Old gander's weepin',
Old gander's weepin'
Because his wife is dead.

5. The goslin's are mournin',
The goslin's are mournin',
The goslin's are mournin'
'Cause their mammy's dead.

6. She only had one fe-eather,
She only had one fe-eather,
She only had one fe-eather
A-stickin' in her head.

4.

Leatherwing Bat

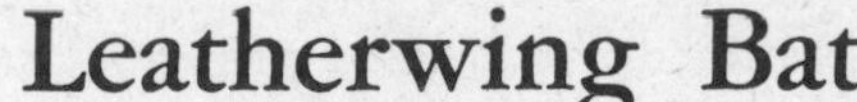

Words adapted and arranged by
John A. and Alan Lomax

Piano arrangement by
Charles and Ruth Seeger

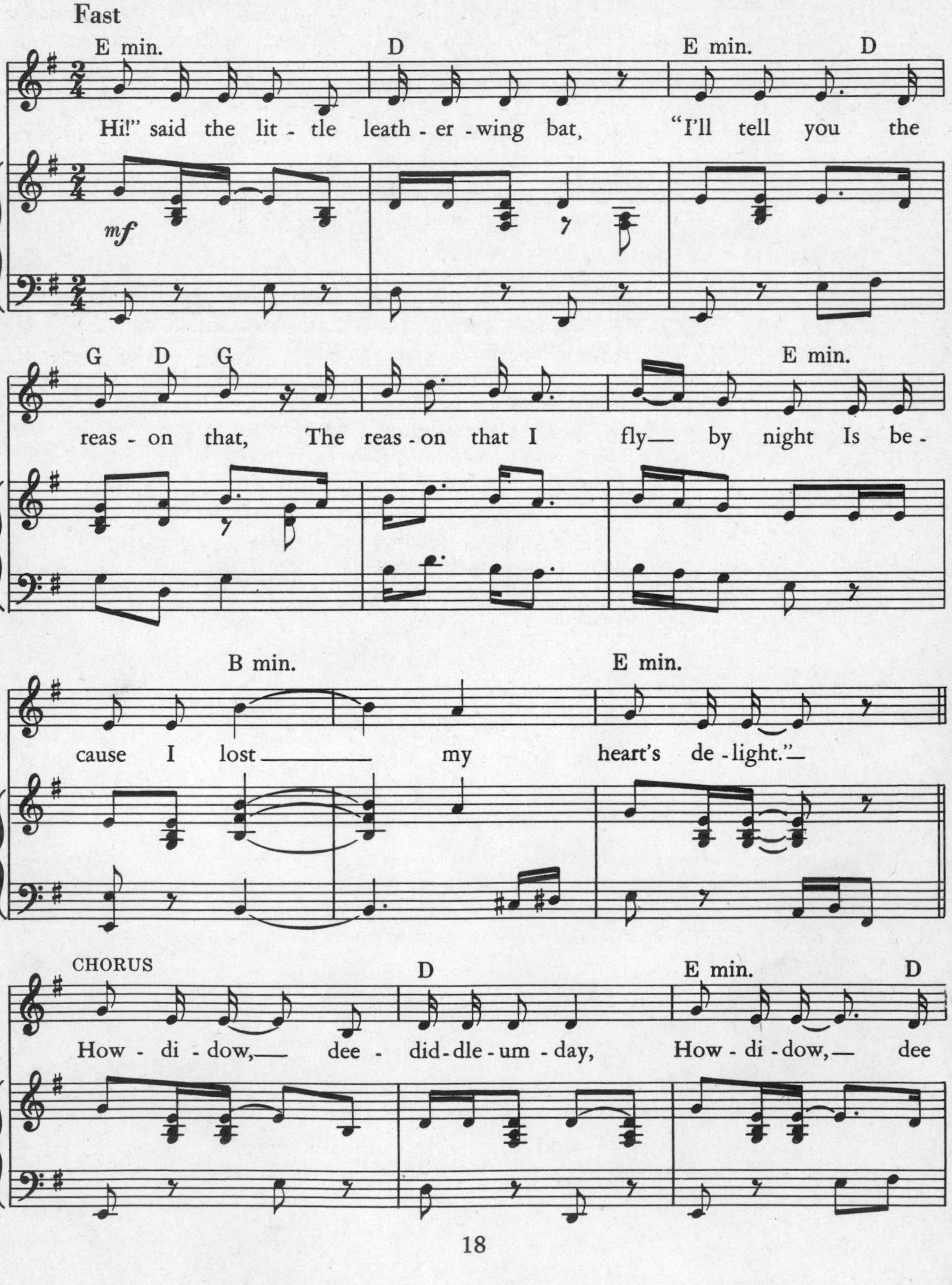
Fast
E min.
D
E min.
D
Hi!" said the lit - tle leath - er - wing bat, "I'll tell you the
mf
G D G
E min.
reas - on that, The reas - on that I fly— by night Is be -
B min.
E min.
cause I lost my heart's de - light."—
CHORUS
D
E min.
D
How - di - dow,— dee - did-dle - um - day, How - di - dow,— dee

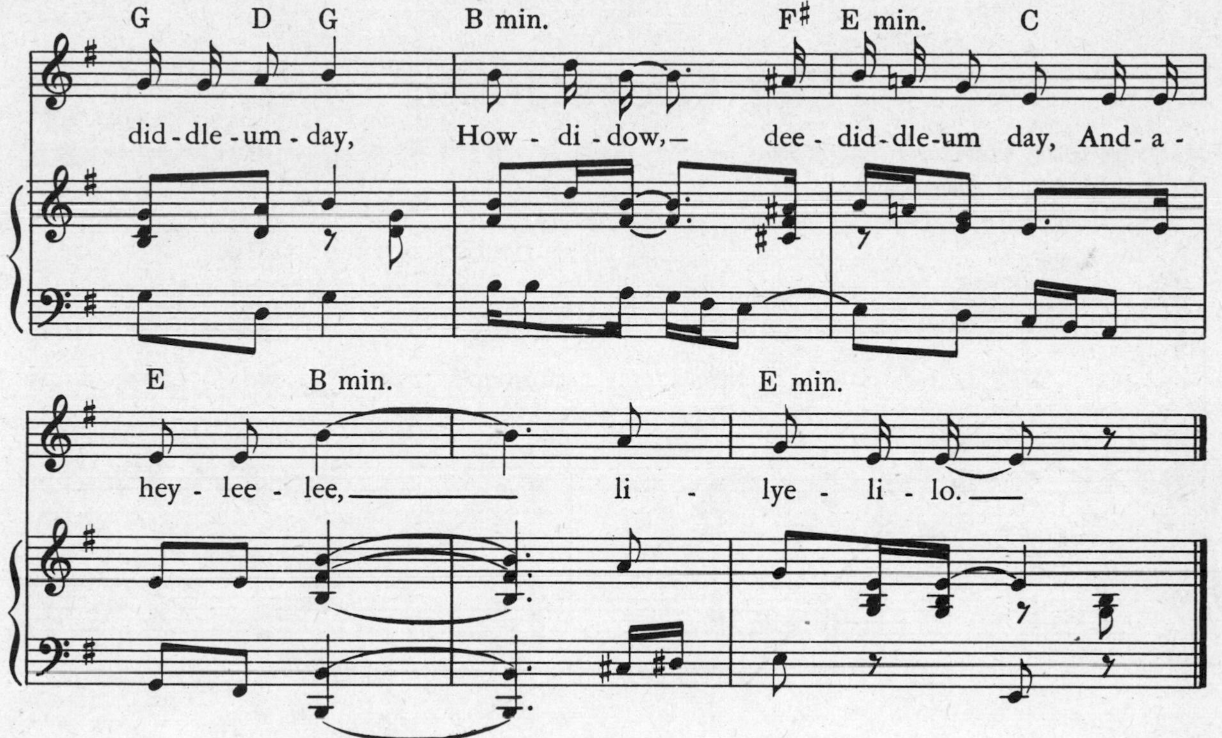

1. "Hi!" said the little leather-wing bat,
"I'll tell you the reason that,
The reason that I fly by night
Is because I lost my heart's delight." CHORUS:

2. "Hi!" said the red-bird sittin' on the fence,
"Once I loved a handsome wench,
But she got saucy and from me fled,
And ever since my head's been red."

3. "Hi!" said the blue-bird, as he flew,
"Once I loved a young gal, too,
But she got saucy and wanted to go,
So I bought me a new string for my bow."

4. "Hi!" says the robin as he flew,
"When I was a young man, I choosed two.
If one didn't love me, the other one would,
And don't you think my notion's good?"

5. "Hoot!" says the owl with her head so white,
"A lonesome day and a lonesome night.
Thought I heard some pretty girl say,
She'd court all night and sleep all day."

6. "No, no," says the turtle dove,
"That's no way for to gain his love.
If you want to gain your heart's delight,
Keep him awake both day and night."

5.

The Grey Goose

Words and melody adapted and arranged by
John A. and Alan Lomax

Piano arrangement by
Charles and Ruth Seeger

1. Well, las' Monday mornin',
Lawd, Lawd, Lawd,
Well, las' Monday mornin',
Lawd, Lawd, Lawd.

*Later stanzas may be played *p* *mp* *mf* ad lib.

2. My daddy went a-huntin',
Lawd, Lawd, Lawd,
He was huntin' for de grey goose,
Lawd, Lawd, Lawd.

3. An' he went to de big wood,
Lawd, Lawd, Lawd,
An' he took along his zulu,
Lawd, Lawd, Lawd.

4. Long come a grey goose,
Lawd, Lawd, Lawd,
Well, he up to his shoulder,
Lawd, Lawd, Lawd.

5. An' he ram back de hammer,
Lawd, Lawd, Lawd,
An' he pull on de trigger,
Lawd, Lawd, Lawd.

6. An' de zulu went *boo-loo*,
Lawd, Lawd, Lawd,
An' de zulu went *boo-loo*,
Lawd, Lawd, Lawd.

7. Down he come a-fallin',
Lawd, Lawd, Lawd,
He was six weeks a-fallin',
Lawd, Lawd, Lawd.

8. An' he put him on de waggin,
Lawd, Lawd, Lawd,
An' he taken him to de white house.
Lawd, Lawd, Lawd.

9. An' yo wife an' my wife,
Lawd, Lawd, Lawd,
Dey give a feather-pickin'.
Lawd, Lawd, Lawd.

10. Dey was six weeks a-pickin',
Lawd, Lawd, Lawd,
Dey was six weeks a-pickin'.
Lawd, Lawd, Lawd.

11. An' dey put him on a-par-boil';
Lawd, Lawd, Lawd,
He was six weeks a-par-boil'.
Lawd, Lawd, Lawd.

12. An' dey put him on de table,
Lawd, Lawd, Lawd,
An' dey put him on de table.
Lawd, Lawd, Lawd.

13. An' de fork couldn' stick him,
Lawd, Lawd, Lawd,
An' de knife couldn' prick him.
Lawd, Lawd, Lawd.

14. Well, dey throwed him in de hog-pen,
Lawd, Lawd, Lawd,
An' de hogs couldn' eat him.
Lawd, Lawd, Lawd.

15. Well, he broke de sow's jawbone;
Lawd, Lawd, Lawd,
Well, he broke de sow's jawbone.
Lawd, Lawd, Lawd.

16. So dey taken him to de sawmill,
Lawd, Lawd, Lawd,
An' he broke de saw's teeth out.
Lawd, Lawd, Lawd.

17. An' de las' time I seed her,*
Lawd, Lawd, Lawd,
An' de las' time I seed her,
Lawd, Lawd, Lawd.

18. She was flyin' 'cross de ocean,
Lawd, Lawd, Lawd,
Had a long string o' goslin's
Lawd, Lawd, Lawd.

19. An' dey all went "Quonk, quonk,"
Lawd, Lawd, Lawd,
An' dey all went "Quonk, quonk."
Lawd, Lawd, Lawd.

**Don't be concerned about this sudden change of sex on the part of the grey goose. Remember everything she (he) had been through.*

6.

Mister Rabbit

Piano arrangement by
Charles and Ruth Seeger

Fast

F

"Mis - ter Rab - bit, Mis - ter Rab - bit, your tail's might - y white."

mp

B♭ F

"Yes, bless God, been git - tin' out - a sight."—

mf

REFRAIN

B♭ F

Ev - 'y lit - tle soul gwine- a shine, shine,—

1. "Mister Rabbit, Mister Rabbit, your tail's mighty white."
"Yes, bless God, been gittin' outa sight."

REFRAIN: Ev'y little soul gwine-a shine, shine,
Ev'y little soul gwine-a shine along.

2. "Mister Rabbit, Mister Rabbit, your coat's mighty grey."
"Yes, bless God, been out 'fo' day."

3. "Mister Rabbit, Mister Rabbit, your ears mighty long."
"Yes, bless God, been put on wrong."

4. "Mister Rabbit, Mister Rabbit, your ears mighty thin."
"Yes, bless God, been splittin' the wind."

7.

Old Blue

Words and melody adapted and arranged by
John A. and Alan Lomax

Piano arrangement by
Charles and Ruth Seeger

2. Shouldered my axe and I tooted my horn,
Gonna get me a possum in the new-ground corn.
"Go on, Blue, I'm comin', too."

3. Old Blue treed, I went to see,
There sat the possum in a 'simmon tree.
"Go on, Blue, I'm comin', too."

4. Possum clumb down on a swingin' limb,
Blue barked at the possum, possum growled at him.
"Go on, Blue, you good dog, you."

5. He grinned at me, I looked at him,
I shuck him out, Blue tuck him in.
"Go on, Blue, you good dog, you."

6. Baked that possum good and brown,
And I laid them sweet potatoes round and round.
"Come on. Blue, you kin have some, too."

7. "Blue, what makes your eyes so red?"
"I've run them possums till I'm almost dead."
"Go on, Blue, I'm comin', too."

8. When old Blue died, he died so hard
Till he shook the ground in my backyard.
"Go on, Blue, I'm comin', too."

9. Old Blue died, I laid him in the shade,
I dug his grave with a silver spade.
"Go on, Blue, I'm comin', too."

10. I let him down with a golden chain,
Link by link slipped through my hand.
"Go on, Blue, I'm comin', too."

11. There's only one thing that bothers my mind,
Blue went to heaven, left me behind.
"Go on, Blue, I'm comin', too."

12. When I get to heaven, first thing I'll do,
Grab me a horn and blow for Old Blue,
Come here, Blue, I got here, too."

13. Then when I hear that Blue dog bark,
Blue's treed a possum in Noah's Ark.
"Come here, Blue, you good dog, you."

8.

Ground Hog

Words and melody adapted and arranged by
John A. and Alan Lomax

Piano arrangement by
Charles and Ruth Seeger

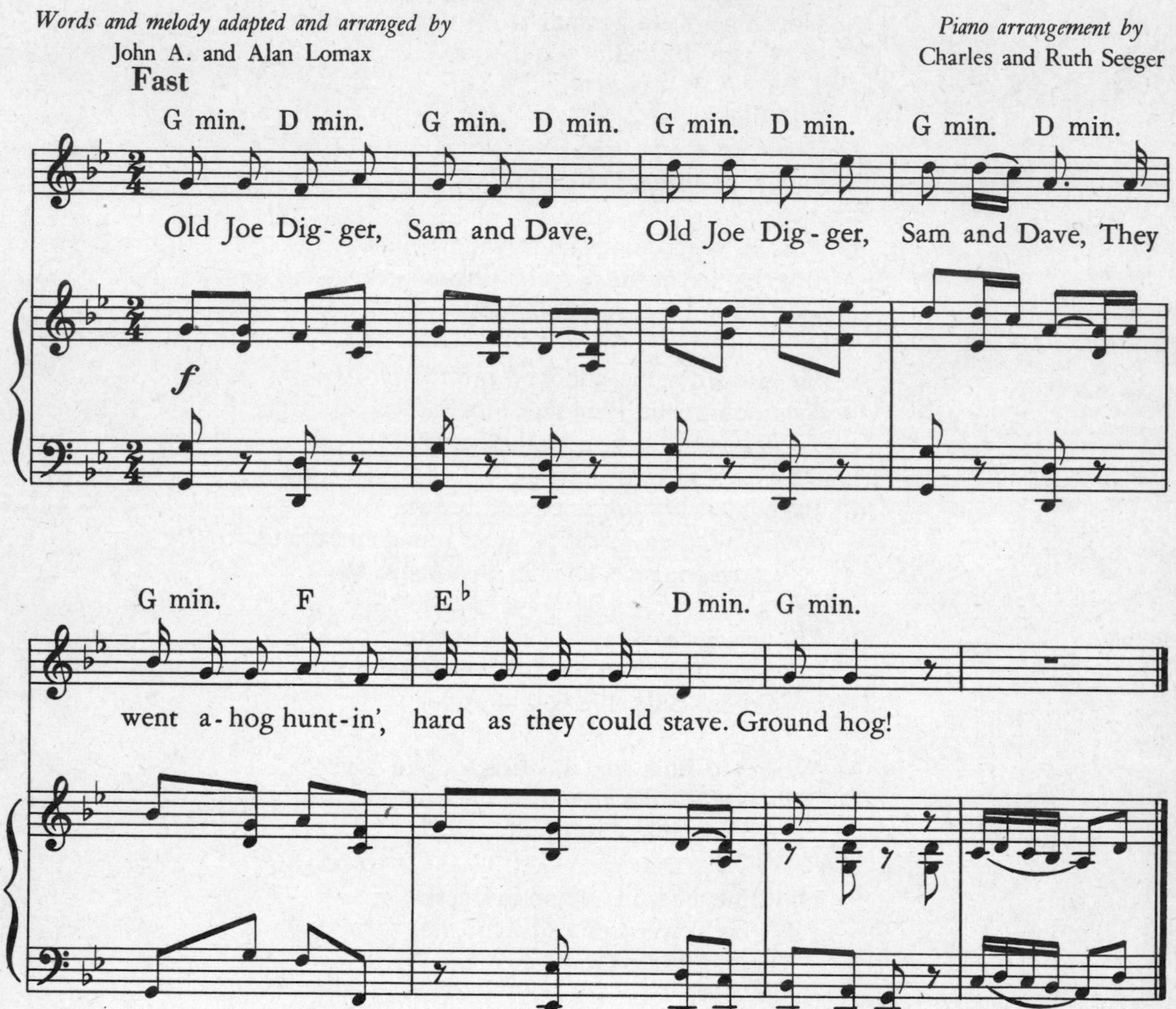

1. Old Joe Digger, Sam and Dave,
   Old Joe Digger, Sam and Dave,
   They went a-hog huntin', hard as they could stave,
   Ground hog!

2. They picked up their guns and went to the brash,
   By gum, Joe, here's the hog sign frash.

3. Too many rocks and too many logs,
   Too many rocks to catch ground hogs.

4. He's in here, boys, the hole's wore slick,
   Run here, Sam, with yer fork-ěd stick.

5. Stand back, boys, and let's be wise,
Fer I think I see his beaded eyes.

6. Hold them dogs, boys, don't let 'em howl,
I thought I heered the ground hog howl.

7. Up jumped Sam with a ten foot pole,
To roust that ground hog outen his hole.

8. Work, boys, work, jest as hard as ye kin tear,
The meat'll do to eat and the hide'll do to wear.

9. Stand back, boys, and le' me git my breath,
Catchin' this ground hog's might nigh death.

10. I heered him give a whistle and a wail,
I've wound my stick right in his tail.

11. Here he comes all in a whirl
He's the bigges' ground hog in this worl'.

12. Sam cocked his gun and Dave pulled the trigger,
But the one killed the hog was old Joe Digger.

13. They took him by the tail and wagged him to a log,
And swore by gosh, he's a hell of a hog.

14. Carried him to the house and skinned him out to bile.
I bet you forty dollars you could smell him fifty mile.

15. The children screamed and and the children cried,
They love ground hog cooked and fried.

16. Hello mama, make Sam quit,
He's eatin' all the hog and I can't get a bit.

17. Hello, boys, ain't it a sin,
Watch that gravy run down Sam's chin.

18. Hello, mama, look at Sam,
He's eat all the hog 'n' a-soppin' out the pan.

19. Watch him, boys, he's about to fall,
He's eat till his pants won't button at all.

9.

Springfield Mountain

Piano arrangement by
Charles and Ruth Seeger

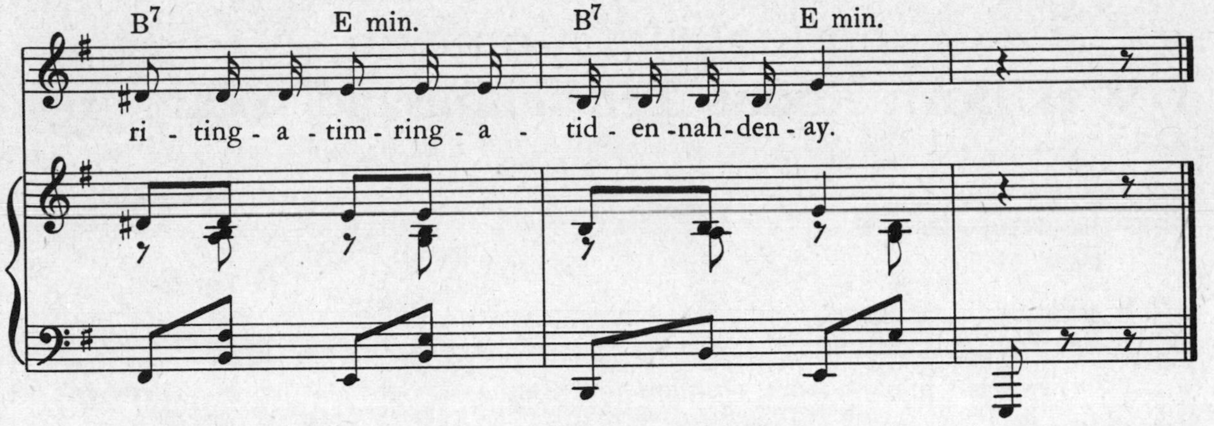

1. On Springfield Mountain there did dwell
A lovely youth whom I knew well,

2. This lovely youth one day did go
Down to the meadow for to mow.

3. He mowed a while and then did feel
A pizenous sarpint bite his heel.

4. He turned around and with a blow
He laid that pesky sarpint low.

5. They carried him to his Sally dear,
Which made her feel so very queer.

6. "O Johnny dear, why did you go
Down in your father's field to mow?"

7. "Why, Sally dear, I suppose you knowed
When the grass gits ripe it must be mowed!"

8. Now Sally had two ruby lips,
With which the pizen she did sip.

9. Dear Sally had a hollow tooth,
And so the pizen killed them both.

10. So Johnny died, gave up the ghost,
And off to heaven he did post.

11. Come all young girls, and shed one tear
For this young man that died right here.

12. Come all young men, and warning take,
And don't get bit by a rattle-snake.

10.

I Was Born About Ten Thousand Years Ago

Words and melody adapted and arranged by
John A. and Alan Lomax

Piano arrangement by
Charles and Ruth Seeger

2. I saw Satan when he looked the garden o'er;
I saw Adam and Eve driven from the door;
And from behind the bushes peepin', I saw the apple they were eatin'
And I swear I was the guy what et the core.

3. I taught Sampson how to use his mighty hands;
I first showed Columbus this happy land;
And for Pharoah's little kids I built all the pyramids
And to Sahara carried all the sands.

4. I taught Solomon his little ABC's;
I was the first man to eat limburger cheese;
And while floatin' down the bay with Methusalah one day
I saw his whiskers floatin' in the breeze.

5. I was there when Alexander crossed the sea,
And I always cheered him on to victory—
And when King Darius died, I was fighting by his side,
So he gave his cha-ri-ot to me.

6. I was present at the battle of the Nile;
And did the bullets fly, well I should smile:
And when Pharoah hit the King with a cutlass on the wing,
I was lying at the bottom of the pile.

7. I saw Nero fiddling when he burnt up Rome;
I told him it looked like his future home;
When he had the nerve to swear, I dragged him from his chair
And broke a Pilsner bottle on his dome.

8. Queen Elizabeth she fell in love with me;
We were married in Milwaukee secretly,
But I got tired and shook her and went off with General Hooker,
A-fightin' skeeters down in Tennessee . . .

CHAPTER II

When You Go A-Courtin'

11. *WHEN YOU GO A-COURTIN'*

As every singer knows there is no better and quicker way to court a young lady than to sing to her. As every young lady knows, there is no easier way to soften your man up than to croon a ditty in your softest and gentlest voice. It doesn't matter too much what you sing. All of the ballads in this book, all of the hymns, all of the wildest melodies have served as courting songs. This chapter, however, samples the garland of songs Americans have created for "carrying on with or about the gals." In such ballads as these the people expressed their deepest convictions about love, and, if you look between the lines, you cannot help but be struck by two repeatedly expressed attitudes toward love and courtship. First, love is dangerous—

I often have wondered, how women loved men,
Then I've looked back and wondered how men could love them.
It ain't nothin' but a notion that is gone with the wind.
They'll cause you hard labor, they'll cause your downfall,
They'll cause you hard labor all behind those prison walls.

Second, love is for laughter and courtship is a comedy—

Love, hit is a funny thing,
Shaped just like a lizard,
It'll run right up your backbone
And nibble at your gizzard.

Apparently these people, who weren't afraid of Indians or loneliness or the varmints of the woods or freedom or wild horses or prairie fires or drouth or deserts or six-guns, were afraid of love. It troubled them, made them feel like a "lonesome turtle dove"; or it tickled their risibility so that they sniggered or guffawed out loud. The comedy of courtship was recorded in hundreds of frontier stories, but nowhere better than in the real-life tale of "The Nettle Bottom Ball" included in J. S. Robb's *Streaks of Squatters' Life*, published in 1847:

I had bin a long time hankerin' arter old Tom Jones' darter on the branch below the Bottom, and she *was* a critter good for weak eyes. Maybe she hadn't a pair of her own! Well, if they warn't a brace of movin' light-houses, I wouldn't say it. There was no calculatin' the extent or handsomeness of the family that gal could bring up around her with a feller like me to look arter them. Talk about gracefulness, did you ever see a maple saplin' moving with the south wind? It warn't a crooked stick to compar to her. But her old dad was *awful.* He could jest lick anything that said *boo* in them diggins, out-swar Satan, was cross as a she-b'ar with cubs . . . and he was precious fond of usin' his shootin' iron. I detarmin'd anyhow, to ask for his daughter, Betsy, to be my partner at the Nettle Bottom Ball.

"Well, my sister, Marth, made me a bran new pair of buckskin trousers to go in, and rile my picture, ef she didn't put stirrups to 'em to keep 'em down. She said straps wur the fashion and I should wear 'em. I jest felt with 'em on as if I had somethin' pressin' me down. All my joints wur sot tight together, but Marth insisted, and I knew I could soon dance 'em off, so I gin in, and started off to the branch for Betsy Jones.

When I arriv, the old feller wur sittin' smokin' arter his supper, and the younger Jones' wur sittin' round the table takin' theirs. A whoppin' big pan of mush stood rite in the center, and a large pan of milk beside it, with lots of cornbread and butter, and Betsy was helpin' the youngsters, while old Mrs. Jones sot by, admirin' the family collection. Old Tom took a hard star' at me, and I kind a shook, but the straps stood it, and I recovered myself and gave as good as he sent, but I wur near the door and ready to break if he took in after me.

"What in Satan are you doin' in disguise? Come to steal somethin'?" says the old man. He swore dreadfully. I riled up at that. Says I, "Ef I wur comin' for sich purpose, you'd be the last I'd hunt up to steal offen."

"You're right," says he, "fur I'd make a hole to light your innards, ef you did." And the old savage chuckled. I meant because he had nothin' worth stealin' but his darter, but he tho't 'twas because I was afear'd on him.

Well, purty soon I gethered up courage and told him what I cum down fur, and invited him to the dance and take a drink and see that all went on rite. Betsy was in an awful way fur fear he wouldn't consent. The old 'oman here spoke in favor of the move and old Tom thought of the licker and gi'n in to the measure. Off bounced Betsy up a ladder into the second story, and one of the small gals with her to help put on the fixups. I set down in a chair and fell a-talkin' to the old 'oman. While we wur chattin' away as nice as relations, I could hear Betsy makin' things stand around above. The floor wus only loose boards kivered over wide joice, and every step made 'em shake and rattle like a small hurricane. Old Tom smoked away and the young ones at the table would hold a spoon of mush to thur mouths and look at my straps, and then look at each other and snigger, till at last the old man seed 'em.

"Well, by gun flints," says he, "ef you ain't makin' a josey—" Jest at that moment, somethin' gi'n way above, and may I die, ef Betsy, without anythin' on yearth on her but one of those starn cushins, didn't drop right through the floor, and sot herself flat into the pan of mush! I jest tho't fur a second that heaven and yearth had kissed each other, and squeezed me between 'em. Betsy squealed like a 'scape pipe; a spot of the mush had spattered on the old man's face and burnt him and he swore dreadful; I snatched up the pan of milk, and dashed it over Betsy to cool her off; and the old 'oman knocked me sprawlin' fur doin' it and away went my straps. The young ones let out a scream, as if the infarnal pit had let loose, and I'd jest gi'n half my hide to have bin out of the old man's reach. He did reach fur me, but I sent him one of my half-lows on the smeller that spread him, and may be I didn't leave sudden! I didn't see the branch, but as I soused through it, I heerd Tom Jones swar he'd "chaw me up, ef an inch big of me was found in them diggins in the mornin'!"

Here is the same story that our first version of "When You Go A-Courtin'" tells—the terrors of courtship on the frontier, when a father still ruled his family like a Biblical patriarch. The second version is a teasing (flyting) song, very popular with the ladies at pioneer parties. . . . Following the frontier from old Virginia to the plains, this song has warned girls of the hardships they would face in marrying boys from states further west.

12. *LOLLY-TOO-DUM*

After the girls had sung "The Texian Boys" or, a song like—

Johnson Boys raised in the ashes,
Didn't know how to court a maid,
Hang their heads and hide their faces,
Sight of a pretty girl makes them afraid—

to the great annoyance and embarrassment of the young men at a country party, the boys would answer back with something like "Lolly-Too-Dum." If the heroine of the song strikes you as a trifle young for marriage, remember that the practice of pioneer America differed from our own. In the early days of Illinois a bearded squatter brought a barefooted girl to the office of the justice of the peace and asked the "jedge" to marry them:

"How old is the young lady?" asked the judge.

" 'Bout fourteen, I reckon," said the squatter.

"Don't you think she's a little young to make a wife, Tom?" said the judge.

"No, I don't, jedge," said the squatter. "I figger it like this. Gals is like new potatoes. They're old enough as soon's they're big enough."

According to the dictates of the frontier (and of some isolated mountain communities of today), the squatter was right. Childhood was short in a log cabin. By the time a girl was six or eight, she'd have charge of one or two of her baby sisters and brothers. Soon she had to pitch in and help her overworked mother with the cows and chickens and housework. By the time she was fourteen she was thinking seriously about marriage, since marriage meant an escape from a hard and dreary life at home. If she wasn't married at twenty-one, people would already be wondering whether she was cut out to be an old maid.

In the new country "where men were men and women were scarce," however, a girl had little excuse for staying single. This letter from young Sophy, who had gone West to improve her fortunes, tells the story:

I got here two weeks ago and here I shall certainly end my days, fur I've had five fellers to spark me since I cum here, and another one wants to cum, but I give him the bags. One of my sparks has got three quarter sections and hous, is six foot tall, and four yoke oxen, and is widdorer, and wants to marry me next week, but I shall wait and see if I can do anny better, for between us, widdorers are so queer, and talk rite up so, they alwis frighten me—but howsumever I s'pose they don't mean more than other men.

This country is very large and so is men and the prarys they say is rollin' but I don't see but they are as still as any other plase. . . . Now you must cum out, I know you'll make your fortun here. Jim sez ther's only one gal here with golden hair like yourn, and she got an offer every day in the week after she got here. Now she's got a husband, a nice hous and farm and a pare of twins. You just can't help liking this country. . . .

Tell Amy if she'll come here she won't have to keep a-wishing and a-looking for the fellers as we used to do in Westbrook—out here theyr rite after you before you think of it. Give my luv to Jane, and ask her how she and Bill gits on, and if hees popped the question yet. She may have him for all of me—I can do better. I can pick my likin's 'mong the fellers here. *Nobody* can't help likin' this country.

For these men the rivers swarmed with fish and game abounded in the woods. The land was theirs in return for their blood and sweat. And for the women there were plenty of men to pop the question. A gal could hardly wait to grow up!

We recorded this song from the singing of Abner Boggs, "widdorer," in the mountains of Harlan County. He liked to sing in his mountain fields so that his children in the cabin a mile away could hear him and his neighbors across the mountains would say, "Ol' Ab's a-hollerin' like a mountain jack."

13. *WHEN I WAS SINGLE (I AND II)*

The frontier may have been a single woman's paradise, but it was hell on married women. Courtships were short and exciting, and weddings were hilarious frolics ending in "charivaris" that frightened the couple into each other's embrace. Afterward, a woman faced years of back-straining labor and the inevitable cabinful of children to be birthed and raised. Before she could sit down to her own table, according to country etiquette, the menfolks must be served and waited on. She carded, spun, and wove the wool and cotton that clothed her family. She worked side by side with her man in the fields at harvest time. Therefore, unless she was a woman of unusual vitality, she lost her beauty by the time she reached thirty, and by forty-odd had become a sallow, snaggle-toothed, gaunt old lady, always "complaining of a misery" in her back, always "feeling po'ly."

Separation and divorce were not uncommon, either. A man could simply drift on west in the night and leave his family to shift for themselves. Bachelors of this sort populated the new settlements. Yes, the frontier was a man's world and hell on women and horses. The first version of "I Wish I Was Single," still current among poor-white singers, tells the married woman's side of the story.

Still, as always, when a woman turned "ornery," she could give the man aces and kings and beat him with the spots in the deck. The men have had their troubles and they have howled about them. In May 24, 1826, the following notice appeared as a paid advertisement in a newspaper called the *Argus of the West*.

Whereas about three months since I took to my bed and board the reputed Widow Demarias Conklin, whom I supposed to be as *chaste* as an *icicle* and as *virtuous* as the *Goddess Diana*—and whereas since my marriage with the said reputed widow, I have learnt she has other husbands living, on whom I presume all her love and affections are placed, as she exhibited none toward me—and whereas the said widow Conklin has frequently wandered from the path of rectitude and conducted herself in such unbecoming manner that my breast has been filled with jealousy, my days with trouble, and my nights with sorrow—and whereas I wish to lead the life of a good and peaceable citizen, instead of being henpecked and tormented with an insatiable wife whose conduct is a disgrace to her sex. Now, therefore, be it known, that without the formalities of the law, I have separated myself from my unruly rib, and all good people are cautioned against trusting her on my account, as I will hereafter pay no debts of the contracting of the said Widow Conklin. I have no objection to her being harbored by any of my fellow citizens, but as to paying any of her debts I will not. I now enjoy myself remarkably well, being out of reach of tongs, broomsticks and ladles, and sleep quietly in my own shop, having none to molest me or make me afraid.

The man who signed this advertisement quite evidently felt he had been fighting with a whole tribe of Cherokees single-handed. He shares his sentiments with the singer of the second and well-known music-hall version of "When I Was Single."

14. *THE SPORTING BACHELORS*

The oldest of all the wars and the one that seems likely to go on forever has been described in many an American folk tale, but nowhere more tellingly than in this Negro folktale from North Carolina:

When de Lawd made Adam and Eve, he made them equal strength. They fit and they fit, but neither one could overcome the other. So Adam he goes to the Lawd and he say, "Dis woman got me down. I sho be oblige if you makes me stronger dan Eve."

"So be it," say de Lawd, "Look at yoself, Adam." Well, Adam look at his arms. Where befo' dey was smooth an' round, now de muscle bump up like prize yams. "Thank you kindly, good Lawd," say Adam.

So Adam hightail it home an' bust in de front do'. Eve was settin' rockin' in de rocker. Eve lookin' mean. When Adam come struttin' in, she retch down in de woodbox for a big stick of kindlin'. Adam jes' grab de stick an' heave it out de window. Den he give her a lazy little slap dat sail her clean across de room. "My feets must slip or somethin'," say Eve, an' she come up kickin' an' clawin'.

So Adam he pick her up an' throw her on de bed an' 'fo' she know what, he start layin' into her wid de flat of his hand. 'Fo' long Eve bust out bawlin'.

She say, "Please quit dat whackin' me, Adam honey."

"Is I de boss round here?" say Adam.

"Yes, honey," she say, "You is de man boss."

"Then fry me some catfish, woman."

"Yes, Adam, honey," she say.

But old Eve was mad enough to bust. Next mornin' she hunt up the Lawd, drap him a pretty curtsy and say, "Could you do me a little old favor, Lawd?"

"Name hit," say de Lawd.

"See dem two little ole rusty keys hangin' on dat nail," Eve say. "If you ain't usin' 'em, I wish I had dem little ole keys."

"I declare," say de Lawd. "Dey been hangin' on dat nail ten million years an' I ain't found de locks yet. If you want 'em, take 'em."

'Fo' long Adam comes outa de garden. "Gimme some food, woman!" he say.

"Can't, Adam, de kitchen do' locked." Adam tried to bust de kitchen do' down, but de Lawd built dat do' an' Adam can't even scratch hit. By an' by, first dark, he git sleepy, say, "Come on, honey, let's me an' you hit de froghair."

"Can't, Adam, de bedroom do' locked."

"Now, what we gonna do?" say Adam.

"Well, maybe, if you go out in de woods and rustle up some firewood, maybe I can put a conjure trick on dem do's an' git 'em open."

"I do it dis once," say Adam. "An' see can you open dem two do's." When he come back wid de wood, Eve has dem do's open an' from den on out Eve kep' de keys and use 'em to suit herself an' Adam haul in de wood. So dat de reason, de very reason, why de mens *thinks* dey is de boss and de wimmins *knows* dey is de boss, 'cause dey got dem two little ole rusty keys. An' if you don't know *dat* already, you ain't no married man.

"The Sporting Bachelors," a song which smacks of an Irish origin, makes a suitable companion piece for this old story of masculine defeat.

15. *JENNIE JENKINS*

As the young folks at a literary, a church sociable, a quilting, a bean-hulling, or an apple-peeling began to edge a little closer to each other, they would leave off the satirical songs and someone might next propose an "answer-back" piece. A dialogue song provided a fine way for a shy couple to court right out in public without overstepping the bounds of propriety or modesty. These old-time dialogue songs suited the teasing relationship that existed between young folks in the country. There was "Billy Boy," where the young fellow poked fun at an imaginary Miss Betsy Jane. There was "No, Sir, No" in which the young man "pursued and pursued and pursued her until she finally caught him." There was "Paper of Pins," where the girl turns the young man down when he sings—

Will you accept the keys to my chest
So you may have gold at your request?

but accepts his proposal, when he sings —

Will you accept the keys to my heart,
So we may wed and never part?

There were "The Deaf Woman's Courtship" and "The Quaker's Wooing," but none of these have the charm and bounce of "Jennie Jenkins," the color song.

The old folk beliefs about the colors generally followed a definite pattern in the British Isles. Most American singers, however, paid so little mind to these beliefs that they neglected to sing the rhyme in the concluding stanza of the British piece—

Will you wear blue, my dear, O my dear,
Will you wear blue, Jennie Jenkins?
Yes, I will wear blue, for your love is true—

in order to have a final joke.

"Jennie Jenkins" has been found in rocky Vermont, in the Southern Appalachians, and among the Okies of California, so we may suppose that at one time it was fairly common in all the country. Our version comes from Mr. and Mrs. F. C. Ball, whom we found courting one evening on the front porch of their Blue Ridge Mountain cabin.

16. *BLACK, BLACK*

If you should ever go ballad-hunting, it will do you no good to ask for "ballads" or "folk songs" or "songs from England" or anything of that kind. If you want to hear the ancient ballads, the romantic ballads of Lord Douglas or the Golden Willow Tree or Barbara Allen, ask around until you find someone who knows "old-timey love-songs," for that is how American folk-singers describe the ancient ballads of tragic love and morbid jealousy and passion murder. These long, doleful accounts of the dangers of love suited the attitudes of our pioneer ancestors exactly. They may not have wept over them, as we have seen the old-timers sing and weep at weddings in the Cajun country, but, when they heard them, they felt as lonesome as

A poor little turtle dove
Setting on a vine,
Mourning for his own true love,
Just as I mourn for mine.

Along with the ancient courtly ballads of the British Isles, life in the wilderness preserved, at the same time that it purified and refined, the great tradition of English lyric song. Sufficient traces of Elizabethan love-song survived to warrant the impression of Anglophile collectors that "the mountaineers of the Southern Appalachians were contemporary Elizabethans," although we now know that these songs were once common to the whole population.

When I forsake you, my old true love,
The rocks shall meet the sun;
The fire shall freeze like ice, my dear,
And the raging sea shall burn.

O don't you see yon little turtle dove,
A-skipping from vine to vine,
A-mourning the loss of its own true love,
Just as I mourn for mine.

Often, however, the golden fancies of British song were transmuted into cold steel or warm copper, a coinage of poetry better suited to the lives of hard-favored pioneers, small farmers, coal miners, coon-hunters, and their women.

The answer that she made him
With tears all in their eyes—
She loved the man that loved her
And she'd love him till she died.

If I had the wings of an eagle,
I'd fly to East and West,
I'd come down without ary fall
And marry the one I love best.

From somewhere in the foothills of Colorado, like a wildflower lifting its head among the grey rocks, came this cowboy love song:

Eyes like a morning star,
Cheeks like a rose,
Laura was a pretty girl,
God Almighty knows.

Weep, all ye little rains,
Wail, ye winds, wail,
All along, along, along
That Colorado Trail.

The banjo pickers, the pokerfaced lads who studied how to make a guitar talk the song, laid the basis for hillbilly ballads with lines like these:

I'd rather be in some dark holler,
Where the sun refuse to shine,
Than to see you another man's darling
And know you'll never be mine.
I don't want yore green-back dollars,
I don't want yore diamond ring,
All I want is yore love, darling,
Won't you take me back again?

Just as sure as the dew falls
Upon the green corn,
Last night she was with me,
Tonight she is gone.

Here was the tradition out of which the blues lyrics sprang when the clash and roar of the industrial age burst in upon the country singers.

Lemme be yore side-track,
Honey, till yore mainline come.
I can do more switchin'
Than yore mainline ever done.

"Black, Black" is an American original which Jack Niles has recast in the image of an English courting song.

17. *COME ALL YOU FAIR AND TENDER LADIES*

We asked one old mountain woman and she said, "It's a mighty sorrowful sounding song, but I like it. It's one my sweetheart used to sing when he came over the mountain a-courtin' me. He made it sound as mournful as he could so's to make me pity him."

"Did you pity him?"

"Well, I reckon so. I been married to him thirty years."

Another lady from Kentucky told us: "A lot of times a woman would be singing that and the men would say, 'Oh sing something else, for there's no truth in that song.' Songs that women makes up about men—about their husbands and about their sweethearts—the men think that we've given them the wrong kind of a deal and it's not justice and they have protested and everly have as far back as I can remember."

18. *OLD SMOKEY*

Think back a century or more to the days when most roads in America were pack-trails, when you packed your produce to the store from your little farm and packed your coffee and sugar and calico back to your family in the little clearing in the big woods. Remember the time when the United States government undertook to finance the building of a wagon road from Washington to St. Louis, the Old Pike, which some folks felt was a crackpot idea, the old-timers called the Old Pike, crackpot foolishness. These were the days when the wagoner with his six spanking horses and his big Conestoga wagon cut a romantic figure everywhere he traveled. The small boys gawked at him and wanted nothing more than to be such a man when they grew up. The gals all had a specially soft spot in their hearts for him.

The Conestoga wagon was built to carry a tremendous load and to withstand the shocks of the wilderness roads it had to navigate. It was a regular frigate of the land, and, according to experts, the best wagon ever invented anywhere. Solid oak, thirty feet long, with their white canvas tops, their bright red sides and their blue underbodies, a caravan of Conestogas was a colorful sight in the unrelieved green of the American wilderness. The rumbling of their huge iron-tired wheels (eight feet in diameter), the screeching of their wooden axles, the swearing of their drivers, and the jingling of the bells on the horses made a real show for the country folk as the caravan rolled along. In those days a boy could tell whose wagon was coming down the road by the sound of the harness bells.

The wagoners were a reckless, devil-may-care lot—singers, dancers, lads with a rambling mind. They found a new girl in every settlement. The sound of their bells has died away; the ruts of their old Pike have faded in the meadows and on the hills; but their story still lives in this song, a lonesome love ditty with its roots in England and its trail winding across all the forty-eight states.

19. *DOWN IN THE VALLEY*

This is another lonesome tune, distilled out of the quiet of the mountain coves, but the aloofness of "Come All You Fair and Tender

Ladies" has departed from this song. There is, instead, a frank nostalgia, a looking out over the rim of the mountain world into the valley where the train rumbles and whistles along, where the world begins to break in upon the peace and isolation of the laurel thickets. The sugar and spice of popular song has come into the hills now; the guitar with an instruction booklet from Sears Roebuck has taught the banjo-player his four-square chords; hillbilly music, which stands for the adaptation of the ancient rural music to city standards, has emerged.

Ever since hillbilly songs began to be heard on records and over the radio, new versions of "Down in the Valley" have been spread abroad. One variant, a prisoners' song called "Twenty-one Years," was recorded on five sides by one company, as well as imitated by others. So, in the last twenty-five years, this tune has become national property, along with "Home on the Range" and "You Are My Sunshine," which it closely resembles. As few of our folks songs, it has crossed the boundaries of geography and background and has become a national song, its stanzas a distillation of many love songs now forgotten. It is a song for many people to sing together with harmony thrown in. Blow it out soft on a harmonica by yourself and it may make you cry.

20. *CARELESS LOVE*

For our singers, courtship was a rather cruel comedy and marriage a dangerous battle, but love, especially "keerless love," would

—make a preacher lay his Bible down,
—make a jack-rabbit hug a hound,
—make a grandmother marry her oldest son,
—make a good boy leave his happy home.

Careless love would give you the blues, blues enough to make a newborn baby cry. Indeed, "Careless Love" is one of the earliest, if it is not actually the first, blues. Our guess is that it originated among white singers (if one can say that any relatively modern Southern song was not a joint product of the two peoples), but it has changed hands across the race line so frequently that it has acquired a pleasant coffee color. Ask an old-time Negro blues singer in the Mississippi Valley the name of the earliest blues he knows and he will probably tell you "Careless Love," or one of its close relatives—"Make Me A Pallet on Your Floor" or "Easy Rider." They all have the same metrical form—iambic tetrameter, with the first line repeated thrice and the "punch" or rhyming line as the fourth and final line of the stanza. Whatever the origin of "Careless Love," you may hear it any day on a hillbilly radio program or wherever a Negro moans the blues.

21. *DINK'S SONG*

. . . is a beautiful Negro variant of "Careless Love." John A. Lomax tells how he found the song in 1904, when he made his first field trip for Harvard University:

"I found Dink scrubbing her man's clothes in the shade of their tent across the Brazos river from the A. & M. College in Texas. Professor James C. Nagle of the College faculty was the supervising engineer of a levee-building company and he had invited me to come along and bring my Edison recording machine. The Negroes were trained levee workers from the Mississippi River.

" 'Dink knows all the songs,' said her companion. But I did not find her helpful until I walked a mile to a farm commissary and bought her a pint of gin. As she drank the gin, the sounds from her scrubbing board increased in intensity and in volume. She worked as she talked: 'That little boy there ain't got no daddy an' he ain't got no name. I comes from Mississippi and we never saw these levee niggers, till us got here. I brung along my little boy. My man drives a four-wheel scraper down there where you see the dust risin'. I keeps his tent, cooks his vittles and washes his clothes. Some day Ize goin' to wrap up his wet breeches and shirts, roll 'em up in a knot, put 'em in the middle of the bed, and tuck down the covers right nice. Then I'm going on up the river where I belong.' She sipped her gin and sang and drank until the bottle was empty.

"The original Edison record of 'Dink's Song' was broken long ago, but not until all the Lomax family had learned the tune. The one-line refrain, as Dink sang it in her soft lovely voice, gave the effect of a sobbing woman, deserted by her man. Dink's tune is really lost; what is left is only a shadow of the tender, tragic beauty of what she sang in the sordid, bleak surroundings of a Brazos Bottom levee camp.

"The lyrics and music of 'Dink's Song' are to me uniquely beautiful. Professor Kittredge praised them without stint. Carl Sandburg compares them to the best fragments of Sappho. As you might expect, Carl prefers Dink to Sappho.

"When I went to find her in Yazoo, Mississippi, some years later, her women friends, pointing to a nearby graveyard, told me, 'Dink's done planted up there.' I could find no trace of her little son who 'didn't have no name.' "

22. *SEE, SEE, RIDER*

. . . is a blues, not a false blues like the Tin Pan Alley "Wabash Blues," or a long-hair blues for piano and seventy-five instruments, but a real Negro blues—first line twice or thrice sung with a rhyming "punch" line. A folk blues has a simple tune you can sing all night and never tire of and an easy beat that rocks you with a steady roll. No Tin Pan Alley sharpie had anything to do with this blues, measuring the sweet and the bitter into a salable mixture. It came out of the great dark valley of the blues, the Mississippi Delta, where the earth and the people are equally fertile and burdened with troubles.

"The blues ain't nothin' but a good man feelin' bad, the blues ain't nothin' but a woman on a poor man's mind, the blues ain't nothin' but the poor man's heart disease—" so they say. "If the blues was money, I'd be a millioneer; if the blues was whiskey, I'd stay drunk all the time, 'cause I can't be satisfied, I can't be satisfied—" so the people, who are deprived and truly desperate, see their deprivation and their desolation. "The blues come from Texas lopin' like a mule; the blues come walkin' like a nachul man; the blues run a rabbit, run him a solid mile and when the blues overtaken him, he hollered like a baby chile; woke up this mornin', the blues all round my bed, went to eat my breakfast and the blues all in my bread—" so the people personify him. They say "hello" to the blues, because he's somebody they know so well.

Good mornin', blues, blues how do you do?
He says, "I'm feelin' putty well, good partner, how are you?

Elizabethans spoke of the "blue devils," having in mind the same feeling that our own singers describe as "the blues." The African slaves kept up their ancient custom of "hollering and moaning" mournful tunes while they worked. Sometime near the turn of the century, a Negro somewhere sat down with an instrument and set one of these "hollers" within the confines of a regular rhythm with a chordal progression. He called this kind of song, "the blues" because he felt "low and worried in his mind." The blues soon replaced all other kinds of music at country Negro dances or in the barrel houses in the slums where the Negroes, just come to town, gathered for their fun. The jazz boys, down from Perdido Street in New Orleans, and Handy, traveling through rural Arkansas, heard this music and made their own uses of it. Now this lonesome melody of the Mississippi has uncoiled in the ear of the whole world.

The blues not only formed jazz, but it has influenced all of Southern white music, lending its chords and its color to our new "hillbilly" songs. The blues have crept into the churches in the guise of "gospel songs." The blues are staple, if not quite respectable, fare on record jockey programs, at late-hour nighteries, even in Western movies. The blues have, more than any other song-form, become *the American song,* much as *cante hondo* is the national song form of Spain or the *corrido* is the national ballad form of Mexico.

"See, See Rider," said to have been composed by an Arkansas Negro in the early part of this century, is the song of "the midnight creeper," "the kid-man," "the sweet-back man," "the nachul-born easman." If you want to understand what these terms mean and what the song has to tell you, here is a little yarn-spinning by Left Wing Gordon, Negro blues singer, wanderer, and philosopher:

I had some mighty, fine women. Had so many I can't count 'em. Take me till day after tomorrow to tell 'bout 'em. Find fifteen or twenty in different cities, an' I been in a heap of cities. . . . Lot's o' times I be in a strange city, jes' come to town. Ain't got no money, ain't got no friends. So I see a nice-lookin' lady at the station or on the street on my way lookin' for a place to stay or maybe some work to do. So I ask her name an' street number an' address. Then I asks her if she's got a friend. Sometime she say "yes" an' sometimes she say "no." So I say I'm in town, lonesome an' want a friend, so what about us bein' friends? I say I'm a man makes good money an' knows how to get it, but jes' now happen to be out an' lonesome boy. Well, if she let me be her friend, I go stay with her a while and sweethearts with her. . . .

Pity po' boy 'way from home,
Good old boy jes' ain't treated right,
Freezin' ground my foldin' bed last night.

Sometimes I ask 'em if they like to drink, an' they say yes. Well, I ask 'em if they ever practice bein' sweet to a person, an' maybe they say yes, they like to be pleasant. So I says I'll do to be pleasant to, and so they git pretty soft on me. Always anxious fer strange feller.

Now a good-lookin' man have a home anywhere he go,
Reason I know is the women tell me so. . . .

Some of these creepers an' rounders more smarter'n mos' women. Sho' do fool 'em. I done learned tricks myself a long time ago. I hides my money in bottom of my shoe or some place. I outtalks 'em an' I plays all sorts of tricks on 'em, how to beat 'em. Howsomever I done learned my tricks by losin' a heap first. . . . Still I don't pay 'em no mind 'cause women can beat men double-crossin'—jes' won't be straight. Always do something crooked in spite of eve'thing. . . . Looks like when I'm with 'em I has to quarrel and fight an' when I'm long way from home an' ain't got no friends, blues drive me crazy. Can't never be satisfied.

Don't never git one woman on yo' mind,
Keep you in trouble and bothered all the time.

You don't know, you don't know my mind,
When you think I'm lovin' you,
I'm leavin' you all the time.

23. *SHORTY GEORGE*

Once a month, on Sunday about sunset, a little gasoline motor-car, whistling as it heads for Houston, leaves Central State Prison Farm near Sugarland, Texas. This "runty little train," the Negro convicts call Shorty George. It is carrying away their wives and sweethearts who, according to custom, have been allowed to spend the day with their menfolks. Especially favored are the trusties who are free to go with their lady friends anywhere in camp limits.

The Shorty George blues is mournfully sad, full of pathetic longing. Iron Head, in prison for life ("I'm a 'habish,'" he told us proudly, "habitual criminal, you know! De roughest nigger dat ever walked de streets of Dallas."), broke down and cried when he sang "Shorty George." "My woman she's scaid to come to me, she might as well be dead. So I gits restless an' wants to run away f'um dis place. I jes' cain't hardly stand to sing dat song."

The song was known among the Negro convicts at Sugarland as Iron Head's personal property. He wouldn't sing it before any of his fellow inmates, and he always cried when he sang about burying his woman. "I couldn't hear nuffin but de coffin's sound."

11.

When You Go A-Courtin'

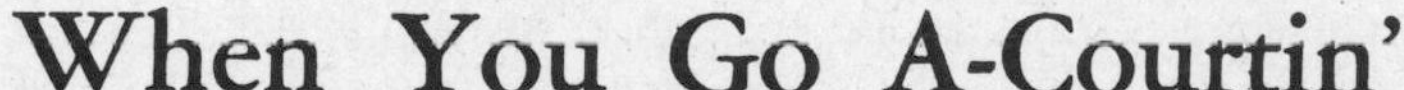

Words and melody adapted and arranged by
John A. and Alan Lomax

Piano arrangement by
Charles and Ruth Seeger

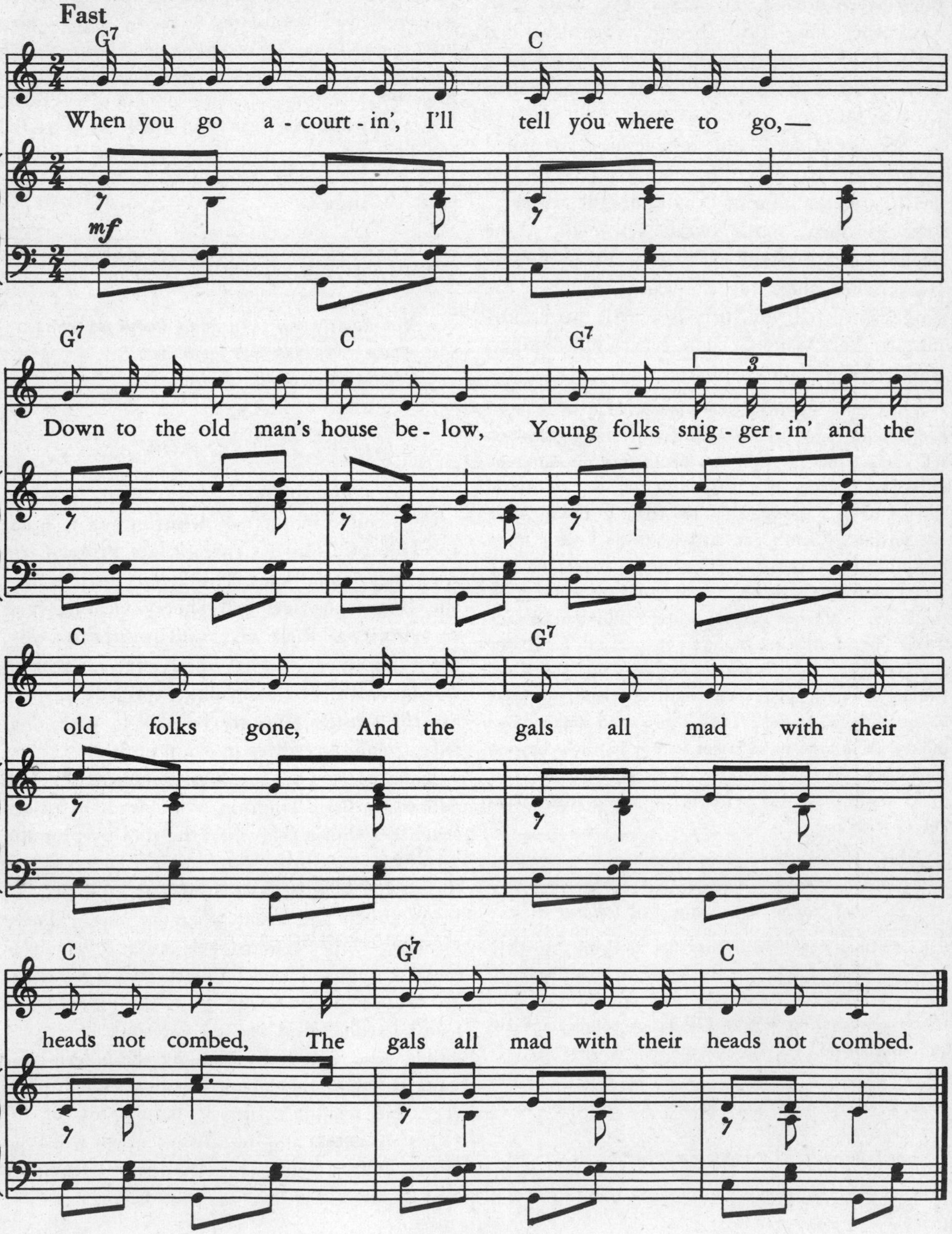
Fast
G7 C
When you go a-court-in', I'll tell you where to go,—
mf
G7 C G7
Down to the old man's house be-low, Young folks snig-ger-in' and the
C G7
old folks gone, And the gals all mad with their
C G7 C
heads not combed, The gals all mad with their heads not combed.

1. When you go a-courtin', I'll tell you where to go,
Down to the old man's house below.
Young folks sniggerin' and the old folks gone,
And the gals all mad with their heads not combed,
The gals all mad with their heads not combed.

2. The old dirty clothes were hangin' on a loom,
The house not swept, for they had no broom;
Had a long-tail coat, Lord, greasy all around,
And an old leather bonnet with a hole in the crown,
An old leather bonnet with a hole in the crown.

3. Well, I stayed and I sparked till I got ashamed—
Every few minutes its "What's your name?"
I told them it was Johnny and they seemed satisfied,
For they laughed and they giggled until they both cried,
They laughed and they giggled until they both cried.

4. Asked me in and invited me to eat,
All they had was a little piece of meat,
An old dull knife and a little bitty fork,
Sawed a half an hour and I never made a mark,
Sawed a half an hour and I never made a mark.

5. Sawed and I sawed till I got it off my plate,
They said, "Young man, you'd better wait."
Sawed and I sawed till I got it on the floor,
Took my foot and I kicked it out the door,
Took my foot and I kicked it out the door.

6. Here come the old man with a doubled-barreled gun,
They said, "Young feller, you'd better run."
Stood there and fought him just as brave as any bear,
Tangled my fingers in the old man's hair,
Tangled my fingers in the old man's hair.

7. He smashed my nose and my clothes he tore,
He knocked out my teeth and threw me on the floor,
He blacked my eyes and kicked me in the pants,
Swear, by heck, I'll never take another chance,
Swear, by heck, I'll never take another chance.

The Texian Boys

(Version II of "When You Go A-Courtin' ")

1. Lou'siana gals, come and listen to my noise,
Don't go marry those Texian boys,
For, if you do, your fortune will be
Johnnycake and venison and sassafras tea,
Johnny cake and venison and sassafras tea.

2. When they go to farming, you needn't be alarmed,—
In Feb'uary they plant their corn.
The way they tend it, I'll tell you how—
With a Texas pony and a grasshopper plow,
With a Texas pony and a grasshopper plow.

3. When they go to preachin', let me tell you what they wear,—
An old leather coat all picked and bare,
An old straw hat more brim than crown,
And a pair of dirty socks they've worn the winter round,
A pair of dirty socks they've worn the winter round.

4. When they go a-courtin', I'll tell you what they ride,—
An old pack-saddle all covered with hide,
An old hair girth made out of a rope,
A-straddle of a horse that can't fetch a lope,
A-straddle of a horse that can't fetch a lope.

5. When he comes in first thing you hear,—
"Madam, your daddy has killed a deer."
And the next thing he says when he sits down,
"Madam, the johnnycake's too damn brown,
"Madam, the johnnycake's too damn brown."

6. For your wedding supper there's beef and cornbread,
There it is to eat when the ceremony's said;
And when you go to milk, you'll milk in a gourd,
Set it in a corner and cover it with a board,
Set it in a corner and cover it with a board.

7. They live in a hut with a hewed log wall,
But it ain't got any windows at all;
With a clapboard roof and a puncheon floor,
And that's the way all Texas o'er,
And that's the way all Texas o'er.

8. They will take you out on a live-oak hill,
And there they'll leave you against your will.
They'll leave you on the prairie and starve you on the plains,
For that is the way with the Tex-i-ans,
For that is the way with the Tex-i-ans.

9. Brandy is brandy any way you mix it,
A Texian's a Texian any way you fix him,
When other good folk are all gone to bed,
The devil is a-workin' in a Texian's head,
The devil is a-workin' in a Texian's head.

12.

Lolly-Too-Dum

Words and melody adapted and arranged by
John A. and Alan Lomax

Piano arrangement by
Charles and Ruth Seeger

1. As I went out one morning to breathe the morning air,
Lolly too-dum, too-dum, lolly too-dum day,
As I went out one morning to breathe the morning air,
I heard a dear old mother saying "O my daughter fair,"
Lolly too-dum, too-dum, lolly too-dum day.

2. "You better go wash them dishes and hush that flattering tongue,
You know you want to marry and that you are too young."

3. "O pity my condition, just as you would your own,
For fourteen long years I have lived all alone."

4. "Supposing I were willing, where would you get your man?"
"Why, Lordy mercy, mammy, I'd marry handsome Sam."

5. "Supposing he would slight you like you done him before?"
Why, Lordy mercy, mammy, I'd marry forty more."

6. There's doctors and lawyers and men of high degree,
And some of them wants to marry and some will marry me."

7. "There's peddlers and tinkers and boys from the plow,
Lordy mercy, mammy, the fit comes on me now."

8. "Now my daughter's married and well for to do,
Lordy mercy, boys, I'm on the market, too."

13.

When I Was Single (I)

(Woman's Story)

Words and melody adapted and arranged by
John A. and Alan Lomax

Piano arrangement by
Charles and Ruth Seeger

1. When I was single, went dressed all so fine,
Now I am married, go ragged all the time.
Lord, don't I wish I was a single girl again.

2. Dishes to wash, spring to go to,
When you're married, Lord, you've got it all to do.
Lord, don't I wish I was a single girl again.

3. When I was single, my shoes they did screak,
Now I am married, my shoes they do leak.
Lord, don't I wish I was a single girl again.

4. Three little babies, lyin' in the bed,
All of them so hungry they can't raise up their head.
Lord, don't I wish I was a single girl again.

5. Wash their little feet and send them to school,
Along comes the drunkard and calls them a fool.
Lord, don't I wish I was a single girl again.

6. When I was single, I eat biscuit and pie,
Now I am married, Lord, it's eat cornbread or die.
Lord, don't I wish I was a single girl again.

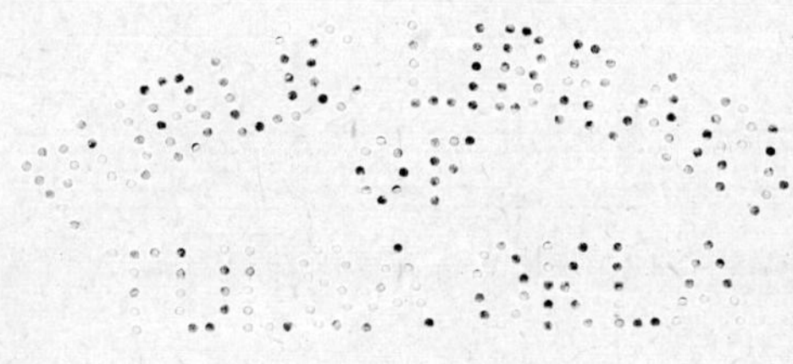

When I Was Single (II)

(Man's Complaint)

Words and melody adapted and arranged by
John A. and Alan Lomax

Piano arrangement by
Charles and Ruth Seeger

1. When I was single, O then, O then,
When I was single, O then,
When I was single,
My pockets did jingle,
And I wish I was single again.

2. I married me a wife, O then, O then,
I married me a wife, O then,
I married me a wife,
She's the plague of my life,
I wish I was single again.

3. My wife she died, O then, O then,
My wife she died, O then,
My wife, she died,
And I laughed till I cried
To think I was single again.

4. I married me another, O then, O then,
I married me another, O then,
I married me another,
She's the devil's grandmother,
And I wish I was single again.

5. She beat me she, banged me, O then, O then,
She beat me, she banged me, O then,
She beat me, she banged me,
She swore she would hang me,
I wish I was single again.

6. She got a rope, O then O then,
She got a rope, O then,
She got a rope,
And she greased it with soap,
And I wished I was single again.

7. The limb did break, O then, O then,
The limb did break, O then,
The limb did break,
My neck did escape,
And I wish I was single again.

8 Young men take warning from this, from this,
Young men take warning from this,
Be good to the first,
For the last is much worse.—
And I wish I was single again.

14.

The Sporting Bachelors

Words and melody adapted and arranged by
John A. and Alan Lomax

Piano arrangement by
Charles and Ruth Seeger

Fast

2. She dresses me in rags,
In the very worst of rags,
While *she* dresses like a queen so fine;
She goes to the town by day and by night,
Where the gentlemen do drink wine, wine, wine,
Where the gentlemen do drink wine.

3. When I come home,
I am just like one alone;
My poor jaw is trembling with fear.
She'll pout and she'll lower, she'll frown and look sour,
Till I dare not stir for my life, life, life,
Till I dare not stir for my life.

4. When supper is done,
She just tosses me a bone,
And swears I'm obliged to maintain her;
O sad the day I married, O that I longer tarried,
Till I to the altar was led, led, led,
Till I to the altar was led.

15.

Jennie Jenkins

Words and melody adapted and arranged by
John A. and Alan Lomax

Piano arrangement by
Charles and Ruth Seeger

1. MAN: Will you wear white, O my dear, O my dear?
O will you wear white, Jennie Jenkins?
WOMAN: I won't wear white,
For the color's too bright,
I'll buy me a fol-di-roldy-tildy-toldy,
Seek-a-double, use-a-cause-a, roll-the-find-me,
MAN: Roll, Jennie Jenkins, roll.

2. MAN: Will you wear red, O my dear, O my dear?
O will you wear red, Jennie Jenkins?
WOMAN: I won't wear red,
It's the color of my head.

3. MAN: Will you wear black, O my dear, O my dear?
O will you wear black, Jennie Jenkins?
WOMAN: I won't wear black,
It's the color of my back.

4. MAN: Will you wear green, O my dear, O my dear?
O will you wear green, Jennie Jenkins?
WOMAN: I won't wear green,
For it's a shame to be seen.

5. MAN: Will you wear purple, O my dear, O my dear?
O will you wear purple, Jennie Jenkins?
WOMAN: I won't wear purple,
It's the color of a turkle.*

6. MAN: Will you wear blue, O my dear, O my dear?
O will you wear blue, Jennie Jenkins?
WOMAN: I won't wear blue,
The color's too true.

*i.e., a turtle (turkle) dove.

16.

Black is the Color

Melody adapted and arranged by
John Jacob Niles

Piano arrangement by
Charles and Ruth Seeger

1. Black, black, black, is the color of my true love's hair,
Her lips are like some rosy fair,
The prettiest face and the neatest hands,
I love the ground whereon she stands.

2. I love my love and well she know-o'-ows
I love the grass whereon she goes,
If she on earth no more I see
My life will quickly fade away.

3. I go to Troublesome to mourn and weep
But satisfied I ne'er could sleep.
I'll write to you in a few little lines,
I'll suffer death ten thousand times.

4. So fare you well, my own true love,
The time has passed and I wish you well;
But still I hope the time will come
When you and I will be as one.

5. Black, black, black is the color of my true love's hair,
Her lips are like some rosy fair,
The prettiest face and the neatest hands,
I love the ground whereon she stands.

17.

Come All You Fair and Tender Ladies

1. Come all you fair and tender ladies,
Be careful how you court young men,
They're like a star of a summer's morning,
They'll first appear and then they're gone.

2. They'll tell to you some loving story,
They'll declare to you their love is true;
Straightway they'll go and court some other,
And that's the love they have for you.

3. I wish I was some little sparrow,
That I had wings, could fly so high;
I'd fly away to my false true lover,
And when he's talkin' I'd be by.

4. But I am not a little sparrow,
And neither have I wings to fly;
I'll sit down here in grief and sorrow
To weep and pass my troubles by.

5. If I'd a-known before I courted,
I never would have courted none;
I'd have locked my heart in a box of golden,
And pinned it up with a silver pin.

18.

Old Smoky

Words and melody adapted and arranged by
John A. and Alan Lomax

Piano arrangement by
Charles and Ruth Seeger

1. On top of old smoky
All covered in snow,
I lost my true lover
By courtin' too slow.

2. For meetin' is a pleasure
And partin' is a grief
And a false hearted lover
Is worse than a thief.

3. A thief, he'll but rob you
And take all you have,
But a false hearted true love
Will drive you to your grave.

4. Your grave will decay you
And turn you to dust,
Not one girl in fifty
That a poor boy can trust.

5. They will tell you they love you
Just to give your heart ease,
And, as soon as your back's turned
They'll court who they please.

6. They'll hug you and kiss you
And tell you more lies,
Than cross ties in a railroad
Or stars in the skies. . . .

7. "It's a-rainin', it's a-hailin',
The moon gives no light,
Your horses can't travel
This dark, lonesome night.

8. "Go put up your horses
And feed them some hay,
And seat yourself by me
As long as you stay."

9. "My horses ain't hungry,
They won't eat your hay,
So farewell, my little darling,
I'll feed on the way.

10. "I will drive on to Georgy
And write you my mind.
My mind is to marry
And leave you behind."

11. "I'll go up on Smoky
On the mountain so high
Where the wild birds and the turtle doves
Can hear my sad cry.

12. "As sure as the dewdrops
Fall on the green corn
Last night he was with me
Tonight he is gone."

19.

Down in the Valley

Words and melody adapted and arranged by
John A. and Alan Lomax

Piano arrangement by
Charles and Ruth Seeger

1. Down in the valley, valley so low,
Hang your head over, hear the wind blow.
    Hear the wind blow, love, hear the wind blow,
    Hang your head over, hear the wind blow.

2. If you don't love me, love whom you please,
But throw your arms round me, give my heart ease.
    Give my heart ease, dear, give my heart ease.
    Throw your arms round me, give my heart ease.

3. Down in the valley, walking between,
Telling our story, here's what it sings:
    Here's what it sings, dear, here's what it sings,
    Telling our story, here's what it sings:

4. Roses of sunshine, vi'lets of dew,
Angels in heaven knows I love you,
    Knows I love you, dear, knows I love you,
    Angels in heaven knows I love you.

5. Build me a castle forty feet high,
So I can see her as she goes by,
    As she goes by, dear, as she goes by,
    So I can see her as she goes by.

6. Bird in a cage, love, bird in a cage,
Dying for freedom, ever a slave;
    Ever a slave, dear, ever a slave,
    Dying for freedom, ever a slave.

7. Write me a letter, send it by mail,
And back it in care of the Birmingham jail.
    Birmingham jail, love, Birmingham jail,
    And back it in care of the Birmingham jail.

20.

Careless Love

Words and melody adapted and arranged by
John A. and Alan Lomax

Piano arrangement by
Charles and Ruth Seeger

1. Love, O love, O careless love,
Love, O love, O careless love,
Love, O love, O careless love,
You see what careless love has done.

2. It's gone and broke this heart of mine,
It's gone and broke this heart of mine,
It's gone and broke this heart of mine,
It'll break that heart of yours sometime.

3. When I wore my apron low,
When I wore my apron low,
When I wore my apron low,
You'd follow me through rain or snow.

4. Now my apron strings won't pin,
Now my apron strings won't pin,
Now my apron strings won't pin,
You pass my door and won't come in.

5. I cried last night and the night before,
I cried last night and the night before,
I criea last night and the night before,
Gonna cry tonight and cry no more.

6. How I wish that train would come,
How I wish that train would come,
How I wish that train would come,
And take me back where I come from.

7. I love my mama and papa, too,
I love my mama and papa, too,
I love my mama and papa, too,
I'd leave them both for lovin' you.

8. Now you see what careless love will do,
Now you see what careless love will do,
Now you see what careless love will do,
Make you kill yourself and your sweetheart, too.

9. Many a po' girl has left her home,
Many a po' girl has left her home,
Many a po' girl has left her home,
For love, O love, O careless love.

21.

Dink's Song

Words and melody adapted and arranged by
John A. and Alan Lomax

Piano arrangement by
Charles and Ruth Seeger

1. Ef I had wings like Norah's dove,
I'd fly up de river to de man I love.
Fare thee well, O honey fare thee well.

2. Ize got a man an' he's long an' tall,
Moves his body like a cannon ball.
Fare thee well, O honey, fare thee well.

3. One uh these days, an' it won't be long,
Call my name an' I'll be gone.
Fare thee well, O honey, fare thee well.

4. 'Member one night, a-drizzlin' rain,
Roun' my heart I felt a pain.
Fare thee well, O honey, fare thee well.

5. When I wo' my ap'on low,
Couldn't keep you from my do'.
Fare thee well, O honey, fare thee well.

6. Now I wears my ap'on high,
Sca'cely ever see you passin' by.
Fare thee well, O honey, fare thee well.

7. Now my ap'on's up to my chin,
You pass my do' an' you won't come in.
Fare thee well, O honey, fare thee well.

8. Ef I had listened to what my mama said,
I'd be at home in my mama's bed.
Fare thee well, O honey, fare thee well.

22.

Easy Rider

Words and melody adapted and arranged by
John A. and Alan Lomax

Piano arrangement by
Charles and Ruth Seeger

1. Easy rider, see what you done done, Lawd, Lawd,
Easy rider, see what you done done,
Easy rider, see what you done done,
Hey, hey, hey, hey.

2. Made me love you, now yo' man done come, Lawd, Lawd,
Made me love you, now yo' man done come,
Made me love you, now yo' man done come,
Hey, hey, hey, hey.

3. When you see me comin', h'ist yo' windows high, Lawd, Lawd,
When you see me comin', h'ist yo' windows high,
When you see me comin', h'ist yo' windows high,
Hey, hey, hey, hey.

4. When you see me leavin', hang yo' head an' cry, Lawd, Lawd,
When you see me leavin', hang yo' head an' cry,
When you see me leavin', hang yo' head an' cry,
Hey, hey, hey, hey.

5. If I was a headlight on some western train, Lawd, Lawd,
I'd shine my light on cool Colorado Springs,
I'd shine my light on cool Colorado Springs,
Hey, hey, hey, hey.

6. I'm goin to the nation and the territo', Lawd, Lawd,
Tryin' to fin' a honey gal I know,
Tryin' to fin' a honey gal I know,
Hey, hey, hey, hey.

7. If I was a catfish swimmin' in the deep blue sea, Lawd, Lawd,
I'd keep those women from fussin' over me,
I'd keep those women from fussin' over me,
Hey, hey, hey, hey.

23.

Shorty George

1. Well-a, Shorty George, he ain' no friend of mine,
Well-a, Shorty George, he ain' no friend of mine,
Taken all de womens an' leave de mens behin'.

2. O when I get back to Dallas, gonna walk an' tell
Dat de Fort Ben' bottom is a burnin' Hell.

3. My mama died, Lord, when Ize a lad,
An' ev'y since I been to de bad.

4. Well, my babe caught de Katy, I caught de Santa Fe;
Well, you cain' quit me, babe, cain' you see?

5. Well, I wen' down to Galveston, work on de Mall'ry Line,
Babe, you cain' quit me, ain' no need you tryin'".

6. Got a letter f'um my baby, "Come at once, she's dyin'"—
She wasn' dead, she was slowly dyin'.

7. How kin you blame po' man f'um cryin',
When his babe ain' dead, but slowly dyin'?

8. Well, I followed her down to de buryin' groun',
You oughta heered me holler when dey let her down.

9. I took my babe to de buryin' groun';
I never knowed I loved her till de coffin' soun'.

CHAPTER III

Swing Your Pardner

Swing your pardner round and around,
Till the hollow of her foot makes a hole in the ground.
Meet your pardner, pat her on the head,
If she don't like biscuits give her cornbread.
Give the fiddler a dram,
Give the fiddler a dram,
Then dance all night
With the bottle in your hand.

WHEN THE FIRST SETTLERS CAME FROM England to the New World, the violin was still a folk instrument, popular at country dances in the shires, but not yet accepted in polite society. For frontier America, however, the fiddle was not just another musical instrument, it was music itself. Played butt against chest, rather than under the chin, sounding the old English and Irish reels and the wild bagpipe melodies of the Scottish Highlands, its wailing, throbbing voice rang through the wilderness like the crow of a rooster, calling the folks to their hoedowns, husking bees, log-rollings, corn-shuckings, weddings, and infares. How our ancestors turned out for one of these old-fashioned country frolics can best be judged from this excerpt from the story of a Knoxville, Tennessee, square dance. The story appeared, in 1845, in the sporting magazine, *Spirit of the Times:*

Old Joe lives in a log house about ten yards square; it has two rooms—one at the bottom and one at the top of the ladder—has about all outdoors fur a yard and all the South fur its occupants at times. He gives a frolic onst in three weeks in plowin' time and one every Saturday night the balance of the year, and only axes a "fip" fur a reel and two bits fur what corn-juice you suck. The gals are thrown in. The supper is made up by the fellers; everyone fetches somethin'; some a lick of meal, some a middlin' of bacon, some a ham, some a possum and some only fetches a good appetite and a skin chock full of perticeler deviltry. He gives Jim Smith, the storekeeper, warnin' to fetch a skane of silk fur fiddle strings. Joe then mounts old Punkinslinger bar-backed, about three hours afore sundown and gives all the gals warnin'. He just rides past in a right peart rack, singin'—

O I met a frog with a fiddle on his back
Inquirin' his way to the frolic—

That's enuff! By sundown the gals come pourin' out of the woods like ants out of an old log when t'other end's afire—jest as fine as silk and full of fun and fixed out in all sorts of fancy doin's from striped homespun to sunflower calico. As for silk, if one had a silk gown, she'd be too smart to wear it to Joe's, fur the homespun would tear it off her quicker nor winkin'.

You may talk about your bar hunts, mister, and your deer hunts, and knottin' tigers' tails through the bungholes of barrels, but if a reg'lar bilt frolic in the "Nobs" of "Old Knox" don't beat 'em all, then I'm no judge of fun, that's all—from a kiss that cracks like a wagon-whip up to a fight that rouses up all outdoors—and as to laughin', why they invented laughin'. And the last laugh will be hearn at old Joe's Nob dance about three in the mornin'.

The ingredient most necessary to the fun at a frolic like this one was the fiddle. Its resin scream could cut through the racket of the rowdiest of country balls, echoing the screech of the catamount, the war-cry of the Indian, the sobbing of a woman, the soft and tender voice of the little turtle dove. Light and portable, it rode the packs of the men who walked across the Appalachians into the dark forests beyond, it sailed all the great inland rivers with the raftsmen, the keelboatmen, and the stevedores, it stowed away in the covered wagons that lumbered over the Rocky Mountains to the western ocean, it was tied in the saddle strings of cowboys moving their wild herds north from Texas to Montana. So the fiddle traveled with the pioneers from the Atlantic to the Pacific, acquiring on the way a bag of tunes the names of which, themselves, make a catalogue of early American fancies and folkways:

Forky Deer, Ground Hog, Wild Horse, Flop Eared Mule, Possum Up a Gum Stump, Old Zip Coon, Shoo Fly, Cacklin' Hen, Turkey in the Straw, Pop Goes the Weasel, Hell Among the Yearlings. . . .

The Virginia Reel, The Tennessee Waggoner, Alabama Jubilee, Cripple Creek, Cumberland Gap, Hell Broke Loose in Georgia, Mississippi Sawyer, Arkansas Traveler. . . .

Paul Jones, Hull's victory, Bonaparte's Retreat, Fire in the Mountain, Devil's Dream, Glory in the Meeting House, Soldier's Joy, Leather Breeches, Sugar in the Gourd, Rye Whiskey. . . .

Hop Light Ladies, Liza Jane, Sally Anne, Black-eyed Susie, Cindy, Sally in the Garden, The Irish Washer-woman, Jenny Put the Kittle On, What'll we Do with the Baby-o.

Thomas Jefferson was a fine fiddler who learned country tunes from his neighbors and played them for his children in the evenings. Lincoln was an active fellow in a square dance. . . . They say that Davy Crockett had one of his most curious adventures where a fiddle was concerned. On his way to Texas through the wilderness, Davy heard a fiddle crying in the deep swamps of Mississippi. He followed the sound and came to a swift creek. In the middle of the creek a minister sat in his buggy, the water foaming up dangerously, sawing "Cripple Creek" on a fiddle. "What in tarnation air ye doin', ye ridiculous idjit?" halloes Crockett. "Why," says the preacher, "here I was stuck in this torrent, ready to drown at any moment. I knew I could holler my lungs out and no one would come, but, if I played me a tune on this devil's music box and there was a buckskin sinner in ten mile, he'd come a-trottin'!"

For these frontier folk there was something magic about the violin. Old-timers will tell you with great earnestness of how master fiddlers who played certain sympathetic notes with such tremendous fire that huge buildings and bridges have collapsed. The ancient folk belief that the fiddle is Old Nick's instrument has only been strengthened by the minister's promises of eternal damnation for the "fiddling and dancing crowd" if they did not give up "fooling with Satan's business." This is one of the many tales told by Americans about a fiddler's encounter with the devil—the story of a Georgia Negro fiddler named Balaam:

. . . Balaam, he say,

"Co'se I know I got all dese here other niggers beat, but I want to show 'em some real fiddlin'!"

Wid dat Balaam taken an' scrape a few sof' notes on he fiddle an' say, "Ole fiddle, you do very well now, but I aims to make you natchelly talk one dese days." De words want outen he mout' 'fo' a voice come right out de fiddle an' say, "If you wants me to talk, Balaam, I talkin' now."

"Well, den, I want you to make us 'nough money to buy us freedom."

"All right," say de fiddle, "but you cain't play good 'nough yet, Balaam. You jes' startin' good."

"Why, I 'lowed I could play pretty good now," say Balaam.

"Pretty good ain't to say plum good," say de fiddle.

"What I hafta do to git plum good?" Balaam ax.

"Nuttin' much," say de voice. "All you got to do is to go to de crossroads ever' night for nine nights an' make a crossmark in de middle o' de road. On de las' night you make de mark somebody'll be dar to tell you what to do nex'." . . .

When he git to de crossroad Balaam say to hisse'f, "Shorely can't be no harm jes' makin' one crossmark. Maybe I'll go to de big meetin' nex' fall an dat'll make it all right."

So's he gone on an' taken he foot an' make a crossmark. An' jes' as he turn 'roun' to go, dar been an ole rabbit a-settin' in de moonlight a-laughin' at him. Balaam light out for home, but by the nex' night he right back to the same place makin' another crossmark. De ole rabbit laugh at him again. Dis here business kep' up for six mo' nights, an' Balaam study so much people think he gittin' mindless.

Well, dat las' night, Balaam slip off ag'in an' he head straight for de crossroads dis time. He walk fas' an', when he git dar, he make he crossmark quick, so's he won't have time to change he mind. Atter he make de mark hit didn' look like nuttin' gwine happen an' Balaam begin to breathe easy when he hear somebody call he name. He look up an sho' 'nough dar been dat same ole rabbit a-settin' right whar he allus set.

Balaam 'gin a screech an' de rabbit jes' disappear. In de place Balaam see a black cloud full of smoke an' sulphur, an' he hear a fiddle comin' from de cloud an' a voice singin':

Munanee, munanee, ho!
Munanee, munanee, ho!
Munanee, munanee, ho!
Big pot o' mush I gwine to git dar.

Wid dat de cloud part in two an' out step de natchel ole Bugger Man hisse'f, lookin' jes' like people say he look. He had a long tail wid a arrer pint, he hoofs was clove an' he tote a long, slim, narrer li'l pitchfork. He look to be 'bout six-foot tall an' he had on a black robe lined wid red velvet on de inside. He step out an' bow perlite, "Evenin', Mister Foster, sho is pretty fiddle you got dar. . . ."

By dis time Balaam so scared he han' he fiddle right over to de Bugger Man. De ole Bugger Man take he fiddle an' bow low an' switch he tail sassy-like, an' start in for to play. He make de air natchelly ring like silver bells; he make hit soun' like all de mockin'-birds in de whole worl' a-bustin' dey throats at de same time. Hit soun' like cow-bells late in de evenin' an' de songs of little frogs down by de mill pon'. He make dat fiddle sob an' cry. Hit soun' like a 'ooman moanin' for her los' man. Hit soun' like people singin' acrost still water. Den he turnt 'roun' an' play dance chunes an' reels. Den an' dar de Bugger Man make Balaam promise him he'd serve him all he life an' let him have he soul when he die.

By'm'by Balaam play 'nough money to buy he freedom. He kep' on playin' for ever' dance an' party he hear 'bout. One day after Balaam no tellin' how ole, he call he ole 'ooman an' all he chillun an' gran'chillun 'roun' him, an' tell 'em he gwine die. After he tell 'em dat, hit seem like he feel better an' he git out de bed an' fetch he fiddle out de trunk an' start to play "Turkey in de Straw." Den he walk back to de bed, lie down an' breave he las', but whilst dey all standin' 'roun' lookin' at de corpse de fiddle in de trunk commence to play. Hit play de lonesomes' chunes you ever hear, an' ever' note hit play soun' like hit was sayin', "Po' los' soul! Po' los' soul!"

Tell me nuttin' 'bout no fiddlin! Dese days dey got fiddles in de chu'ches an' ever'whars else, but us ole people what know 'bout Balaam, us ain't got no use for fiddlin'.

The fiddle might be the devil's own instrument, the godly might step aside when it began to squawl, preachers might shower fire and brimstone on the heads of the dancers, whole communities might be devastated by the brawls and killings that sometimes took place at the country breakdowns, but the people kept flocking around the fiddler. The strenuous and democratic nature of his breakdown dances suited the frontier; they were just the thing to loosen a fellow up after a hard week of bear-hunting, stump-grubbing, hog-chasing, sod-busting, or brush-popping. "Thunder and lightning, a man has to have a chance to git to the gals, sometimes!"

No, the hellfire and brimstone boys never had a chance against the fiddler and the square dance where he officiated. As the people unrolled the map of the new country, new dances appeared in the raw young communities. Based on the country dances of Great Britain and Ireland, hundreds of new steps and patterns popped up between Maine and California. The dance callers, who directed the couples as they circled left, swung, changed partners and docey-doed, developed a whole literature of calls with a frontier flavor as distinctive as cornbread or son-of-a-gun stew. Larry Chittenden, one of the best of Western versifiers, has caught the flavor of these "cow-drilles" in his "Cowboys' Christmas Ball":

'Way out in Western Texas, where the Clear Work's waters flow,
Where the cattle are a-browsin', and the Spanish ponies grow;
Where the Norther comes a-whistlin' from beyond the Neutral Strip
And the prairie dogs are sneezin', as if they had the grip,
The boys had left the ranches and come to town in piles,
The ladies—kinder scatterin'—had gathered in for miles.
The music was a fiddle and a lively tambourine,
And a viol come imported by stage from Abilene.
The wimmin folks looked lovely—the boys looked kinder treed,
Till their leader commenced yellin': "Whoa, fellers, let's stampede."
The music started sighin' and a-wailin' through the hall,
As a kind of introduction to The Cowboys' Christmas Ball.

The leader was a fellow that came from Swenson's Ranch,
They called him Windy Billy, from Little Deadman's Branch.
His rig was kinder keerless, big spurs and high-heeled boots;
He had the reputation that comes when fellers shoots.
His voice was like the bugle upon the mountain's height;
His feet were animated and a mighty movin' sight,
When he commenced to holler, "Neow, fellers, stake yer pen!
Lock horns to all them heifers, an' russle 'em like men.
Saloot yer lovely critters; neow, swing and let 'em go,
Climb the grapevine round 'em—all hands do-ce-do!
You Mavericks, jine the round-up—jest skip her waterfall."
Huh! hit wuz gittin' happy, The Cowboys' Christmas Ball!

The boys were tolerable skittish, the ladies powerful neat,
That old bass viol music just got there with both feet.
That wailin' frisky fiddle, I never shall forget;
And Windy kept a-singin'—I think I hear him yet—
"Oh yes, chase you squirrels, an' cut 'em to one side,
Spur Treadwell to the center, with Cross P Charley's bride,
Doc Hollis down the middle, an' twine the ladies' chain,
Varn Andrews pen the fillies in big T Diamond's train.
All pull yer freight together, neow, swallow fork an' change,
Big Boston lead the trail herd, through little Pitchfork's range.
Purr round yer gentle pussies, neow rope 'em! Balance all!"
Huh! hit wuz gittin' active—The Cowboys' Christmas Ball!

The calls, the tunes, and the dance patterns grew with the frontier. Indeed, except for a slump during the early part of the century when the hot musicians and the strait-laced folks unconsciously joined forces against it, the American square dance has continued to grow and is still growing today, even in big cities. Every summer thousands of young people swing and change in the parks of New York City. Up and down the country, callers are meeting and swapping dances, thus creating patterns with the flavor of the whole country in them. Young bucks with fancy bowing technique keep turning up at the Old Fiddler's Contests and winning them. Maybe some of their capers would have surprised the old bucks at the dance on the Knobs of Old Knox, but the spirit is essentially the same.

We regret that we are unable to teach you how to square dance in this chapter. That would, however, require another book as big as the present one, plus several albums of records and a good dance caller.* All that we can do is to offer you some of the best of the old breakdown tunes as songs. These verses, shouted out over the noise of the dancers and the sawing of the fiddle, reflect, better than any other poetry, the wild, foolish, skylarking, monkey-shine spirit of the frontier fandangoes.

24. *SOURWOOD MOUNTAIN*

In this fiddling piece from the Southern mountains, with its lilting refrain, the singer looks out across the green tangle of the hills to the cabin of his sweetheart, remembers what a fine young filly she is, imagines himself asking her old man for her and then decides he wouldn't have her for sour apples.

25. *OLD JOE CLARK*

Some say that Old Joe Clark ran a moonshine still in the Blue Ridge Mountains. Some say he located in Kentucky. Some say he was an ornery peace officer. But nobody really knows more than that he has been memorialized in the most popular and the longest of breakdown songs. Out of the hundreds of stanzas attached to his song, we have chosen enough to give you a notion of what the people can do with a good old tune, a common name like Joe Clark, and plenty of time to sit around and think up rhymes. The last of the Joe Clark songs originated in the 1940's in New York City. Norman Corwin used it on the first of his wartime broadcasts and on his last, the celebrated "On A Note of Triumph."

* A number of good instruction books and phonograph albums are cited in the Appendices.

26. *RAISE A RUKUS*

The South was the meeting place of two very musical peoples. There the folk from the British Isles and the folk from the West Coast of Africa pooled their tunes, their rhythmic patterns, and their song-styles. The sharing of songs and the musical competition between these radically different groups gave rise to the most interesting things in American music—the music of the minstrels, the spiritual, the blues, hot jazz and, now, hillbilly.

Imagine what happened, for instance, when the fiddler who formed "Sourwood Mountain" or "Old Joe Clark" heard a Negro slave, slapping out an intricate, syncopated rhythm on his thighs and chanting—

> *JU*ba dis an' *JU*ba dat an'
> *JU*ba killed my *YAL*low cat, O
> *JU*ba,
> *JU*ba, *JU*ba, *JU*ba, *JU*ba, *JU*ba. . . .

You may be sure that fiddler slipped out back of the cowshed that night, and tried to "mock" that little song on his instrument. His "Juba" took on a character distinctively different from its original. You can think of scores of tunes that have this flavor: "Cindy," "Old Dan Tucker,"

"Buffalo Gals," "O Susannah," to mention only a few.

Reverse the situation. The song-leader from the slave quarters stands in the kitchen door and watches an Irish music master play his lively jig tunes, while the white folks swing and turn in a quadrille. He makes himself a one-string fiddle and practices until he can amuse his white master and his guests. Later he gets his hands on an old broken-up fiddle and works hard to learn a few tunes, because he knows that, as plantation fiddler, he can earn release from some of the harder tasks and punishments that now fall upon him. . . . This is precisely the story of Balaam and hundreds of other slave musicians; and we know that even in colonial times Negro fiddlers were playing for the most elegant balls, as well as for their own dances in the slave quarters.

Out of such competition and emulation came songs like "Raise A Rukus," an ante-bellum Negro hoedown or jig tune with an overlay of minstrel-show influence. In the slave quarters, where no instruments were available, the typically African song leader improvised new lines against an insistent vocal and rhythmic refrain to make dancing music. An ex-slave has described a jigging contest in "the quarters," where songs of this kind began:

> Master always wanted to help his colored folks live right, and he always 'ranged for parties and such—no foolishment, just good, clean fun. There was dancing and singing most every Saturday night. He had a little platform built for jigging contests. Colored folks came from all around to see who could jig the best.
>
> I must tell you about the best contest we ever had. One nigger on our place was the jiggingest fellow ever was. He could put a glass of water on his head and make his feet go like trip-hammers and sound like a snare drum. Now it gets noised around a fellow been found to beat him and a contest was arranged for Saturday evening. There was a big crowd and money was bet.
>
> So they starts jigging. Tom starts easy and gits a little faster and faster and it look like Tom done met his match, but there am one thing he ain't done—he ain't made a whirl. Now he does it. Everybody holds he breath, and the other fellow starts to make a whirl and he makes it, but just a spoonful of water slops out of his cup, so Tom was the winner.

As background for the bitterly satirical lines of "Raise A Rukus," here is an anecdote from the childhood of Jenny Proctor, Alabama ex-slave:

> I recollects once when I was tryin' to clean house like old Miss tell me, I finds a biscuit and Ize so hungry, I et it, 'cause we never see such a thing as a biscuit only sometimes on Sunday morning. Well, she come in and say, "Where's that biscuit?" I say, "Miss, I et it 'cause I'm so hungry."
>
> Then she grab the broom and start beating me over the head with it, and I guess I clean lost my head 'cause I knowed better than to fight her if I knowed anything, but I start to fight her, and the driver comes in and starts beating me with that cat-o'-nine-tails, and he beat me till I fall to the floor. I still got those scars on my back just like my grandmother have when she die, and Ize a-carryin' mine right on to the grave just like she did.

The refrain of this ditty, "raise a rukus tonight," has two meanings: to start trouble, to have fun. This contrast in meanings aptly hits off the dual aspects of the song: a song of protest and irony—a crazy "black-face minstrel song" which will tickle "the white folks." In this latter guise, the song is known and loved all over the South, both among Negroes and whites. Ironically enough, it is one of the few secular songs that Negro ministers will officially permit their congregations to sing at picnics and church socials.

27. *OLD DAN TUCKER*

From the days of the first navigators along the African coast, down to the latest "expeditions" north of 110th Street into Harlem, the white man has always been impressed by the talent of Negroes for dancing. The Negro slave left much of his African culture behind him when he was transported in chains to our shores, but the rhythmic characteristics of his culture he kept. It was in the early years of the nineteenth century that his talent for rhythmic expression made its first impression on American life, an impression that has only deepened with the years.

A young vaudevillian, named E. D. Rice, was walking along the streets of a Southern city one day in 1828 when he heard a voice singing,

Turn about and *wheel* about and *do just so,*
And *ev*erytime I *wheel* about, I *jump Jim Crow.*

An old Negro man was singing, snapping his fingers, performing for himself a subtle little soft-shoe dance as he moseyed down the streets. He was dancing out his song; everyone who has lived in an area of Negro culture has seen things like this scores of times. But Rice was fascinated. He stared and stared, memorizing every gesture and inflection of the old man.

Sometime later, during an engagement in Pittsburgh when his act was wearing a little thin, Rice decided to try out his new material. He looked up a Negro longshoreman, whose only name was Cuff and whose clothes made up in picturesqueness for their dilapidation, lured him into the theatre, borrowed his rags, blacked his face, and, when his call came, soft-shoed on the stage and sang "Jump, Jim Crow." The house came down. Rice had to improvise new verses for a half an hour and might have been improvising yet, if poor Cuff, who heard another steamboat blowing for a landing, had not crept on stage in his drawers, loudly demanding that Rice give him back his trousers.

This incident, this little act made Rice one of the most popular and one of the highest-paid performers of his day. His imitators, among them Emmett and Christy, formed themselves into blackface companies called "minstrel shows." The "minstrel show" was the most important form of American theatrical entertainment until the end of the nineteenth century. Around the minstrel show there grew up scores of songs which became national favorites and some of which were taken over by the people, polished and changed by oral transmission to become folk songs.

Among these few (and here but two * songs of Stephen Foster can be included, since his songs have rarely changed perceptibly from their original forms) the darn-fool ditty, "Old Dan Tucker" by Dan Emmett, stands first. American folk-singers have honored Dan Emmett (he was of Irish extraction, born in Southern Ohio, and ran away with a circus at the age of sixteen) by assuming that this song was of their own making. It has turned up as a play party in the Southwest, a square set in New England, and a banjo song wherever Americans have wandered.

28. *CINDY*

Wherever the minstrel show and its music penetrated in America, it carried along the five-string banjo, which might be said to be America's only original folk instrument. It is related on its mother's side to certain primitive West African stringed instruments; it was raised up by Negro slaves; it was polished and given its fifth string by one Joe Sweeney of North Carolina in 1840; and, strangely, it found its final home, after everyone else had grown tired of it, in the lonesome hollers of the Southern mountains. When the mountain fiddlers heard it, they gave up their fiddles, sat down with the contraption and worked on it till they had produced a kind of music that was neither Afro-American, nor minstrel-style, nor a transcription of their old-time tunes, but a peculiar and wonderful mixture of all of these. "Darlin' Corey," "John Hardy," "Black-eyed Susie," and "Cindy" are among the tunes in this book

* "O Susannah" and "Camptown Races."

that bear, strongly, the influence of the mountain five-string banjo style.

"Cindy," according to one singer, was so stupendously sweet that he wanted to sew her onto his coattails so as always to keep her by his side. Others have painted her as a rather brash mountain gal, mainly interested in getting herself a man, who, on first meeting, "threw her arms around me and hung on like a leech." Then again, Cindy was the kind of gal who went to church and "got so full of glory that she shook her stockings down."

So it seems that Cindy is a pretty complex personality. At any rate, she is a much-traveled young lady, for the song which celebrates her name has traveled as far as mountain fiddlers and banjo pickers have been able to take it, as far as the highways run, the busses roll, and the fast freight rattles—and that includes, via the radio and phonograph records, the entire United States and points East, North, West, and South. Cindy's song is a dance tune for fiddle or banjo and fit for a square dance or a reel. But it's more fun if you sing it, swapping off verses. Everyone gets in his harmonies on the chorus; it's a lung-buster.

29. *BLACK-EYED SUSIE*

She travels right along with Cindy, but in a slightly rougher crowd.

30. *SKIP TO MY LOU AND OTHER PLAY-PARTY TUNES*

Respectable folk in Protestant communities have always regarded the fiddle as the devil's instrument and dancing as downright sinful. Not many years ago a popular young lady in an East Texas community was called before her church to answer the charge that she had danced a set at a country frolic. The minister asked whether she was sorry for what she had done.

"Yes," said the young lady, "I'm sorry that I joined a Christian church that has such stupid rules." Then she walked out of the church for good, and, by that act, moved beyond the pale of her community. She lived and died a bitter old maid.

Faced with such violent religious prejudices, the young people of the frontier developed the play-party, in which all of the objectionable features of the square dance were removed or so masked that their grave elders could approve. No instruments were permitted—the dancers sang and clapped their own music. Drinking and love-making were taboo. The waist swing was frowned on and the fancy steps and intricate figures of the country dances were abandoned in favor of the simpler dramatic patterns of children's games. In many and many a frontier community the bear-hunters, the Indian fighters, the rough keelboatmen, and the wild cowboys could be seen dancing innocently with their gals, like so many children at a Sunday school picnic.

The play-party, however, soon acquired a life and vitality of its own. It was an ideal amusement for the teen-age group and the younger married people. For a square dance one had to have a fiddler and an experienced caller, as well as dancers who knew the figures; but for a play-party all that was required was a friendly crowd that knew a few simple songs and movements. So, once created, the play-party followed the frontier, flourishing wherever the people were dependent on "home-made" or "make-it-yourself-or-do-without" amusements. It lives today in rural communities throughout the Southwest. Turn off the main roads in West Texas or Oklahoma almost any summer night, and somewhere out in the moonlight you're likely to hear the distant voices chanting—

Can't get a redbird, a blue-bird'll do. . . .

West Texans don't believe in exclusive parties. When you give a frolic out on the plains, you spread the word around the community and everybody comes that wants to, regardless of age, sex, or class. If you're a stranger, just come along to the house about good dusk-dark and join in the fun; but don't get too nosey, unless you want the whole bunch to pile on you.

The least children are put to bed on pallets in the bedroom. The furniture is all moved into the back. The girls in their stiff calicoes sit giggling against the walls. The boys begin to drift in, not dressed up specially, but in white shirts, blue trousers, and with their broad hats pulled down over their eyes. The "life of the party" starts the dance off with some simple choosing-the-partners games, getting folks acquainted, poking mild fun at some of the tough boys—but very mild because he knows how easy a fight can start.

The older men join in from time to time to have the pleasure of jollying some young gal. The eight- and ten-year-olds can dance, too, if they've a mind to. The leader goes on with more intricate games like "Old Dan Tucker" or "Coffee Grows on White Oak Trees" or "Jingle at the Windows." Maybe a couple steps out to the well for a cool drink; he hands her the dipper, then drinks, himself, from the same side. Lots of country romances have started that way.

Toward the end the leader may call for "Weevily Wheat" or one of the games that involves a "waist swing." Some dancers drop out then and just look on, wishing, probably, that their folks weren't so strict. . . . At eleven o'clock there'll be watermelon or ice cream and cake. . . . Then around twelve o'clock, it's time to go home. The young folks walk home across the fields or down the dusty roads, some couples holding hands, the married ones walking Indian file, with the man in the lead. Next week all the young folks will talk about what went on at Maybelle's party.

SKIP TO MY LOU—THE DANCE

This is a simple game of stealing partners. It begins with any number of couples hand in hand, skipping around in a ring. A lone boy in the center of the moving circle of couples sings—

Lost my pardner, what'll I do?

As the girls whirl past him, the awkward young man in the center may hesitate, bashfully, while he decides which of these Black-eyed Susans to choose. As he sings—

I'll get another'n purtier'n you,

he grabs for the hand of the young lady he's decided on. He then joins the circle, while her partner takes his place alone in the center of the dancing ring. This young man steals himself a partner in the same way as the first and the game continues. "Skip to My Lou" is a good game to start a play-party with, good to loosen a crowd up and get the young ladies in the notion for swinging later on.

31. *COFFEE GROWS ON WHITE OAK TREES*

You'll enjoy this Southwestern play-party game as a song, but, in case you want to try the play-party which it describes, we give the directions herewith.

This one is for any number of couples. They join hands, with the ladies on the left, form a ring, and march around and around a lone man, who stands inside the circle. As they march, they sing the introduction in slow tempo. The man inside the circle chooses a partner from the ring. Then, while the dancers in the ring skip around him, singing—

Two in the middle and I can't dance Josie—

he swings his partner, first by the right hand and then by the left. Then the introductory stanza is sung again, while the dancers in the ring circle round and round and the two dancers in the middle each choose themselves a partner. All sing—

Four in the middle and I can't dance Josie—

while the two couples in the middle of the ring swing by the right and the left. The introduction is repeated, while all four dancers in the center of the ring choose partners. Then on—

Wheel around and whirl around, I can't dance Josie—

the eight dancers now inside the ring break into groups of four and swing by the right and left. Then, as all dancers sing at a slow tempo—

Railroad, steamboat, river an' canal—

six of the dancers inside rejoin the ring and all march around the couple that remains inside. They sing at a livelier tempo—

O she's gone, gone, gone—

to allow the couple remaining in the middle to swing right and left. The game then begins again with the introduction, skipping the first stanza this time, since a couple now stands in the center of the ring. Use any of the remaining haywire stanzas that you care to in repeating the dance pattern until everyone has had enough.

32. *SHOOT THE BUFFALO*

John A. Lomax, who was raised in Bosque County, Texas, where play-parties protected the young folks from the devilish business of square dancing, gives the following account of "Shoot the Buffalo," and of Bob Hanna, who led it at country gatherings.

Every spring Bob rode behind or alongside a herd of long-horns up the trail to Kansas. He wintered on the home ranch on the Bosque River. For me he was a romantic figure—a young Lochinvar or Jeb Stuart. His work gave him leisure. He was young, light-hearted, handsome. He loved music and color. He sang as he rode, in harmony with the jingle of his shining big-belled spurs, the creaking of his saddle gear. The glossy sheen of his well-groomed pony, bright conchos on bridle, martingale and saddle, showed Bob's care for his equipment. Even the two saddle girths were woven from colored strands; and his saddle blanket was a blaze of color. His own dress was simple and artistic: a broad-brimmed Stetson; a heavy flannel shirt, sometimes soft gray, sometimes pure white, oftener with a dash of red among the lighter colors; buff-colored corduroy trousers covered to the knees by high-topped, high-heeled boots. Mexican flower patterns were stitched in colored thread in the upper fronts of his shiny, knee-high boots. Sometimes the four boot-straps were covered by bright tassels. Bob wore a loosely knotted, red silk handkerchief about his throat. Even the quirt which hung from his wrist was plaited from leather or rawhide strips of contrasting colors. Bob's experience in riding up the trail had given him poise and assurance. He was a natural leader. So when the sitting-down games of "Slap-in and Slap-out," "Club Fist," "William-a-Tremble-Toe" and the skipping games of "Hog Drovers," "Johnny Brown," and "Skip-to-my-Lou," grew less thrilling to the group of youngsters, Bob Hanna would walk to the center of the room and shout, "Get your partners for 'Jingle at the Window' "—a rollicking song with a beat as lively as "Money Musk" or "Arkansas Traveler." Here's where we cheated the Baptists and the Methodists; for we followed all the figures of the standard square dance, "swinging partners and corners," "do-ce-do-ing," "sashaying," "grand-right-and-left-ing" and "promenading" to our seats—(but not until we had repeated each movement over and over again). All the time we sang lustily through all the stanzas of the song.

Come jingle at my window, tidy-o,
Come jingle at my window, tidy-o,
Come jingle at my window, tidy-o,
Come jingle at my window, low.

In Chaucer the lover "tirl-ed at the pin"; in the Deep South the Negro "fo' day creeper" scratches on his true love's window sill. Bosque County boys and girls innocently "jingled at the window" and loved it.

Other songs of rapid tempo followed, but Bob's tour-de-force, the final dance song, was "Shoot the Buffalo." We shot buffalo by thousands, the stamp of our boot heels imitating the crack of Needle gun (the rifle that carried so far the bullet did not land until next day!); and we danced all night till near daylight, till time to ride home with the girls in the morning.

33. *BUFFALO GALS*

A song which runs—

Lubly Fan, woncha come out tonight. . . .
was published by Cool White, one of the early blackfaced minstrels, in 1844. We suspect that he took it on permanent loan in the same way that Daddy Rice borrowed Cuff's old rags. The minstrel boys very soon began changing it to "New York Gals," "Philadelphia Gals," or "Bowery Gals," depending on the theatre they were playing. Around 1848, "Buffalo Gals" (probably for poetic reasons) became the favorite version and, as such, it has been for a hundred years one of the most popular and most-parodied American songs. In Pennsylvania they sing about the "Lusbaugh Gals"; in West Virginia about the "Jimtown Gals"; in Indiana, Illinois, and Idaho about the "Cincinnati Gals"; in Iowa and Texas about the "Lou'siana Gals." Lately, the Andrews sisters made a fortune out of a swing version of the same old tune, when they harmonized on—

Danced with a dolly, with a hole in her stocking,
And her knees kept a-knockin' and her feet kept a-rockin'— *

Before the swingsters revived the "Buffalo Gals," however, it had been played on squeaky fifes, sawed by country fiddlers, tickled out by five-string banjo pickers, roared out as a sea chantey by the blue-water boys, sung by Mississippi raftsmen as their favorite tune, and clapped out at every play-party on the Great Plains. We give you here the Texas play-party version, the one that cowboy Bob Hanna used to liven the gals up in Bosque County seventy-five years ago.

When Bob Hanna led off with "Buffalo Gals," he came right out in the open and called a conventional square dance. You can dance it this way or else you can follow these directions for a simple swinging game.

Four couples take their places in a ring. The girl from the lead couple and the girl next to her left catch right hands and swing around one time. Then their partners each swing their partners once around. Meanwhile the other two couples are singing and clapping the rhythm.

Each boy then swings the girl to his left once around by the left hand. Then he swings his partner half around by the right hand, releasing her to catch left hands with the next girl to his right. He swings her half-way round and catches right hands with the next girl to the right. Thus, alternating right- and left-hand swings, he moves to his right around the ring until he gets back to his original partner. The couples then promenade once around the ring.

The whole cycle is then repeated, with three couples dancing instead of two, the third couple being the next couple to the left of the first two. When this cycle is completed, begin the final cycle with all four couples dancing.

34. *SWEET THING*

Play-parties were permitted. Square dancing was frowned on but tolerated. And "round dancing," where a couple danced face to face with arms around each other, was something no respectable country girl would do.* It remained for the Negroes to develop their blues and folk jazz tunes, their "slow-drag," "eagle-rock," "ballin' the jack" two-step dances, and, finally, only in this generation, to set all the folks dancing "round dances." "Sweet Thing" is a standard round dance in folk communities along with other fast-stepping tunes such as "John Henry," "New River Train," "Careless Love," "Easy Rider," "Goin' Down the Road Feelin' Bad," "Nine Hundred Miles," and others more modern still.

"Sweet Thing," originally a Negro blues from the levee camps and jook joints, was adopted by white banjo and guitar pickers in the early part of this century, parodied by them in a score of ways for a score of stories, and today it can be heard wherever a hillbilly unlimbers his git-box. It fits the experience of the dispossessed, the downtrodden, the people of shacks and slums, the hungry and the criminal. Name the variants and you open a great volume on deprivation and violence in the South: "Gwineter Harness in the Mornin' Soon," "Ole Bill," "Bugger Burns," "Winnsboro Cotton Mill Blues"—and still this family of song continues to grow.

In this version we give you a partial resume of the story which this great song can tell: first, the Negro's smiling and keenly ironic acceptance of the facts of poverty; six bitter stanzas on the Southern farmer and why he raises hell when he gets hold of a little moonshine whiskey; and, finally some cheerful lines from the folks who depend on crawdading* for their living. When *you* sing this song, sing it as if you had been living on cornbread and flour gravy and greens for your whole life, you were half full of white lightning, you knew everybody in the room was packing a knife and a pistol and you "didn't give a durn."

* Naturally, these remarks do not apply in areas where the waltz, the polka, and such dances, were permitted.

* Fishing for freshwater crawfish.

24.

Sourwood Mountain

Words and melody adapted and arranged by
John A. and Alan Lomax

Piano arrangement by
Charles and Ruth Seeger

*If this setting can be played very fast (approximately ♩=144), the sound of the dulcimer, upon which instrument the tune is often played, may be approached more closely by continuing the left hand throughout as in measure one, that is, without change of harmony from beginning to end — all very lightly and without change of speed or dynamics.

2. My true love lives over the river,
Hey-ho, dee-iddle-um-day,
My true love lives over the river,
Hey-ho, dee-iddle-um-day,
A few more jumps and I'll be with her,
Hey-ho, dee-iddle-um-day.

3. My true love is a blue-eyed daisy,
Hey-ho, dee-iddle-um-day,
My true love is a blue-eyed daisy,
Hey-ho, dee-iddle-um-day,
Ef I don't git her I'll go crazy,
Hey-ho, dee-iddle-um-day.

4. My *true* love lives at the head of the holler,
Hey-ho, dee-iddle-um-day,
My true love lives at the head of the holler,
Hey-ho, dee-iddle-um-day,
She won't come and I won't foller,
Hey-ho, dee-iddle-um-day.

5. My true love lives over the ocean,
Hey-ho, dee-iddle-um-day,
My true love lives over the ocean,
Hey-ho, dee-iddle-um-day,
I'll go to see her, if I take a notion,
Hey-ho, dee-iddle-um-day.

6. "Say, old man, I want yore daughter,
Hey-ho, dee-iddle-um-day,
Say, old man, I want yore daughter,
Hey-ho, dee-iddle-um-day,
To wash my clothes and carry my water,
Hey-ho, dee-iddle-um-day."

7. "Fifteen cents, a dollar and a quarter,
Hey-ho, dee-iddle-um-day,
Fifteen cents, a dollar and a quarter,
Hey-ho, dee-iddle-um-day,
Say, young man, take her if you want her,
Hey-ho, dee-iddle-um-day."

8. Ducks in the pond, geese in the ocean,
Hey-ho, dee-iddle-um-day,
Ducks in the pond, geese in the ocean,
Hey-ho, dee-iddle-um-day,
Devil's in the women if they take a notion,
Hey-ho, dee-iddle-um-day.

25.

Old Joe Clark

Words and melody adapted and arranged by
John A. and Alan Lomax

Piano arrangement by
Charles and Ruth Seeger

CHORUS: Fare thee well, old Joe Clark,
Fare thee well, I say,
He'll foller me ten thousand miles,
To hear my fiddle play.

2. Old Joe Clark had a mule,
His name was Morgan Brown,
And every tooth in that mule's head
Was sixteen inches around.

3. Old Joe Clark had a cow,
She was muley born,
It takes a jaybird a week and a half
To fly from horn to horn.

4. Old Joe Clark had a yellow cat,
She would neither sing or pray,
She stuck her head in the buttermilk jar
And washed her sins away.

5. Old Joe Clark had a dog
As blind as he could be,
Ran a redbug round a stump
And a coon up a holler tree.

6. Old Joe Clark had a house
Fifteen storeys high,
And every storey in that house
Was filled with chicken pie.

7. I went down to old Joe's house,
He invited me to supper,
I stumped my toe on the table leg
And stuck my nose in the butter.

8. I wouldn't go down to old Joe's house,
Tell you the reason why,
Can't get around his garden spot
For tearing down all his rye.

9. I won't go to old Joe's house,
I've told you here before.
He fed me in a hog-trough
And I won't go there anymore.

10. Old Joe Clark's dead and gone,
I hope he's gone to Hell,
He made me wear the ball and chain,
Made my ankle swell.

CHORUS: Rock, rock, old Joe Clark,
Rock, rock, I say,
Rock, rock, old Joe Clark,
You'd better be gittin' away.

11. I would not marry an old maid,
Tell you the reason why,
Her neck so long and stringy, boys,
'Fraid she'd never die.

CHORUS: Fare you well, old Joe Clark,
Fare you well, I'm gone,
Fare you well, old Joe Clark,
With your golden slippers on.

12. Now I wouldn't marry a widder,
Tell you the reason why,
She'd have so many children
They'd make those biscuits fly.

13. I wouldn't marry a schoolteacher,
I tell you the reason why,
She blows her nose in yellow cornbread
And calls it pumpkin pie.

14. I wouldn't marry a yellow gal,
Tell you the reason why,
She'd eat a barrel of sauerkraut
And drink the river dry.

15. Masser had a yaller gal,
Brought her from the South,
Wrapped her hair so very tight
She could not shut her mouth.

16. He took her to the blacksmith shop,
To have her mouth made small,
She backed her ears and opened her mouth
And swallowed shop and all.

CHORUS: Fare you well, old Joe Clark,
Goodbye, Betty Brown,
Fare you well, old Joe Clark,
Fare you well, I'm gone.

17. Sixteen horses in my team,
The leaders they are blind,
And every time the sun goes down,
There's a pretty girl on my mind.

18. Eighteen miles of mountain road
And fifteen miles of sand.
If I ever travel this road again,
I'll be a married man.

19. Never got no money,
Got no place to stay,
Got no place to lay my head,
Chicken's a-crowin' for day.

20. I wish I was in Arkansas
Sittin' on a rail,
A jug of whiskey under my arm
And a possum by the tail.

21. Wish I was in Tennessee
Settin' in a big arm cheer,
One arm round my whiskey jug,
And the other round my dear.

22. Wish I had a sweetheart,
I'd set her on a shelf,
And every time she smiled at me,
I'd get up there myself.

23. I climbed up the oak tree
And she climbed up the gum,
Never saw a pretty lil' gal
But what I loved her some.

Round and Round Hitler's Grave

(Modern adaptation of "Old Joe Clark")

Piano arrangement by
Charles and Ruth Seeger

*Copyright 1942, by Bob Miller, Inc. Written by the Almanacs. Used by the permission of the publishers.

1. Wish I had a bushel,
Wish I had a peck,
Wish I had old Hitler
With a rope around his neck.

CHORUS: Round and round Hitler's grave,
Round and round we go,
We're gonna lay that poor boy down,
And he won't get up no mo'.

2. I'm a-goin to Berlin
To Mister Hitler's town,
Im gonna take my forty-four
And blow his playhouse down.

3. The Germans went to Russia
In search of Russian oil,
But the only oil that they found there
Was the pot in which they boiled.

4. The German Army General Staff
I guess they missed connection,
Traveled a hundred miles a day
But in the wrong direction.

5. Mussolini won't last long,
Tell you the reason why,
We're goin' salt his beef
And hang it up to dry.

6. I don't care exactly
Which way we go in,
Just so the road we're travelin' on
Leads into Berlin.

26.

Raise a Rukus

Words and melody adapted and arranged by
John A. and Alan Lomax

Piano arrangement by
Charles and Ruth Seeger

CHORUS: Come along, little chillun, come along,
While the moon is shinin' bright,
Git on board, down the river float,
We gonna raise a rukus tonight.

2. My ol' mistiss say to me;*
"Sambo, Ize gwine ter set you free."
But when dat haid get slick and bal',
You couldn'-a killed her wid a big green maul.

3. My ol' mistiss never die
Wid her nose all hooked an' skin all dry.
But when ol' miss she somehow gone,
She lef' Uncle Sambo a-hillin' up de corn.

4. Ol' mosser likewise promise me,
When he died, he'd set me free.
But ol' mosser go an' make his will
Fer to leave me a-plowin' ol' Beck still . . .

5. All dem 'taters in dat oven,
How I wish I had some of 'em.
All dem biscuits in dat pan —
If I don't get 'em I'll raise some san'.

6. Way down yonder on Chit'lin' Switch
Bullfrog jumped from ditch to ditch,
Bullfrog jumped from the bottom of de well,
Swore, my Lawd, he'd jumped from Hell.

*In singing this song, be sure to repeat "Raise a rukus tonight" after every line.

27.

Old Dan Tucker

Words and melody adapted and arranged by
John A. and Alan Lomax

Piano arrangement by
Charles and Ruth Seeger

1. Ol' Dan Tucker's a fine old man,
Washed his face in a fryin' pan,
Combed his head wid a wagon wheel
And died with a toothache in his heel.

CHORUS: Git out the way, ol' Dan Tucker,
You too late to git yo' supper,
Supper's over an' dinner's cookin' —
An ol' Dan Tucker jes' standin' there lookin'!

2. I come to town the other night,
To hear the noise and see the fight,
The watchman he was a-runnin' around,
Cryin', "Ol' Dan Tucker's come to town."

3. Ol' Dan Tucker come to town,
Ridin' a billygoat an' leadin' a houn',
Houn' barked and the billygoat jumped,
Throwed ol' Dan right straddle of a stump.

4. Ol' Dan Tucker clumb a tree,
His Lord and Master for to see,
The limb, it broke an' Dan got a fall,
Never got to see his Lord at all.

5. Ol' Dan Tucker went to the mill,
To git some meal to put in the swill;
The miller swore by the p'int of his knife
He never had seed such man in his life.

6. Ol' Dan Tucker he got drunk,
Fell in the fire and he kicked up a chunk;
Red hot coal got in his shoe,
Lord godamighty, how the ashes flew!

7, Ol' Dan Tucker he come to town,
Swingin' the ladies round an' around;
First to the right an' then to the left,
An' then to the one that you love best.

8. Ol' Dan an' me, we did fall out,
An' what do you reckon it was about?
He stepped on my corn, I kicked him on the shin,
An' that's the way this row begin.

9. Ol' Dan Tucker begun in early life
To play the banjo an' the fife;
He'd play the boys and gals to sleep
An' then into his bunk he'd creep.

28.

Cindy

Words and melody adapted and arranged by
John A. and Alan Lomax

Piano arrangement by
Charles and Ruth Seeger

(4)

1. You oughta see my Cindy,
She lives away down South,
An' she's so sweet the honey bees,
Swarm around her mouth.

CHORUS: Git along home, Cindy, Cindy,
Git along home, Cindy, Cindy,
Git along home, Cindy, Cindy,
I'll marry you sometime.

2. I wish I was an apple,
A-hangin' on a tree,
And every time that pretty gal passed
She'd take a bite of me.

3. I wish I had a needle,
As fine as I could sew,
I'd sew that gal to my coat tail
And down the road I'd go.

4. When Cindy got religion,
She thought her time had come,
She walked right up to the preacher
And chawed her chewin' gum.

5. Cindy got religion,
She'd had it once before,
But when she heard my old banjo,
She 'uz the first un on the floor.

6. She took me in her parlor,
She cooled me with her fan,
She swore that Ize the purties' thang
In the shape of mortal man.

7. Cindy hugged and kissed me,
She wrung her hands and cried,
She swore I was the purties' thing
That ever lived or died.

8. She told me that she loved me,
She called me sugar-plum,
She throwed her arms around me
And I thought my time had come.

29.

Blackeyed Susie

Words and melody adapted and arranged by
John A. and Alan Lomax

Piano arrangement by
Charles and Ruth Seeger

1. All I want in this creation,
Pretty little wife and a big plantation.

REFRAIN: Hey, blackeyed Susie,
Hey, pretty little blackeyed Susie,
Hey—.

2. All I need to make me happy,
Two little boys to call me pappy.

3. One name "Sop" and the other name "Gravy",
One gon' sop it up, the other gon' save it.

4. Up Red Oak and down salt water,
Some old man gonna lose his daughter.

5. Blackeyed Susie went huckleberry pickin',
The boys got drunk and Susie took a lickin'.

6. Some got drunk and some got boozy,
I went home with blackeyed Susie.

7. Blackeyed Susie is a sunburnt daisy,
If I don't get her, I'll go crazy.

8. Blackeyed Susie about half grown,
Jumps on the boys like a dog on a bone.

9. I asked her to be my wife,
She come at me with a barlow knife.

10. Love my wife, love my baby,
Love my biscuits sopped in gravy.

30.

Skip to My* Lou

Words and melody adapted and arranged by
John A. and Alan Lomax

Piano arrangement by
Charles and Ruth Seeger

Moderately fast

C G
Lost my part - ner, what - 'll I do? Lost my part - ner, what - 'll I do?

C G C
Lost my part - ner, what - 'll I do? Skip to my Lou, my dar - lin'.

CHORUS

G7
Lou, Lou, skip to my Lou, Lou, Lou, skip to my Lou,

C G7 C
Lou, Lou, skip to my Lou, Skip to my Lou, my dar - lin'.

*To be sung "muh".

(6)

1. Lost my partner, what'll I do?*
Lost my partner, what'll I do?
Lost my partner, what'll I do?
Skip to my Lou, my darlin?

CHORUS: (to be sung when you feel like it)
Lou, Lou, skip to my Lou,
Lou, Lou, skip to my Lou,
Lou, Lou, skip to my Lou,
Skip to my Lou, my darlin'.

2. I'll get another one, purtier'n you,
I'll get another one, purtier'n you,
I'll get another one, purtier'n you,
Skip to my Lou, my darlin' . . .

3. Can't get a red bird, a blue bird'll do,
Can't get a red bird, a blue bird'll do,
Can't get a red bird, a blue bird'll do,
Skip to my Lou, my darlin' . . .

4. Little red wagon, painted blue.

5. Fly in the sugar-bowl, shoo, fly, shoo.

6. Gone again, what'll I do?

7. Hair in the butterdish, six feet long.

8. Cows in the cornfield, two by two.

9. Rats in the breadtray, how they chew.

10. One old boot and a run-down shoe.

31.

Coffee Grows on White Oak Trees

Words and melody collected by
B. A. Botkin

Piano arrangement by
Charles and Ruth Seeger

A
D
D.C.
FINALE
Hel - lo, Su - san Brown. Rail - road, steam - boat, riv - er an' ca -
A7
D
nal, I lost my true love on that ra - gin' ca - nal. O she's
G
D
A
E7
A
A7
gone, gone, gone, O she's gone, gone, gone, O she's
D
G
D
A7
D
gone, on that ra - gin' ca - nal.

INTRODUCTION:

Coffee grows on white oak trees,
The river flows with brandy-o,
Go choose some one to roam with you
As sweet as 'lasses candy.

1. Two in the middle and I can't dance Josie,
Two in the middle and I can't get around,
Two in the middle and I can't dance Josie,
Hello, Susan Brown.

2. Four in the middle and I can't dance Josie,*
Four in the middle and I can't get around,
Four in the middle and I can't dance Josie,
Hello, Susan Brown.

3. Wheel around and whirl around, I can't dance Josie,
Wheel around and whirl around, I can't get around,
Wheel around and whirl around, I can't dance Josie,
Hello, Susan Brown.

4. Rats in the boots and the boots turn over, etc.

5. Cow in the well and can't jump Josie, etc.

6. Briar in my heel and I can't dance Josie, etc.

7. Fiddler's drunk and I can't dance Josie, etc.

(Just before the end you sing. . .)

FINALE:

Railroad, steamboat, river an' canal,
I lost my true love on that ragin' canal.
O she's gone, gone, gone,
O she's gone, gone, gone,
O she's gone on that ragin' canal . . .

*You can sing this song with as many stanzas as you have breath for; if you want to perform it as a play party, turn to the note at the beginning of this chapter.

32.

Shoot the Buffalo

Words and melody adapted and arranged by
John A. and Alan Lomax

Piano arrangement by
Charles and Ruth Seeger

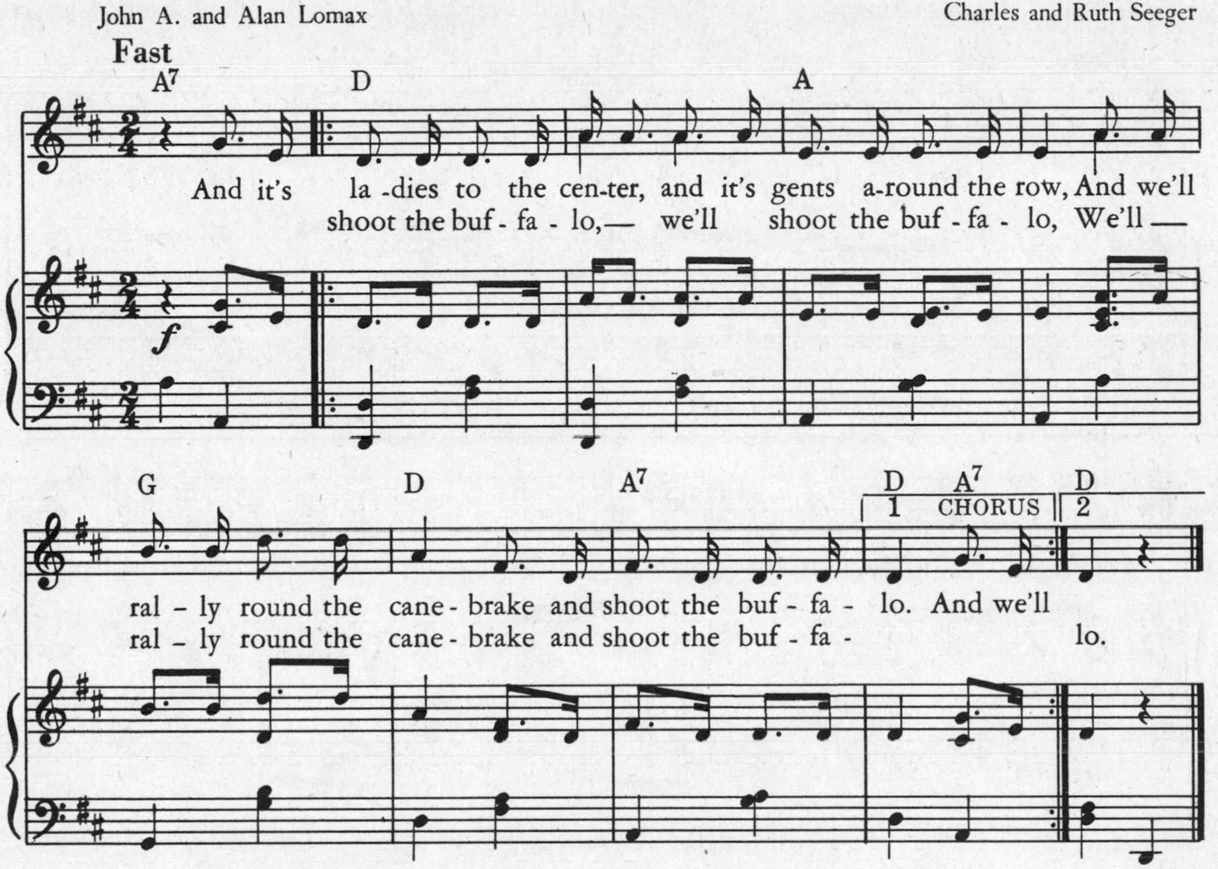

1. And it's ladies to the center and it's gents around the row,
   And we'll rally round the canebrake and shoot the buffalo.

CHORUS I: And we'll shoot the buffalo, we'll shoot the buffalo,
We'll rally round the canebrake and shoot the buffalo.

2. Rise you up, my dearest dear, present to me your hand,
   I'll lead you in procession to a far and distant land.

CHORUS II: And we'll promenade, you know, and we'll promenade, you know,
And we'll all meet together and we'll shoot the buffalo.

3. Rise you up, my dearest dear, present to me your paw,
   I'm sure you've got terbacker, I'd like to have a chaw.

4. The girls will sit and spin, and the boys will sit and grin,
   Rally round the barnyard and chase the old blue hen.

5. The girls will go to school, the boys will act the fool,
   Rally round the barnyard and chase the old gray mule.

6. The girls will sew and patch, the will fight and scratch,
   And we'll all meet together in the sweet potato patch.

7. Oh, the hawk shot the buzzard and the buzzard shot the crow,
   And we'll rally round the canebrake and shoot the buffalo.

Buffalo Gals

Words and melody adapted and arranged by
John A. and Alan Lomax

Piano arrangement by
Charles and Ruth Seeger

*Has been sung about *Lousi'ana Gals, Kansas Gals,* etc. Can be sung about or to any gals you're courting.

2. O yes, pretty boys, we're comin' out tonight,
   We're comin' out tonight, we're comin' out tonight,
   O yes, pretty boys, we're comin' out tonight,
   And dance by the light of the moon.

CHORUS: I danced with a gal with a hole in her stockin',
And her heel kep' a-rockin' an' her toe kep' a-knockin',
I danced with a gal with a hole in her stockin',
An' her heel kep' a-rockin' to the moon.

34.

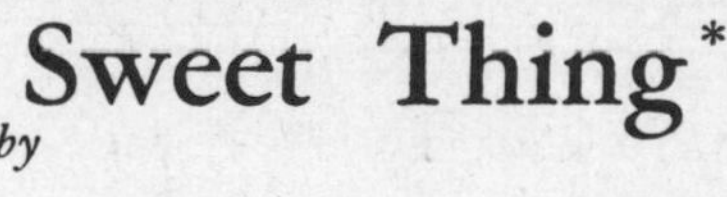

Sweet Thing*

Words and melody adapted and arranged by
John A. and Alan Lomax

Piano arrangement by
Charles and Ruth Seeger

Moderately fast

F
What you gon-na do when the li-quor gives out,_ sweet thing?

mf

F⁷ F
What you gon-na do when the li-quor gives out, sweet thing?

F⁷ F
What you gon-na do when the li-quor gives out, Stand a-round the cor-ner with your

C⁷ F
mouth in a pout, Sweet thing, sweet thing, sweet_ thing.

*Also known as *Sugar Babe, Sometime, Crawdad Song,* etc.

2. What you gonna do when your shoes give out, sweet thing?
What you gonna do when your shoes give out, sweet thing?
When my shoes give out, I'm gonna quit the street,
Take a chair and put a fan at my feet,
Sweet thing, sweet thing, sweet thing.

3. What you gonna do when your chair gives out, sweet thing?
What you gonna do when your chair gives out, sweet thing?
When I got no liquor, no chair, no shoes,
I'll lay 'cross the bed, with my head in the blues,
Sweet thing, sweet thing, sweet thing.

4. Slats on the bed go blamety-blam, in the mornin',
Slats on the bed go blamety-blam, in the evenin',
Slats on the bed go blamety-blam,
But I'll keep on a-sleepin' like I don't give a damn,
Sweet thing, sweet thing, sweet thing.

Crawdad Song

(Version 2 of "Sweet Thing")

1. Wake up, old man, you slept too late, this mornin',
Wake up, old man, you slept too late, this evenin',
Wake up, old man, you slept too late,
The crawdad wagon done passed your gate,
In the mornin', in the evenin', so soon.

2. You get a line and I'll get a pole, this mornin',
You get a line and I'll get a pole, this evenin',
You get a line and I'll get a pole,
I'll meet you down at the crawdad hole,
In the mornin', in the evenin', so soon.

3. A-settin' on the ice till my feet got cold,
A-watchin' that crawdad dig his hole.

4. Crawdad, crawdad, you better dig deep,
For I'm gonna ramble in my sleep.

5. A-settin' on the bank till my feet got hot,
A-watchin' that crawdad rack and trot.

6. Crawdad, crawdad, you better go to hole,
If I don't catch you, durn my soul.

Sugar Babe
(Version 3)

1. Look at them farmers comin' to town, sugar babe,
Look at them farmers comin' to town, sugar babe,
Look at them farmers comin' to town,
Clothes all ratty and head hangin' down,
Sugar babe, O baby mine.

2. A little sup of whiskey er a taste of gin, sugar babe,
A little sup of whiskey er a taste of gin, sugar babe,
A little sup of whiskey er a taste of gin,
Straighten right up and they're gone agin!
Sugar babe, O baby mine.

3. Shoot your dice and roll 'em in the sand, sweet thing,
Shoot your dice and roll 'em in the sand, sweet thing,
Shoot your dice and roll 'em in the sand,
I ain't gonna work for no durned man.
Sweet thing, sweet thing, sweet thing.

4. Danced all night with a bottle in my hand, sweet thing,
Danced all night with a bottle in my hand, sweet thing,
Danced all night with a bottle in my hand,
A-lookin' for a woman ain't got no man.
Sweet thing, sweet thing, sweet thing.

5. I got drunk and reel against the wall,
Good corn liquor was the cause of it all.

6. Put your hand on your hip and let your mind roll by,
'Cause your body's gonna swivel when you come to die.

CHAPTER IV

Johnny Has Gone for A Soldier

AMERICAN SOLDIERS HAVE ALWAYS FELT that war was pretty absurd. Even in the American Revolution, the favorite song of the men was "Yankee Doodle," a British slur on the ragged, unprofessional army of the colonists. In World War I, "Mademoiselle from Armentières," the soldier's No. 1 song was a rambling, and often bawdy, satire on their officers and on the French women they had crossed the sea to defend. Finally, in World War II, the American citizen soldier took most kindly to songs which had this burden—

When the war is over, we will all enlist again,
When the war is over, we will all enlist again,
When the war is over, we will all enlist again,
In a —— —— —— we will.

Not that this man was never fired by patriotic songs. In the Revolution he marched to the grim measures of "Chester," which that fiery old blacksmith musician, William Billings, had composed for the Revolution:

Let tyrants shake their iron rod;
And slav'ry clank her galling chains,
We'll fear them not; we trust in God,
New England's God ever reigns.

The foe comes on with haughty stride,
Our troops advance with martial noise,
Their vet'rans flee, before our youth
And Gen'rals yield to beardless boys.

His own campfire ballads, stories of the battles in his eight-year agonizing struggle for freedom, sometimes rang like bugle calls:

Come unto me, ye heroes, whose hearts are true and bold,
Who value more your honor, than others do their gold,
Give ear unto my story and the truth to you I'll tell,
Concerning many a soldier, who for his country fell.

In the War of 1812 the "eagle screamed" in lines like—

You parliament of England, ye lords and commons, too,
Consider well what you're about and what you mean to do,
If you go to war with Yankees, I'm sure you'll rue the day,
You've roused the sons of liberty in North Amerikay.

The song of that conflict which caught on with the people and remained in oral currency among the folk was the "Hunters of Kentucky":

We are a hardy, free-born race,
Each man to fear a stranger;
Whate'er the game we join in chase,
Despising time and danger;
And if a daring foe annoys,
Whate'er his strength and forces,
We'll show him that Kentucky boys
Are alligator horses.
Oh! Kentucky, the hunters of Kentucky,
Oh! Kentucky, the hunters of Kentucky.

Certainly the Civil War, because it was a war of issues and ideas, produced more serious songs than any other war in which Americans have fought. "The Battle Hymn of the Republic" and its popular form "John Brown's Body," "Kingdom Comin'," and "Marching Through Georgia," "Tenting on the Old Camp Ground" and "The Bonny Blue Flag"—the soldiers sang all of these, marched to them, sentimentalized over them at post-war conventions. Yet the songs they made themselves for themselves had the usual satirical soldier's spirit. Johnny Reb sang:

Just before the battle, the gineral hears a row,
He says the Yanks are comin', I hear their rifles now,
He turns around in wonder and what do you reckon he sees,
The Georgia militia, eatin' goober peas.

The Yankee army, too, produced its own song of the empty belly, a parody of "The Battle Cry of Freedom" which told of the sad fate of Mary's little lamb:

. . . and frequently she turned it loose upon the bank to play,
The soldiers eyed it from the shore in a kleptomaniac way.
Mary never more did see her darling little lamb,
For the boys in blue they chawed it up and they didn't give a damn,
Shouting the battle cry of freedom.

The great song of the Spanish-American War, "There'll Be a Hot Time in the Old Town Tonight," had more to do with celebrating than with soldiering. Even the fervor of 1917, which produced "Johnny Get Your Gun," "Keep the Home Fires Burning," "Over There," and other valorous, patriotic pieces, could not long sustain the disillusioned doughboy. He made his grinning parodies—about training:

They took him on the parade ground, to march, to rush, to crawl,
The first was bad, the next was worse, the last was worst of all;
He bruised his belly on a tack, he tore it on a nail,
He'd have made a damn good lizard if he'd only had a tail.

on army rations:

Dear army beans,
You know I love you,
For I eat you every day.

on his little companions in the trenches, a parody on "Pack Up Your Troubles":

Wrap both your elbows up around your back
And scratch, scratch, scratch. . . .

on a dying aviator:

Take the cylinders out of my kidneys,
The connecting rod out of my brain,
The crankshaft out of my backbone,
And assemble the engine again.

and even disrespectful and impudent verses about old man Death:

The worms crawl in, the worms crawl out,
The worms play pinochle on your snout.

Of course, the favorite song of them all, the song to which the doughboys gave their undivided loyalty, improvising a ditty of hundreds of stanzas, celebrated the dissolute and charming little lady from Armentières.

World War II produced little or no inspirational music which will be remembered. On the one hand, the commercial music business felt the marching songs might hurt the dance-band trade; on the other, official Washington was too busy to promote singing in the services on a broad scale.

35. *JOHNNY HAS GONE FOR A SOLDIER*

The ragged Continentalers, Andy Jackson's volunteers, the Texas Rangers, the Indian fighters, and the boys from the backwoods who fought in the Civil War, these young men and the girls they left behind them adopted the ballads of their grandparents as their principal wartime folk songs. Such British pieces as "The Soldier and the Lady," "Jackie Monroe," "The Pretty Little Miss All in Her Garden," "The Bold Soldier," "Turtle Dove"—these songs of parting and joyful reunion have been sung by the folk as contemporary songs in all our wars. We have asked many an old ballad-singer which war produced such ancient pieces as "Jackie Monroe." Almost invariably the answer has referred to the war which impinged most nearly upon the singer's own past.

It is for this reason that we have chosen to publish a Revolutionary War version of the Irish "Shule Aroon" in an American folk-song book. Although Joyce, the Irish collector, identifies "Shule Aroon" with the period between 1691 and 1745, when the Irish enlisted and fought with the armies of the French, its truly exquisite Irish melody has carried it into every quarter of America. Chantymen on the clippers sung it at the capstan, lumberjacks had their version for the deacon seat, sodbusters made it over into a play-party tune, Negro children used it as a game song, and an old lady from Waco, Texas, sent it to us as a Cherokee Indian song, believing that her garbled Gaelic refrain was Cherokee. Our present version comes from John Allison, whose family have, for generations, lived on the west bank of the Hudson near Butternut Hill. One of the Allisons marched with Washington's army and heard the men singing this, the most haunting of American soldiers' songs.

36. *BRAVE WOLFE*

Of all the topical soldier ballads of early America, the broadside piece that celebrates the British general, James Wolfe, has continued longest in oral currency. Among upstate New York folk-singers he is still a hero; and, although the people sometimes misfire in choosing their heroes, they hit upon a true hero in Wolfe.

When Wolfe, with his redcoats and his American auxiliaries, stormed the heights of Abraham and took Quebec from the French in 1759, the people of the British colonies were vastly delighted. For years the French control of the North and the West had slowed down the westward advance of the frontier, and the Indian allies of the French had harassed the outlying settlements of the thirteen colonies. The colonists had been so occupied with these problems that they had been forced to ignore their differences with the British king. When the French were defeated in Canada, the Americans were left free to prepare for their struggle for independence.

Not only did James Wolfe become a popular hero for historical reasons, he was just naturally cut out to be one. His whole career was a succession of gallant attitudes. He wrote about his appointment to lead the Canadian campaign:

> I have this day signified to Mister Pitt that he may dispose of my slight carcass as he pleases, and that I am ready for the undertaking. . . . I am in a

very bad condition both with the gravel and with rheumatism; but I'd rather die than decline any kind of service that offers.

When a courtier complained to King George that a madman (Wolfe) had been appointed commander, the King replied, "Mad is he? Then I hope he'll bite some others of my generals. . . ."

Wolfe and his nine thousand men laid siege to Quebec where Montcalm held sixteen thousand troops in readiness to throw him back into the St. Lawrence, but Wolfe and his men believed in each other. Wolfe said, "Our troops are good and, if valor can make amends for numbers, we shall probably succeed." One of Wolfe's grizzled old sergeants remarked that his men were ready for anything—"Nay, how could it be otherwise, being at the heels of gentlemen whose whole thirst, equal with their general, is for glory?"

Wolfe fell gravely ill a few days before his planned attack up the sheer cliff toward the city. He told his physician, "I know perfectly well you cannot cure me, but pray make me up so that I may be up without pain for a few days and able to do my duty." Struck down by three rifle balls on the Plains of Abraham before the city, Wolfe told his men, "Don't grieve for me. I shall be happy in a few minutes." When they brought him the news of victory, he said, "Now, thank God, I can die contented."

Thus James Wolfe died on the field of battle as his opponent, the gallant French general Montcalm, was bleeding to death from his wounds behind the French lines. Here was a situation for the ballad-makers; here was a hero people could weave legends about. Wolfe was a plain man; he died well; and on his breast hung a locket enclosing the picture of his beautiful fiancée. This ballad has lived on, in broadsides, in patriotic songbooks, and on the lips of old-timers like Yankee John Galusha, lumberwoods singer of upstate New York, who gave Frank Warner this version.

37. *JOHN BROWN'S BODY*

The Civil War melody that will be longest remembered is that one which rolls through both the "Battle Hymn of the Republic" and "John Brown's Body." Earlier it was set to Sunday school words in the hymn, "Say, Brothers, Will You Meet Me," attributed to William Steffe. Steffe would probably have shaken right out of his "Sunday-go-to-meetin' " trousers if he had ever encountered the gentleman whom his melody has immortalized.

John Brown, a descendant of Peter Brown, who came over in the Mayflower, was born in Torrington, Connecticut, May 9, 1800, and hanged in Charlestown, Virginia, December 2, 1859; but his soul goes marching on.

John Brown believed that slavery was an abomination in the eyes of the Lord. He called it "a barbarous and unprovoked warfare of one portion of the citizens upon another portion in utter disregard and violation of those eternal and self-evident truths set forth in the Declaration of Independence."

John Brown stood over six feet tall. He had the eye of an eagle and a voice that rumbled like a prairie storm. When guerrilla warfare broke out in Kansas over the slavery issue, John Brown led his sons and his neighbors against the "slavers," and soon John Brown became a name of terror to all the Quantrell sympathizers. The Federal troops harried his band and drove him out of Kansas.

John Brown studied guerrilla warfare. He took council with Frederick Douglass, Harriet Tubman, and other Abolitionist leaders. In the lonesome hours of the night he conceived a plan—God-given, so old John Brown thought—to set the burning issue of slavery before the country in such fashion that the American people would put an end to slavery forever.

John Brown proposed to capture the arsenal at Harper's Ferry with a small force of men, call upon the masses of the slaves to take arms against their master and join him. Then, with a force of ten thousand men, he dreamed of holding out in the Southern mountains until the whole South, the whole country, rose up and smashed the slavery system.

Colonel Robert E. Lee took John Brown and what remained of his pitiful twenty-five after a few hours of hopeless fighting at Harper's Ferry. When Lee asked him what was his purpose and by what authority he acted, John Brown replied, "To free the slaves——by the authority of God Almighty."

John Brown wrote to his people from the Charlestown jail:

> I have been whipped, as the saying is; but I am sure I can recover all the lost capital occasioned by this disaster by only hanging a few minutes by the neck. . . . It affords me some satisfaction to feel conscious of having tried to better the condition of those who are on the underhill side, and now I am in hopes of being able to meet the consequences without a murmur. . . . I charge you all never to forget the griefs of the poor that cry and of those who have none to help them. Farewell, farewell.

John Brown was sentenced by a Virginia court to be hanged by the neck till he was dead. When they asked the prisoner if he had anything to stay, he told them this:

> Had I interfered in the manner which I admit has been proved in behalf of the rich, the powerful, the intelligent, or any of their friends, and suffered and sacrificed what I have in this interference, it would have been all right. Every man in this court would have deemed it an act worthy of reward, rather than punishment. . . . I say that I am too young to understand that God is any respecter of persons. I believe that to have interfered in behalf of His despised poor I did no wrong, but right. Now if it is deemed necessary that I should forfeit my life for the furtherance of the ends of justice, and mingle my blood further with the blood of my children and the blood of the millions in this slave country, I say, let it be done.

He stood calmly while they placed the rope around his neck. He died calm. John Brown's body moldered in the grave, but the people remembered him. They took an old, thundering hymn tune and they made a song about old John Brown that was sung by both sides during the Civil War and that still rolls his name around the world, wherever men march and fight for their freedom.

38. *MADEMOISELLE FROM ARMENTIERES*

In World War I the American troops catalogued their amorous adventures, their gripes against the army, and their soldier's cynicism in the familiar "Mademoiselle from Armentières." An anonymously and privately published work in two volumes, appearing under the imprint of the press of the Wooly Whale, New York, 1935, gives a saltier version of the song than we can publish, as well as some particulars about its history.

One of the familiar stanzas of the "Mademoiselle" song begins:

Two German officers crossed the Rhine,
To kiss the women and drink the wine.

Apparently this was a development of an older song in which a little marine or a little Dutch Soldier . . .

. . . crossed over the Rhine,
And stopped at the house of a lady so fine.

This song, whose melody so closely resembles "Mademoiselle," goes on as follows:

Oh madam, have you a daughter fine,
Snapoo,
Oh, madam, have you a daughter fine,
Snapoo,
Oh madam, have you a daughter fine,
That's fit for a soldier from over the Rhine,
Snapoo, snapeeda, filanda-go-sheeta,
Snapoo.

Obviously the refrain line is a satirical approximation of some foreign language, which indicates that "Snapoo" was derived from some foreign original. Various authorities have proposed the French ballad "Le Retour du Marin," and the German songs, "Der Wirthin Tochterlein," and "Drei Reiter Am Thor" as sources. None of these, however, seems probable to us. In all likelihood, we shall never track down "Parlez-vous" to its beginnings. The curious moral, however, is that American soldiers have marched through two wars singing a song of suspiciously foreign origin.

39. *GEE, BUT I WANT TO GO HOME*

How much genuine soldier verse and soldier balladry came out of this last of our citizen armies, we will not know until the collections are published. "Mademoiselle from Armentières" was given new stanzas. The Negro troops made for themselves a stirring and bitter marching song.

Jody's got your gal and gone,
And left you here a-singin' this song.
You had a good wife and you left,
You right!
You had a good home and you left,
You right!

From the very first days of training, however, the most popular of all soldier songs in World War II was "Gee, But I Want to Go Home." This was an adaptation of a British song of World War I composed by Lt. Gitz Rice:

I want to go home, I want to go home,
The bullets they whistle, the cannons they roar,
I don't want to stay here anymore;
Take me over the sea,
Where the Germans can't get me,
O my, I'm too young to die,
I want to go home.

One must conclude from their songs that American citizen soldiers don't care for wars, but up to now they have won them.

35.

Johnny has Gone For a Soldier

Words and melody adapted and arranged by
John A. and Alan Lomax

Piano arrangement by
Charles and Ruth Seeger

Moderately slow

A min. E A min. E C

Sad I sit on But-ter-nut Hill, Who could blame me, cry my fill? And

mp

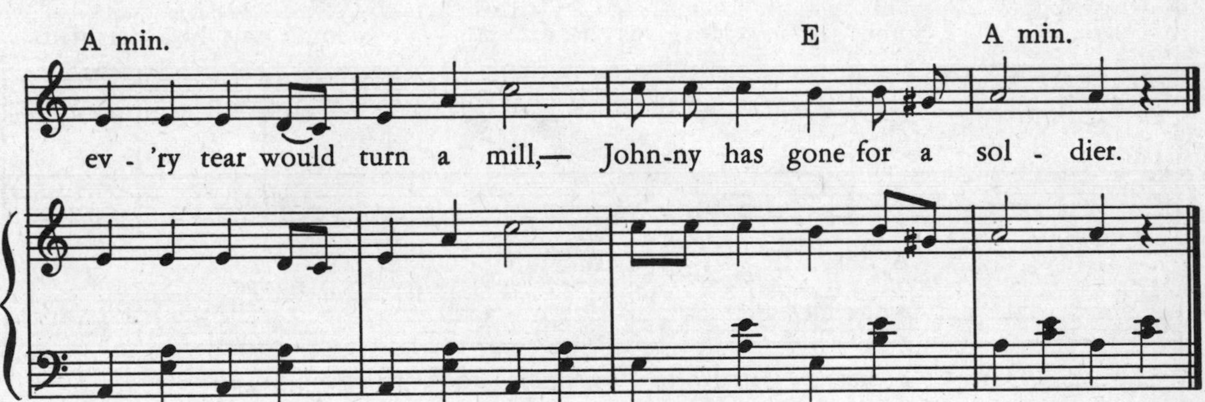

1. Sad I sit on Butternut Hill,
Who could blame me, cry my fill?
And ev'ry tear would turn a mill—
Johnny has gone for a soldier.

2. Me O my, I loved him so,
Broke my heart to see him go,
And only time will heal my woe,—
Johnny has gone for a soldier.

3. I'd sell my clock, I'd sell my reel,
Likewise I'd sell my spinning wheel
To buy my love a sword of steel—
Johnny has gone for a soldier.

36.

Brave Wolfe

Words and melody adapted and arranged by
John A. and Alan Lomax

Piano arrangement by
Charles and Ruth Seeger

1. "Bad news has come to town, bad news is carried,—
Some say my love is dead, some say he's married.
As I was a-ponderin' on this, I took to weepin',—
They stole my love away whilst I was sleepin'." . . .

2. "I'll go and tell my love that I will leave her,
All in the wars of France I'm bound forever,
All in the wars of France where the cannon does rattle,
There I'll myself advance and face the battle."

3. "Love, here's a ring of gold, long years I've kept it.
Madame, it's for your sake, will you accept it?
When you the posy read, pray think on the giver.
Madame, remember me, I'm undone forever."

4. Then a*way* went this brave youth and embarked on the ocean,
To free Amerikay was his intention.
He landed in Quebec with all his party,
The city to attack, being brave and hearty.

5. He drew his army up in the lines so pretty
On the plains of Abraham, back of the city,
At a distance from the town, where the French would meet him
In double numbers there resolved to beat him.

6. Montcalm and this brave youth together walk'ed,
Between two armies they, like brothers talk'ed,
Till each one took his post and did retire.
It was then these numerous hosts commenced their fire.

7. *Lit*tle did he think death was so near him,
Yes, little did he think death was so near him,—
When, shot down from his horse was this our hero,—
We'll long lament his loss in tears of sorrow.

8. He *rais'*éd up his head where the cannons did rattle
And to his aide he said, "How goes the battle?"
His aide-de-camp replied, "It's ended in our favor."
Then says this brave youth, "I quit this earth with pleasure." . .

9. "Bad news has come to town, bad news has carried,—
Some says my love is dead, some says he's married.
As I was a ponderin' on this, I took to weepin',—
They stole my love away whilst I was sleepin'."

37.

John Brown's Body

Piano arrangement by
Charles and Ruth Seeger

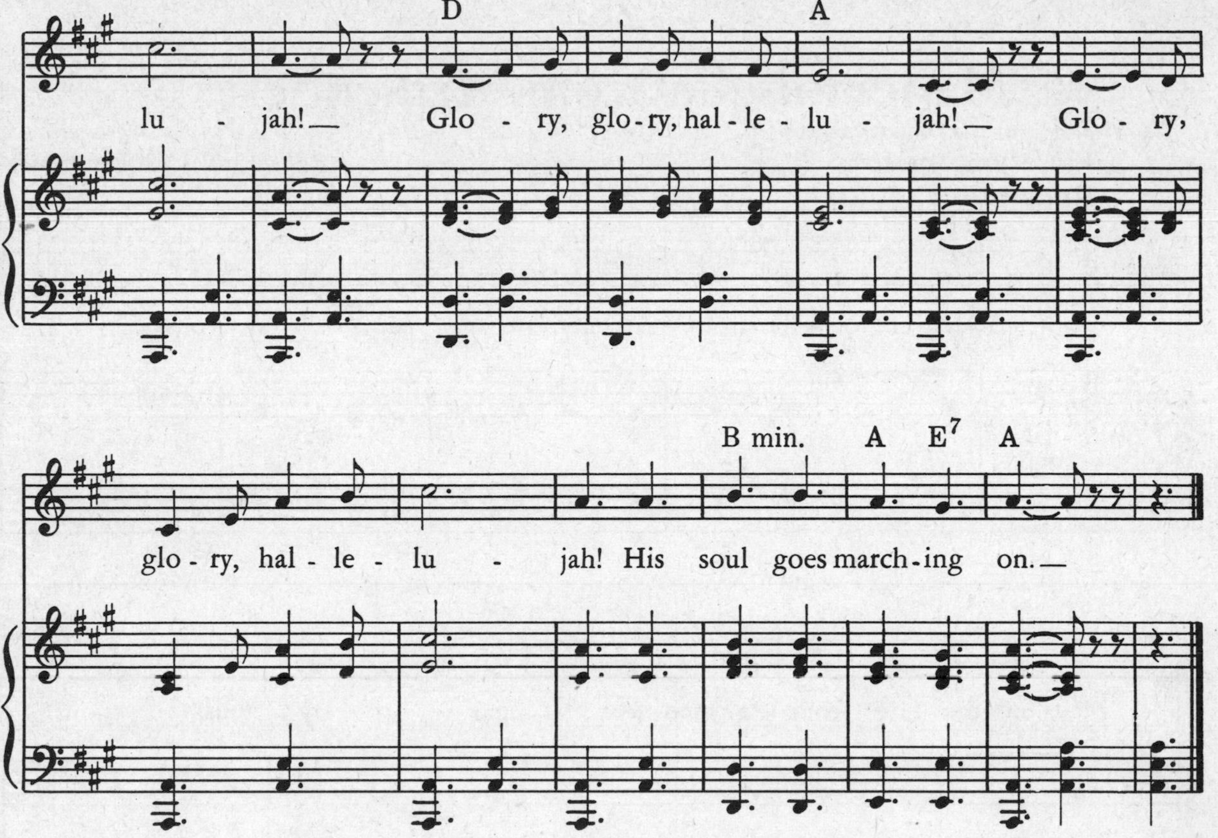

1. John Brown's body lies a-moulderin' in the grave,
John Brown's body lies a-moulderin' in the grave,
John Brown's body lies a-moulderin' in the grave,
But his soul goes marching on.

2. He's gone to be a soldier in the army of the Lord,
He's gone to be a soldier in the army of the Lord,
He's gone to be a soldier in the army of the Lord,
But his soul goes marching on.

3. John Brown died that the slaves might be free,
John Brown died that the slaves might be free,
John Brown died that the slaves might be free,
But his soul goes marching on.

4. His pet lambs will meet him on the way,
His pet lambs will meet him on the way,
His pet lambs will meet him on the way,
But his soul goes marching on.

38.

Mademoiselle from Armentieres

Words and melody adapted and arranged by
John A. and Alan Lomax

Piano arrangement by
Charles and Ruth Seeger

World War I

1. Mademoiselle from Armentières,
   She hadn't been kissed in forty years.

2. She never could hold the love of a man,
   For she took her baths in a talcum can.

3. She might have been old for all we knew,
   When Napoleon flopped at Waterloo.

4. Mademoiselle from Orleans,
   She made me sell my Liberty bonds.

5. The seventy-seventh went over the top,
   A sous-lieutenant, a Jew and a Wop.

6. The medical corps they held the line,
   With pinky pills and iodine.

7. The officers get all the steak,
   And all we get is the bellyache.

8. The general got the croix-de-guerre,
   And the son-of-a-gun was never there.

9. An American soldier on the Rhine,
   He kissed the woman and drank the wine.

10. 'Twas a hell of a war as we recall,
    But still 'twas better than none at all.

World War II

1. The Waves and Wacs will win the war
   So what the hell are we fighting for?

2. The permanent party will have to go,
   The Wacs are here to run the show.

3. O Mississippi* is a hell of a state,
   The garbage can of the forty eight.

4. We're the boys from Keesler Field,**
   We never had a decent meal.

5. Once we had a decent meal,
   It took a general to swing the deal.

6. They say this is a motorized war,
   So what the hell are we marching for?

*Substitute the name of whatever state you trained in and forgive the editors for having to revise this stanza for publication.
**Also and likewise.

39.

Gee, But I Want to Go Home

1. The coffee that they give us,
They say is mighty fine,
It's good for cuts and bruises
And it tastes like iodine.

CHORUS: I don't want no more of army life,
Gee, but I want to go,
Gee, but I want to go home.

2. The biscuits that they give us,
They say are mighty fine,
One fell off a table
And killed a pal of mine,

3. The clothes that they give us,
They say are mighty fine,
Me and my buddy
Can both fit into mine.

4. They treat us all like monkeys
And make us stand in line,
They give you fifty dollars a week
And take back forty nine.

5. The girls at the service club
They say are mighty fine,
Most are over eighty
And the rest are under nine.

CHORUS: I don't want no more of army life,
Gee, but I want to go,
Gee, but I want to go home.

CHAPTER V

Blow, Boys, Blow

A Yankee ship came down the river,
Blow, boys, blow,
Her masts and spars, they shone like silver,
Blow, my bully boys, blow.

IT WAS DURING THE REVOLUTIONARY WAR and the War of 1812 that American sailing ships and American sailors began to run circles around the fleets of all the world. Ship builders laid out blockade runners and privateersmen with keener lines than earlier vessels. The men who manned them took risks that crews had not taken before. They drove their vessels hard, but the profits were high enough to make the danger worth while. The mercantile fortunes accumulated in those war years provided the basis for further experiments in ship design. All along the Atlantic Coast, the shipyards turned out vessels with sharper lines, vessels that sat lower in the water and yet carried more canvas than any ships had carried before. These slim, streamlined, rakish squareriggers came to be called "clippers," and, for almost a hundred years, the white-winged clippers were the queens of all the seas, outdistancing all vessels on all the oceans. Listen to their names, names that roll in epic lines:

The Racehorse, the Staghound, the Antelope and the Wild Pigeon,
The Syren, the Flying Fish, the Sea-Serpent, and the Witch of the Waves,
The Southern Cross, the Northern Light and the Shooting Star,
The Trade Wind, the Monsoon, the White Squall and the Hurricane.

To the men who designed and sailed them, the clippers were beautiful, cruel, and dangerous mistresses. To their owners they brought fat profits. In the highly competitive China tea-trade, in the gold rush to California, in the fur trade with the Arctic, speed paid dividends. Oftentimes a new ship would pay for itself entirely in one voyage. American officers, who had learned their trade and earned their berths as common seamen before the mast, instead of in schools of navigation as privileged members of an upper class, knew how to drive their ships to the last pitch of speed. A French captain, who was lying close-hauled with all sails in before a storm of wind, observed a small white cloud on the horizon—another ship with all sails set. As the ship scudded past him, he said to his first mate, "That man must be crazy to carry sail in a storm like this," to which his mate replied, "He isn't crazy, he's just an American."

Sometimes these crazy Americans drove their ships under or broke them in two. As the supremacy of sail began to be threatened by steam, both vessels and men were driven harder than ever. When an officer said "jump," a seaman jumped or else received at once a kick from a copper-toed sea-boot or a blow from an iron belaying pin. Mates were chosen as much for their ability to whip any man who might come aboard as for their seamanship.

And who do you think was the captain of her?
Blow, boys, blow,
Bully Hayes, that devil's driver,
Blow, my bully boys, blow.

O Bully Hayes, he loves us sailors,
Blow, boys, blow,
Yes, he does, like hell and blazes,
Blow, my bully boys, blow.

And what do you think we had for dinner?
Blow, boys, blow,
Pickled eels' feet and monkey liver,
Blow, my bully boys, blow.

The American sailorman, who roared out these lines, who manned and worked the clippers and who made their record-breaking voyages possible, was tougher and hardier than the ships he sailed. In a howling gale off Cape Horn he would crawl to the top of a mast that swung in a sixty-degree arc eighty feet above the deck and the sea; he would lie there against the yardarm and pull at the stiff canvas until he burst his finger-ends and his red blood spattered the sail. He could live three or four months on hard tack and salt pork and a ration of foul water, sleep on boards in a dripping forecastle, stand twenty-four- or sixty-hour watches in a storm and arrive in port with nothing more serious to complain of than a great thirst. Ashore, the boarding-house masters took him in charge, and filled him with cheap rum; the floozies robbed him of his money. A deadbeat sailor on the beach had no friends. He had no choice but another hell-ship bound out for God knows where.

This American sailor was a lonely man, a master craftsman without whose steel muscles and horny hands the trim clippers would have been helpless in the winds. Above all, he was a great singer. Dana wrote in *Two Years before the Mast,* "A song is as necessary to sailors as the fife and drum to soldiers. We often found a great difference in the effect of the different songs. Two or three songs would be tried, one after another, with different effect—not an inch could be got up on the tackles. When a new song was struck up that seemed to hit the humor of the moment, [they] drove the tackles 'two blocks' in a moment. . . ."

Apparently this custom of calling out at the ropes and tackle is as old as sail. One Friar Fabri, in describing life aboard a Venetian galley in 1493, writes, ". . . there are others who are called mariners, who sing when work is going on, because work at sea is very heavy, and is only carried on by a concert between one who sings out the orders and the laborers who sing in response. . . ." Sailor work songs or shanties (the word is probably derived from the French *chantez*), as we call them, have been sung by men of all the European nations; but it was in the farflung navies of Great Britain that they flowered and matured until the beginning of the nineteenth century. For almost a century thereafter, while the American clippers showed their sterns to the ships of the rest of the world, our shanteymen made *their* contributions to this ancient art of the sea.

Scores of these sturdy and profane old songs were known to every seaman. Some came from the carracks of Queen Elizabeth's fleet, others straight from the music halls along the Bowery or in Limehouse, others from Negro singers who shipped on in Gulf ports. The shanteyman, or work-song leader, had no special rank or privileges. He was a common "able-bodied" seaman, an experienced hand, who, when sail was to be set, laid hold of the rope at the point nearest the mast and decided the timing of the concerted pulls by the rhythm of his chant.

He knew by instinct and long practice how to space the pulls so as to get the last ounce of exertion out of every man on every pull; he knew also how to set the tempo of his songs to allow the men to rest and recover themselves between pulls. When sail had to be reefed in an icy gale, it was his shout of—

We'll pay Paddy Doyle for his BOOTS!

which really brought the inch-thick, icy canvas up to the mast out of the monster grip of the wind.

A shanteyman needed a good, loud, bellowing voice that could be heard above a storm. He needed a good memory, for the men liked to hear the old familiar words and stories, just the way they had heard them before. He needed a ready wit for improvising new lines on the spur of the moment—vulgar slurs on the character and ancestry and personal habits of the first mate and the captain—bawdy stanzas about the female "fire-ships" of the seven seas. A man who could get a laugh out of the men at the ropes or tramping around the capstan could push the work along faster.

When the shanteyman lifted his song, he would often sing the chorus through once alone to make sure everybody knew *his* tune, since these orally transmitted songs varied greatly in small particulars from one singer to the next. Then he would take his solo line. "A good shanteyman," writes Joanna Colcord, the principal American collector, "embellished the bare bones of the air with grace notes and flourishes; he flung his voice aloft like a bird to reach a high note, soaring above it, then swooping down upon it with a careless jubilant swing that was irresistible." Before he had released the final note, the other men took the refrain line all together and roared it out in unison, thus allowing the shanteyman time to breathe and to think of the next line. Another solo line for the shanteyman; another bellow in unison from the crew—then the shanteyman swung his hoarse-voiced, bull-throated herd into the chorus, and, while they flung the burden into the wind's teeth, he cast his eye at the slack of the sail or the state of the pump well and readied his next rhyme.

40. *SANTY ANNO*

The most beautiful and the best-known of shanties were those sung at the capstan or windlass. Since there was no motive power aboard a sailing vessel beyond that which lay in the backs of the crew, the job of raising the anchor off the bottom was accomplished by the whole crew heaving against the capstan bars and tramping them round and round until the muddy flukes of the anchor swung against the ship's bow. The capstan shanties all have a slow march rhythm. Indeed, our common mistake with shanties is to sing them at too fast a clip, for most of them were slow, suited to the tempo of heavy work. They celebrated "Sally Brown, the bright mulatter," "The Maid of Amsterday," "The Gloucester Girls who had no combs," the "The Hog Eye Man"; they charted the sailor's course to "South Australia," "Mobile Bay," "Sacramento," "Liverpool," and "The Rio Grande"; they toasted "Old Stormalong" (as the roughest and readiest of all the officers) and the Mexican General Santa Anna British and American sailors often squabbled and even came to blows over this chantey, since in the British version Santa Anna whipped the American General Taylor, while American sailors preferred to have Taylor do the whipping and old Santy the running. Perhaps an explanation for the importance of Santy to chantey singers is that the Mexican War coincided with the great period of the clippers.

41. *SHENANDOAH*

Old sailormen, who have heard this capstan shantey ringing out across strange anchorages in the far ports of the world, agree that it is the finest of them all. The melody has the roll and surge and freedom of a tall ship sweeping along before a trade wind. The sonorous succession of long vowels and soft and liquid consonants blend perfectly with the romantic air. The lines are a call from the homeland to the sailor wandering far out across the seas, a call not from a sweetheart, a house, or even a town, but from the land itself, its rivers and its familiar and loved hills.

It is quite likely that no one will ever know exactly where or how the song was made. Captain Whall, who compiled one of the earliest and best of shantey collections, says that it may be a *voyageur* or Missouri river boatman's song. Sometimes the song tells of a trader who courts the brown daughter of an Indian chief named Shenandoah. Old-time cavalry officers roar out a lusty version of their own contriving which adds certain bawdy details to this story. Yet the main life of the song was lived under sail in the days of squarerigged ships, when the men were leaning hard on the capstan bars and tramping the anchor up from the bottom. This is one of America's rich returns for the gifts from British shanteymen of "Amsterdam," "Blow the Man Down," "Rio Grande," and "Leave Her, Johnny."

42. *SACRAMENTO*

In 1849, when the whole world began a scramble to get to the Western gold fields, there were two possible routes to California, both equally hazardous and arduous. One was the covered-wagon track across the Great Plains, the desert, and the high Sierras. The other was the wind and water route around Cape Horn, the path of the windjammer, the American clipper ship.

So it was that the gold of California minted a silver-winged fleet. In 1848 two sailing vessels dropped anchor in San Francisco; in 1849 seven hundred and forty-two ships made landfall there, debarking more than ninety thousand gold-seekers. Cargo rates shot up so fast that a clipper could pay for herself in one trip to 'Frisco. A new fleet was built in the next ten years, a fleet of California clippers, "the most lifelike machines ever made by man," the fastest deepwater sailing vessels that ever existed.

The most extreme of all these California clippers and the swiftest was the "Flying Cloud." On the morning of June 3, 1851, she slipped past Ambrose Light bound round the Horn to the California gold fields. Here are some extracts from the captain's log of this record-breaking voyage:

June 6—Lost main and mizzen top gallant sails and main topsail yard.

July 11—Very severe thunder and lightning, double-reefed topsails, split fore and main top-mast staysails. At one p.m. discovered that mainmast had sprung.

July 23—Cape Horn, North five miles. The whole coast covered with snow.

July 31—Fresh breezes. Fine weather, all sails set. By six squally-in lower and top gallant studding sails; 7, in royals; 2 a.m., in fore-top-mast studding sail. Ship very wet fore and aft. Distance run this day 374 miles. (The fastest day ever made by a vessel under sail!)

August 3—Suspended First Officer from duty in consequence of his arrogating to himself the privilege of cutting up rigging, contrary to my orders.

August 30—Anchored in San Francisco Harbor after a passage of 89 days and 20 hours.

On this, the fastest voyage ever made under sail, the captain padlocked the sails to the yards and put the keys in his own pocket, carrying sail until the canvas or the masts gave way. His iron-souled first mate was so terrified that he chopped away the sail with a hatchet because he thought the ship was going under. That's the way records were broken by the California clippers, in the days when the anchor came up to the strain of . . .

Ho, boys, ho, for Californio,
There's plenty of gold, so I've been told,
On the banks of the Sacramento.

43. *LOWLANDS*

The most miserable hard work on a sailing vessel was the job of pumping ship. The wooden vessels always drank water through their seams and there had to be a regular daily turn at the pumps. In rough weather the pumps might work round the clock. It was heartbreaking, back-splitting labor. The wooden windlass pumps squeaked and groaned a mournful song of their own. The chanties that accompanied the groan of the pumps were mournful as well. "Lowlands," the best-known of all the pumping chanties, derives from the popular British ballad, "Edwin in the Lowlands Low," in which a young lady's parents murder her sweetheart for his gold and send his body floating on the "lowlands low." The British version of the chantey recalls this story:

I dreamed a dream the other night,
I dreamed my own true love was dead,
His hair was wet and dim his eye.

The Negro stevedores of Mobile, who adopted this chantey as a cotton-screwing chant, were more concerned with their low pay than with the demise of young Edwin. The song they handed back to the squareriggermen who touched Mobile Harbor, was a far cry from the romantic British version, but more suited to a seaman's taste. Soon the Mobile version was sung in every ocean by chanteymen of every complexion, largely replacing the older romantic song.

44. *BLOW, YE WINDS OF MORNING*

After the last rope had been coiled, after the brasswork had been polished, after all necessary work had been done, the officer on a "smart" ship "made" work for the crew. The old salts had a saying:

Six days shalt thou work and do all thou art able,
And on the seventh holystone the deck and pound the cable.

Even so, in the calm warm latitudes, when a vessel scudded along in a steady trade wind day after day with little trimming of the rigging necessary, there came a time for the seaman to swap yarns, work at his handicrafts, and sing his ballads in the lee of the forecastle. Perhaps one of the men had brought his fiddle or his banjo along on the voyage. Even without instruments, however, ballads were sung—tales of sea fights and fast voyages, stories of wrecks and of vessels lost in storms. One of the favorite tunes for these fo'c'sle ballads was the Elizabethan "Blow, Ye Winds in the Morning." The whalemen of New England used it as the air of a fine forecastle song, a saga of work aboard a whaling ship.

If the existence of a merchant seaman was hard, a whaler's life was hell. Voyages often lasted for two or three years. The vessels were clumsy tubs that stank continually from whale oil. Often months went by without a catch.

When a whale was sighted by the lookout standing his watch aloft, the long double-ended whaleboats were lowered away and either rowed or sailed in pursuit. The harpooner, the highest-paid member of the crew, stood in the bow of the boat, and, if his oarsmen could bring him up to the whale, hurled his heavy weapon into the leviathan's side. Then the real battle began. The whale often sounded—dove straight down—and the line attached to the harpoon would pay out so fast that water had to be poured on it to prevent its catching fire. Sometimes the whale would swim away close to the surface with the boat foaming along behind him like an aquaplane; this, the whalers called a "Nantucket sleigh ride." Before taking him in tow, they lanced him in the eye to make sure that he was no longer alive. The boats were often smashed to bits and the men killed or maimed by the thrashing of the whale's tail or fluke, or by the whale's coming to the surface directly beneath the boat after "sounding."

And when this whale we did harpoon
He gave one splash with his tail
And he upset the boat, we lost five of our crew,
Neither did we catch that whale, my boys,
Neither did we catch that whale.

Once the whale was finally brought alongside the ship, a chain was passed around his flukes and he was hoisted tail-first alongside, for the stowing down to begin. The first operation was "cutting in," in which the lower jaw was cut away and brought aboard with heavy tackles hung from the rigging. The blubber of the body was cut away from the head and hoisted aboard in long blankets peeled in spirals from the rotating carcass. The head was divided in two, as it couldn't be brought aboard whole. The snowy white spermaceti in the upper part of the head (the "case") produced the most valuable oil. To get it out, the men had to climb into the head and work waist-deep in the loose fat. The decks were often awash with oil, and the black and greasy smoke from the "try-works" settled on the ship, the rigging, and the men. The work went on—when necessary, both day and night—for days at a stretch.

For their wages the men received a share in the proceeds of the voyage. This share, or "lay," depended on the man's position in the crew and the line. All advances for the man's equipment, his share in the ship's medicine chest, his "ship's bill." were deducted from the "lay." Also, a poor catch in quality or the number of whales or loss of the cargo through storm, might make the cruise profitless. Many a seaman has come back from a two- or three-year voyage to all latitudes without a penny in his pockets to show for all the hardships and dangers and monotony he had endured.

Like a great many workman's ballads, "Blow, Ye Winds" is a "gripe song"; but like soldiers' "gripe songs," it has spirit—no tears, and the melody has the buoyancy of men who can survive and grow strong on hard work and hard living. It has a tune that will carry in a high wind and blow the blues right out of your system.

45. *THE E-RI-E*

The first enterprise of the thirteen states was to develop a fleet of ships that soon took first place in the mercantile trade of the world. The first great American fortunes were mercantile fortunes. Soon, however, the people began to move inland and to swarm out over the great sea of land that stretched away west of the Appalachians. The easiest route for westward migration lay along the Hudson as far as Albany, and then west to the Great Lakes. A canal that would link Albany to Buffalo, the port at the head of the lakes, became the next business of the young nation.

It took eight years for several thousand wild Irish bog-trotters to muck the Erie Canal through from Albany to Buffalo; but, when the last lock was filled in the fall of 1825 and the "Sequoia Chief" out of Buffalo with Governor De Witt Clinton aboard floated into New York Harbor, the wiseacres knew that New York had become the Empire State and that its canal was the highway to the new states in the West. Twenty years later, Michigan had increased its population by sixty times and Ohio had climbed from the thirteenth to the third most heavily populated state in the Union. Most of these settlers and their goods had moved west along the silver ribbon of the Erie Canal.

By 1845 there were four thousand canalboats and twenty-five thousand canalers afloat on Governor Clinton's 425-mile ditch. The motive power for the barges was furnished by teams of mules or horses plodding along the towpath. There was a towpath boy to touch up the team, a captain to sit on deck and smoke his pipe, a cook in the galley, and, at the tiller, the steersman's hardest job was to dodge low bridges. Old time "canawlers" admit that theirs was an easy life:

> I had a good time on the Erie from the day I started out to drive—a boy of 14—for eight dollars a month and board. When you got to be steersman, you might get as much as thirty; and, if you saved your money, some day you'd own a boat worth three thousand dollars. . . . You moved fast enough: in six hours on duty, you'd go nine or ten miles with a loaded boat and with a light one you could hit 'er up to fifteen or eighteen. We had a pretty good time. By May first we were always ready to go back on the canal.

Apparently the most engrossing diversion of the "canawlers" was fighting—fighting for precedence at the locks, fighting over cargo, or just fighting. They tell how steersman Jack bit off his rival's ear and spat it out on deck, saying: "There's yer ear, Charley." Charley replied, "You bit it off, cuss you. Now eat it!"

But, between scraps and flirting with the cook, there must have been a great deal of singing on the canal. Scores of ballads have been discovered, most of them garrulous lampoons on the imaginary dangers of life on the "raging canawl"—impudent parodies of the romantic forecastle ballads of the blue-water sailors.

46. *THE BIGLER*

When Paul Bunyan, the old lake sailors will tell you, was lumbering up Minnesota and Michigan way, he quite naturally needed ponds for his sawmills. So he and his blue ox, Babe, scraped out the Great Lakes; the dirt from the excavation going to make up the Black Hills of South Dakota, and the water for these ponds coming in through the St. Lawrence ditch from the sea. If you ask how this sea-water became fresh, you will be told about the filtration plants old Paul set up along the St. Clair river.

After Paul moved his camps out to Oregon and the Northwest, his ponds filled up with sailing vessels—a few squareriggers, but mostly schooners and barquetines, keen-lined and specially rigged for lake conditions. They were fine vessels. One of them, the "St. Clair," took a load of gold-seekers from Cleveland round the Horn to 'Frisco in '49. After the Civil War these lake boats carried a million and a half tons of ore into Cleveland. Not until the 1890's did the big lake steamers crowd them out of business.

In the early part of the last century the crews came up from deep water, bringing with them the lore, the knowledge, and the songs of deep-watermen. The shanties were kept alive at the capstan and at the halliards, and new quatrains appeared in the old songs:

We reefed and we furled from dark to daylight,
You never in your life did see such a sight.
Rolling home to old Chicago,
Rolling home to thee.

If some of the old salts thought that they had found an easy berth on calm inland waters, they were soon scared out of their complacency by the cyclonic polar storms and the icy fogs of the lakes. They learned that here no captain could turn and run before a storm; the threat of shoals and islands and an everpresent lee shore made that impossible. The short heavy chop of the inland sea could soon break a boat in half, or else the helpless vessel might be driven against some rocky beach and the maidens of the lake would carry the poor sailors off to their icy underwater caverns that lay beneath the Michigan shore. So many vessels have been lost, it has been said, that the bottom of the lakes is a graveyard, white with the bones of drowned seamen and broken ships.

We drifted with each pounding sea
And then we struck stern on.
Our mainmast by the deck was broke,
Our mizzenmast was gone;

The huge seas raked her fore and aft,
And then she swung broadside
And three men overboard were swept
Into that raging tide.

This is no shipwreck song from blue water, but one of the scores of ballads made and sung in the lee of the fo'castle where the ballad makers wove tales of Great Lakes wrecks and Great Lakes races:

The wind's nor'east and a-blowin' all night,
See them big seas roll their bonnets all white;
The rainbows playing for'ard and the foaming wake aft,
With her decks all aslant beneath her bending mast.
Let the old ponds roar
As they've often done before,
Hooray for a race down the lakes.

The favorite of all the racing ballads told the comic story of the clumsy, snub-nosed canaler, "The Bigler," the slowest of the fleet, the vessel that "could-a beat them all, if they'd hove to and wait." It was a barroom masterpiece and should be sung, if allowable, with a beer mug in hand.

47. *ROCK ABOUT MY SARO JANE*

The great rivers of the central valley—the rivers of the musical names, Ohio, Mississippi, Missouri, Tennessee, Red—have been pathways of folklore and song as well as highways for settlement, for commerce and adventure. The keelboatmen along the Ohio and the Mississippi with their rowdy songs of One-eyed Riley and Shenandoah's complaisant daughter, the blues along the rolling and melancholy Mississippi, the early jazz-bands on the sidewheel paddlers between New Orleans and Chicago—all these are famous; but the songs that are native to the river, that have rung in every crook and bend and over every sand bar and mudflat, are the "rouster" songs—the work songs of the Negroes who did the toting and lifting on the big boats.

From 1811 to 1900 the big double-stacked, scow-keeled wooden steamboats were the white queens of the rivers. Their pilots were lords of all they surveyed. Their menus began with wild duck and cranberries and ended, two pages later, with *fachenettes à la fleur d'orange.* Their main cabins were done in mahogany, the doorknobs were of solid silver, and their passengers spent the long sunny days on the river in gambling, flirtation, and a succession of gay balls and theatricals.

On the freight deck, however, the real work of the river had to go on. While idle passengers leaned on the rail and complained of the heat, the big-footed, brawny stevedores handled the freight. Hogsheads of tobacco and molasses, bales of cotton, or crates of dry goods had to be moved off and on the steamer and moved fast at every landing.

Run here, dog,
And git yo' bone,
Tell me what shoulder
You want it on.

It was handwork, backwork, muscle-work. It was the work of the Negro roustabouts, the laughing, yelling, singing, dancing Negro roustabouts. A human beltline moved along the swinging, dipping gangplank, between the steamer and the shore. Each man bowed down with his burden, his steps a quick sliding shuffle in rhythm with his buddies. Sometimes these men were driven to their work with whips. The tough mates knew all the profanity in the book and on occasion could add new supplies out of their own private stock. And so these songs of the river were made—made by men groaning under heavy loads, made by men who shouted in triumph as the loads were hurled down, made by men who were driven by their own unbridled and beautiful strength to bring melody and a rhythm for weary muscles to the breast of the great rivers.

Most of these roustabout tunes run to the blues. They are moans of poor boys a long way from home or even more primitive African work cries. Some, again, are quicksteps to the shuffling rhythm along the gangplank. Such a one is "Rock About My Saro Jane," which Uncle Dave Macon tells us he learned from Negro singers in Nashville, Tennessee, in 1887. It is the story of a Negro rouster, recruited to serve on one of the Federal gunboats that cut the rebel supply lines in the Civil War. There is charming irony in the chorus lines:

And there's nothin' to do
But set down and sing—

40.

Santy Anno

Words and melody adapted and arranged by John A. and Alan Lomax

Piano arrangement by Charles and Ruth Seeger

*The remainder of this song may be treated as a refrain and be sung after any or all the stanzas.

1. SOLO: We're sailing down the river from Liverpool,
CHORUS: Heave away, Santy Anno!
SOLO: Around Cape Horn to Frisco Bay,
CHORUS: All on the plains of Mexico.

2. SOLO: She's a fast clipper ship and a bully good crew,
CHORUS: Heave away, Santy Anno!
SOLO: A down-east Yankee for her captain, too.
CHORUS: All on the plains of Mexico.

3. SOLO: There's plenty of gold, so I've been told,
CHORUS: Heave away, Santy Anno!
SOLO: There's plenty of gold so I've been told,
CHORUS: 'Way out in Califor-ni-o.

4. SOLO: Back in the days of Forty-Nine,
CHORUS: Heave away, Santy Anno!
SOLO: Those were the days of the good old times,
CHORUS: All on the plains of Mexico.

5. SOLO: When Zacharias Taylor gained the day,
CHORUS: Heave away, Santy Anno!
SOLO: He made poor Santy run away,
CHORUS: All on the plains of Mexico.

6. SOLO: General Scott and Taylor, too,
CHORUS: Heave away, Santy Anno!
SOLO: Made poor Santy meet his Waterloo,
CHORUS: All on the plains of Mexico.

7. SOLO: Santy Anno was a good old man,
CHORUS: Heave away, Santy Anno!
SOLO: Till he got into war with your Uncle Sam,
CHORUS: All on the plains of Mexico.

8. SOLO: When I leave this ship I will settle down,
CHORUS: Heave away, Santy Anno!
SOLO: And marry a girl named Sally Brown,
CHORUS: All on the plains of Mexico.

41.

Shenandoah

Words and melody adapted and arranged by
John A. and Alan Lomax

Piano arrangement by
Charles and Ruth Seeger

1. SOLO: O Shenandoah, I long to hear you,
CHORUS: Away, you rolling river,
SOLO: O Shenandoah, I long to hear you,
CHORUS: Away, I'm bound away,
'Cross the wide Missouri.

2. SOLO: Missouri, she's a mighty river,
CHORUS: Away, you rolling river,
SOLO: The Indians camp along her borders.
CHORUS: Away, I'm bound away,
'Cross the wide Missouri.

3. SOLO: The white man loved an Indian maiden,
CHORUS: Away, you rolling river,
SOLO: With notions his canoe was laden,
CHORUS: Away, I'm bound away,
'Cross the wide Missouri.

4. SOLO: O, Shenandoah, I love your daughter,
CHORUS: Away, you rolling river,
SOLO: For her I've crossed the rolling water,
CHORUS: Away, I'm bound away,
'Cross the wide Missouri.

5. SOLO: Seven long years I courted Sally,
CHORUS: Away, you rolling river,
SOLO: Seven more I longed to have her.
CHORUS: Away, I'm bound away,
'Cross the wide Missouri.

6. SOLO: Farewell, my dear, I'm bound to leave you,
CHORUS: Away, you rolling river,
SOLO: O Shenandoah, I'll not deceive you.
CHORUS: Away, I'm bound away,
'Cross the wide Missouri.

42.

Sacramento

Words and melody adapted and arranged by
Joanna Colcord

Piano arrangement by
Charles and Ruth Seeger

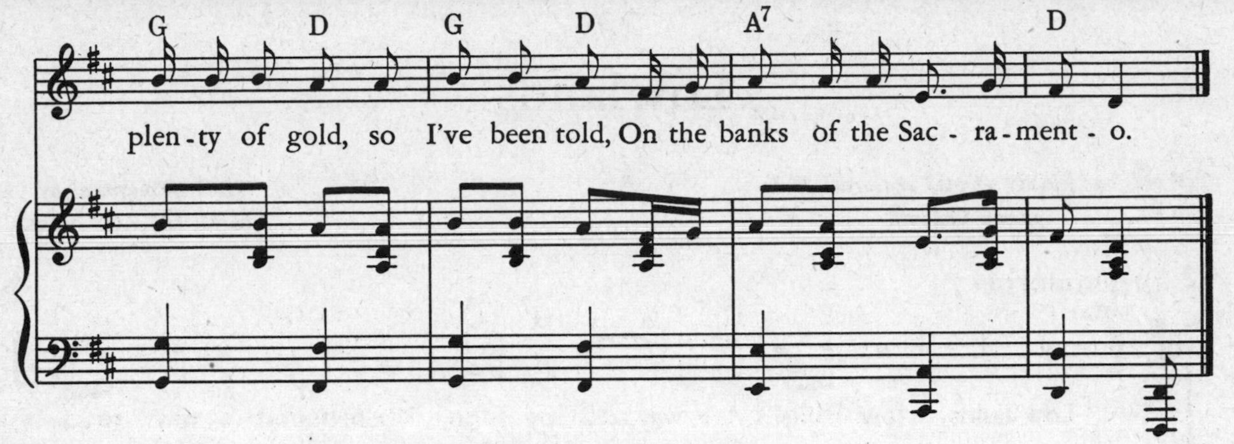

1. SOLO: A bully ship and a bully crew,
CHORUS: Doo-da, doo-da!
SOLO: A bully mate and a captain. too,
CHORUS: Doo-da, doo-da-day.

CHORUS: Then blow ye winds, hi-oh,
For Californy-o!
There's plenty of gold, so I've been told,
On the banks of the Sacramento.

2. SOLO: Round Cape Horn in the month of snows
CHORUS: Doo-da, doo-da,
SOLO: We came to the land where the cocktail flows,
CHORUS: Doo-da, doo-da-day.

CHORUS: Then blow ye winds, hi-oh,
For Californy-o!
There's plenty of gold, so I've been told,
On the banks of the Sacramento.

43.

Lowlands

Words and melody adapted and arranged by
Joanna Colcord

Piano arrangement by
Charles and Ruth Seeger

INTRODUCTION:

SOLO:	Lowlands, lowlands, Away, my John, We're bound away to Mobile Bay.
CHORUS:	My dollar and a half a day.

STANZAS:

1. SOLO: O was you ever in Mobile Bay?
   CHORUS: Lowlands, lowlands,
   Away, my John.
   SOLO: A-screwin' cotton by the day.
   CHORUS: My dollar and a half a day.

2. SOLO: The white man's pay is rather high,
   CHORUS: Lowlands, lowlands,
   Away, my John.
   SOLO: The black man's pay is rather low.
   CHORUS: My dollar and a half a day.

3. SOLO: O my old mother, she wrote to me,
   CHORUS: Lowlands, lowlands,
   Away, my John.
   SOLO: She wrote to me to come home from sea.
   CHORUS: My dollar and a half a day.

44.

Blow, Ye Winds in the Morning

Words and melody adapted and arranged by
Joanna Colcord

Piano arrangement by
Charles and Ruth Seeger

Moderate

F C F
'Tis ad - ver - tised in Bos - ton, New York and Buf - fa - lo, Five

G min. C^7 F G min. G^7 C CHORUS
hun - dred brave A - mer - i - cans, a - whal - ing for to go.— Sing - ing,

F
blow, ye winds in the morn - ing, And blow, ye winds, high - o!

B♭ F G min. C F
Clear a - way your run - ning gear, And blow, ye winds, high - o!

1. 'Tis advertised in Boston, New York and Buffalo,
Five hundred brave Americans, a-whaling for to go.—

CHORUS: Singing, blow, ye winds in the morning,
And blow, ye winds, high-o!
Clear away your running gear,
And blow, ye winds, high-o!

2. They send you to New Bedford, that famous whaling port,
And give you to some land-sharks—to board and fit you out.

3. They tell you of the clipper ships a-going in and out,
And say you'll take five hundred sperm before you're six months out.

4. It's now we're out to sea, my boys, the wind begins to blow,
One half the watch is sick on deck and the other half below.

5. Then comes the running rigging which you're all supposed to know,
'Tis "Lay aloft, you son of a gun, or overboard you go."

6. The skipper's on the quarter-deck a-squinting at the sails,
When up aloft the look-out sights a school of whales.

7. "Now clear away the boats, my boys, and after him we'll travel,
But if you get too near his fluke, he'll kick you to the devil!"

8. Now we've got him turned up, we tow him alongside;
We over with our blubber hooks and rob him of his hide.

9. Next comes the stowing down, my boys 'twill take both night and day,
And you'll all have fifty cents apiece on the 190th lay.

10. And when our old ship is full, my boys, and we don't give a damn,
We'll bend on all our stu'nsails and sail for Yankeeland.

11. When we get home, our ship made fast, and we get through our sailing,
A winding glass around we'll pass and damn this blubber-whaling.

45.

The E-RI-E

Words and melody adapted and arranged by
John A. and Alan Lomax

Piano arrangement by
Charles and Ruth Seeger

1. We were forty miles from Albany,
Forget it, I never shall,
What a terrible storm we had one night
On the E-RI-E canal.

CHORUS: O the E-RI-E was a-risin'
And the gin was a-gittin' low,
And I scarcely think we'll git a drink
Till we get to Buffa-lo-o-o,
Till we get to Buffalo.

2. We were loaded down with barley,
We were chock-up full of rye;
And the captain he looked down on me
With a gol-durn wicked eye.*

3. Two days out from Syracuse
The vessel struck a shoal
And we like to all been founderéd
On a chunk o' Lackawanna coal.

4. We hollered to the captain
On the towpath, treadin' dirt
He jumped on board and stopped the leak
With his old red flannel shirt.

5. The cook she was a kind old soul,
She had a ragged dress,
We heisted her upon a pole
As a signal of distress.

6. The winds begin to whistle
And the waves begin to roll
And we had to reef our royals
On the raging Canawl.

7. When we got to Syracuse,
The off-mule he was dead,
The nigh mule got blind staggers
And we cracked him on the head.

8. The captain, he got married,
The cook, she went to jail,
And I'm the only son-of-a-gun
That's left to tell the tale.

*It is customary to sing the chorus every other stanza.

The Bigler

1. Come all my boys and listen, a song I'll sing to you,
It's all about the Bigler and of her jolly crew,
In Milwaukee last October we chanced to get a sight
In a schooner called the Bigler, belonging to Detroit.

CHORUS: Watch her, catch her, jump up in her juberju,
Give her the sheet and let her go, we're the lads can pull her through,
O don't you hear us howling? O the wind is blowing free
On our down trip to Buffalo from Milwaukee.

2. It was on one Sunday morning, just at the hour of ten,
When the tug, Nickle Roberts, towed the schooner, Bigler, into Lake Michigan,
O there we made our canvas in the middle of the fleet,
O the wind hauled to the south'ard, boys, and we had to give her sheet.

3. The wind come down from the sou' sou'-west, it blowed both stiff and strong,
You had orter seen thet little schooner, Bigler, as she plowed Lake Michigan,
O far beyant her foaming bows the fiery waves to fling,
With every stitch of canvas and her course was wing and wing.

4. We made Skillagalee and Wabbleshanks, the entrance to the straits,
And might have passed the whole fleet there, if they'd hove to and wait,
But we drove them all before us the nicest you ever saw,
Clear out into Lake Huron through the Straits of Mackinac.[2]

5. First, Forty Mile Point and Presque Isle Light, and then we boomed away,
The wind being fresh and fair, for the Isle of Thunder Bay;
The wind it shifted to a close haul, all on the starboard tack,
With a good lookout ahead we made for Point Aubarques.

6. We made the light and kept in sight of Michigan's east shore
A-booming for the river as we'd often done before,
And when abreast Port Huron Light, our small anchor we let go,
The tug, Kate Moffet, came along and took the Bigler in tow.

7. The Moffet took six schooners in tow, and all of us fore and aft,
She took us down to Lake Saint Claire and stuck us on the flat,
She parted the Hunter's towline in trying to give relief,
And stem to stern went the Bigler, smash into the Mapleleaf.

8. Then she towed us through and left us outside the river light,
Lake Erie for to wander and the blustering winds to fight,
The wind was from the sou'west, and we paddled our own canoe,
Her jib boom pointed the dummy, she's hellbent for Buffalo.

1. "Detrite", of course.
2. "Mackinaw".

46.

The Bigler

Words and melody adapted and arranged by
John A. and Alan Lomax

Piano arrangement by
Charles and Ruth Seeger

CHORUS
C
Watch her, catch her, jump up in her ju - ber - ju,
G
Give her the sheet and let her go, we're the lads can pull her through, O
D
A min.
don't you hear us howl - ing? O the wind is blow - ing free On our
F
C
D min.
down trip to Buf - fa - lo from Mil - wau - kee.

47.

Rock About My Saro Jane

Words and melody adapted and arranged by
John A. and Alan Lomax

Piano arrangement by
Charles and Ruth Seeger

2. B'iler busted and whistle done blowed,
The *head* cap'n done fell overboard.
O, Saro Jane!

3. Engine give a crack and the whistle give a squall,
The engineer gone to the HOLE-IN-THE-WALL.
O, Saro Jane!

4. Yankees build boats for to shoot them rebels,
My *musket's* loaded and I'm gonna hold her level.
O, Saro Jane!

CHORUS
G
O there's noth-ing to do But to set down and sing And
f
D7 G
rock a-bout, my Sa-ro Jane. O rock a-bout, my
C
Sa-ro Jane. O rock a-bout, my Sa-ro
G
Jane, O there's noth-ing to do But to

D7
set down and sing And rock a-bout, my Sa - ro
(Fine)
G
C
G
Jane.
(Fine)
D7
G
D7
G
D7

CHAPTER VI

Come All Ye Bold Fellers

THE WORKERS WHO DID THE BIG JOBS IN this country—the men who sailed the ships, drove the freight-wagons, cut down the timber, dug the mines, herded the cattle—the men who, as the lumberjacks' saying has it, "let some daylight into these swamps"—these men composed a world of ballads about themselves which began with lines like these:

Come all ye bold fellows, wherever you be,
Come sit down a while and listen to me. . . .

Sometimes the song was addressed to "ye true-born shanty boys," sometimes to "you Texas Rangers," sometimes to "you loyal union men"; but, however the ballad might commence, it always dealt with the "bold" worker and his job. The death of a brave man at work, the discomfiture of a dishonest or unjust boss, the dangers and hardships of the life, the hardihood of the men who followed the craft—such have been the subjects of thousands of roughhewn and rambling American folk ballads, the ballads of occupations.

As the frontier moved westward, the same loved tunes and the same familiar narrative formulas were used again and again. The sailors turned lumberjacks, the wagoners turned raftsmen, the farmers turned miners, the woodsmen turned buffalo hunters, the Civil War veterans turned cowboys—passing the ballads on West from hand to hand. Very often only the name of the central characters or the details of the setting had to be changed for a new and satisfactory ballad to be born. Ultimately the parent ballads were Anglo-Irish, stemming from the British "come-all-ye" and the Irish street-song styles. These styles had become so popular during the eighteenth century that they all but displaced the older and subtler style of the medieval ballads in Great Britain. The literal and journalistic "come-all-ye's" were concerned with the lives and loves of the common man—apprentices, serving maids, sailor lads, farmers, and common murderers—rather than with the lives and emotions of the upper classes. While these ballad styles were popular in the old country, in America they became the almost exclusive basis for ballad composition. The folks who were carving a new country, rough hewn out of a howling wilderness, were very literal when it came to ballad-making. They wanted to hear just what had happened, just how it had been. They might weave mountain ranges of comic exaggerations and tomfoolery in their jokes and tales, but when it came to ballads they were usually all-fired serious. The highest compliment they could pay a ballad was—"That's pintedly hit!" or "That's just the way it was!" or "That air song is as true as steel." . . . Even their comic songs hew close to the facts of their lives.

A book of these occupational songs would tell the story of how the foundation work for this country was done. In this chapter we can only follow a thin trace of the whole story, a trace that begins in the Northern lumber woods, follows a party of buffalo hunters out into the Western plains, crosses the Sierras with the '49ers, and ends up in a coal mine in Pennsylvania. You will find more of these American "come-all-ye's" in other chapters of this volume *, all of them, by and large, sharing these characteristics. They take themselves very seriously. Most of them are as Irish as Paddy's pig, since the singing Irishman apparently went everywhere on all the tough and dangerous jobs. The commonest metric form was the four-line stanza of six or seven iambic feet. The tunes were freely sung—rubato parlando. In their direct and naively honest way the ballads reflect literally the spirit of the courageous, proud, and hard-working crew of independent Americans who used them. Finally, although they undoubtedly originated, each one of them, in the work of a single man, they are stubbornly anonymous:

My name is nothing extry, so that I will not tell. . . .

48. *ONCE MORE A LUMB'RING GO*

Slightly more flamboyant than most of these workers' ballads is this one, known in Maine, Pennsylvania, and Michigan as "The Logger's Boast." Here is a portrait of a man who was proud of his job. The American lumberjack (who in the old days called himself a "shanty boy" because he lived in "shanties" in the woods) cut a 3000-mile swathe from Maine to Washington, "letting the daylight" into millions of acres of virgin timberland, clearing off the country for the clodhoppers and providing several trillion feet of lumber for a growing nation. Since 1820 they cut and sawed enough boards to stretch a four-foot walk from here to the moon. Here was a job for real heroes, and, since the shanty boys felt small against the tremendous forests they had to tackle, they created a man whose size and imagination matched the job. Although Paul Bunyan was mostly a wood's joke, a come-on for the greenhorns, nevertheless, like the other tall-tale heroes of American folklore, it was comforting to have him in mind when things got too difficult. Here's how old Paul was born, the way they tell it out in the tall timber of Washington State:

If what they say is true, Paul Bunyan was born down in Maine. And he must have been a pretty husky baby, too, just like you'd expect him to be, from knowin' him afterward. . . .

When he was only three weeks old, Paul rolled around so much in his sleep that he knocked down four square miles of standing timber and the government got after his folks and told them they'd have to move away. . . .

When Paul was only seven months old, he sawed off the legs from under his dad's bed one night. The old man noticed when he woke up in the mornin' that his bed seemed considerable lower than it used to be, and so he got up and investigated, and sure enough, there was the legs all sawed off from under it and the pieces layin' out on the floor. . . .

He looked around to see who could have done it and there was Paul layin' sound asleep with his dad's cross-cut saw held tight in his fist and smilin' in his sleep as pretty as anythin'. He called his wife and when she come in he says to her:

"I'll bet that boy of ours is goin' to be a great logger some day. If he lives to grow up, he's goin' to do some great loggin' by an' by, you just see—a whole lot bigger than any of the men around here has ever done."

And they was right, all right. There ain't never been loggin' before nor since like Paul done. . . .

* The Farmer Is the Man; Git Along, Little Dogies; Heroes and Hard Cases; Blow, Boys, Blow.

The trees groaned when they heard the footsteps of the tellers of these tales. They were men who could work all day with the temperature at forty below, who could fell a pine so accurately as to drive a stake into the ground and leave a scurf on the butt of the log as smooth as finished lumber. These were hard men to nick. They carelessly spent their young strength and sometimes their lives slashing and destroying our native timberland; and when they grew old, knotted by rheumatism and rotted by cheap whiskey, they often died with no more possessions than their stained and faded workclothes. We will not soon again see their like in America.

I am a jolly shanty boy, as you will soon discover;
To all the dodges I am fly, a hustling pinewoods rover.
A peavyhook it is my pride, an axe I well can handle.
To fell a tree or punch a bull, get rattling Danny Randle.
Bung yer eye, bung yer eye!

49. *BLUE MOUNTAIN LAKE*

Life in the shanties of an old-style logging camp was rather primitive. After twelve to fourteen hours work in the sub-zero weather of the woods, the men came in to the shanty, sharpened their axes, and sat down to their grub. No talking was allowed at table. The cook, if he was man enough, would slap a jack off his seat for "speaking over his victuals." From suppertime until nine o'clock, the boys sat on the deacon seat around the stove and smoked and gabbed until the air turned blue with Kentucky plug and profanity. Then, after removing their boots and their caps, they rolled into their communal bunks, pulled their communal blankets up to their noses and snored until daylight.

Sixteen men on a pine-slab bunk—
Gosh, how the bullies snore!
Like a buzzsaw hittin' a hick'ry knot,
While the wind through the spruces roared.
What if a blizzard cavorts around?
Loggers ain't blokes to mind,
Sleepin' they're gettin' all rested up
To tackle tomorrow's grind.

Sixteen men in a pine-slab bunk
Facin' the far North Pole.
One of them wantin' a turn, yells "Spoon!"
Then over as one they roll,
Till all their noses are pointin' south
As straight as the wild duck flies,
Their lousy blankets white with frost
That's smokin' in their eyes.

There is a yarn of recent vintage that voices a modern protest against the rigors of shanty life.

Paul Bunyan was all right in his day, but he didn't have the big shots to deal with—and he never was able to get rid of the crumbs. A crumb is what you call a louse.

One time when one of the big shots come out to look things over, he stuck his head in a bunkhouse and he heard a bunch of voices yelling at him, "Hello, brother." It kinda puzzled him. After while, when he seen that the crumbs was coming to meet *him* and was actually calling *him* their brother, the boss got mad.

"What do you mean calling me your brother?" he says. "Well, we are, ain't we?" they says. "We don't need no interpreter," they says. "And we get our living from the same source, don't we? . . . Really, we're your best allies," they says.

"How so?" says the boss.

"Ain't it our gougin' into their hides that keeps 'em so busy scratchin' they can't do any thinkin'? And as long as they can't think, they won't bother to organize or demand improvements."

The ballads record the old-time jack's cheerful acceptance of crumbs, long hours, low pay, bad food, months of isolation in the woods. His pioneer spirit did not quite repress all his resentment of how he had to live in order to eat. He was always honing for a fight. The battle described in the "Blue Mountain Lake" ballad is still remembered by old-timers in the lumbering community of Glens Falls in upstate New York where it happened.

50. *THE JAM ON GERRY'S ROCKS*

Death was a close companion of the shanty boy. Let a sled get out of control on an icy hill and the driver might be pulverized under the runners. A breath of air could send a tree the wrong direction and smash the life out of a good axeman or swamper. At the rollways on the river a little misjudgment could bring a mammoth pile of logs tumbling down on the jack. And in the drive, when the rivermen rode the whirling, leaping logs down the spring freshets toward the mills, a man could go out quick—like "the smoke from a dandelion."

For two or three weeks the boys of the river rode "the mill-tail of hell," catching a couple of hours sleep in their wet clothes where they could, and by day walking the back of the drive, guiding it downstream. The streams that carried the log drives in the spring were usually small and filled with rapids, rocks, and falls. Often a few logs got caught in these narrows and then a "jam" began, the rough timbers piling up "mountains high," the whole mass groaning, thundering, shuddering, and settling into the riverbed as the drive piled up behind it. Then the nerve of the "whitewater men," the river drivers, came to the fore.

With their peavies in their hands, rivermen would scatter over the face of the jam, heaving at a log here, sawing another there, searching for the key to the mixup. When the key log was found and pried loose, the whole jam would shudder like a live thing and then, suddenly, thousands of logs would start moving all at once with the force of the whole river behind them. The river drivers had to run then, skipping for shore across the rolling, tumbling, leaping backs of the logs, the white water churning around their legs, dependent on their daring and their catfootedness for survival. A man who slipped and went down into the maelstrom was a goner. If they found him, they'd hang his boots to the limb of a big pine for remembrance and the drive would roll on—just one more riverman gone and nobody to remember him.

A few of these brave rivermen have been remembered, however, because of the ballads their comrades made about them. Nobody knows any facts about Young Jack Monroe, not even whether he was an American or a Canadian. No one has ever been able to locate "Gerry's Rocks" with certainty; argumentative old-timers claim them for Maine, New York, Pennsylvania, Michigan, and Canada. The ballad, meanwhile, has become by far the best-known and best-loved of all shanty-boy songs, with versions turning up in the Southern mountains, in cow-camps out West, and even in the woods of Scotland.

In the old days it was sung, like the other ballads, at the deacon seat after supper. That was the time for ballads and for storytelling. Every man was warm and belly-filled and peaceful. Sometimes each man in the bunkhouse was required to sing a song or tell a story; otherwise he had to pay a forfeit. Most often, however, the evening's entertainment was turned over to the men with a knack for it. Franz Rickaby, in his book *Ballads and Songs of the Shantey Boy* tells a story that makes clear the importance of these camp entertainers:

> . . . one winter in a Michigan lumber camp, a man named George Burns, an old Scotsman, wandered into the shanties in a freezing condition. He was of course taken in, and in natural order of events was asked if he could sing. In reply he sang "Bonnie Doon" in a fine tenor voice, and after that he couldn't get away. He was given work to do all that winter," although he couldn't shovel snow and do it right," and left camp the following spring with a stake of $135, a favorite member of the crew.

Some of these woods' singers had fine voices. But a good voice was not as important, to a wood's singer as a good memory and a "way of speaking the words out plain so we could git all the story." These wandering singers carried with them romantic ballads like "Andrew Barton" and "Barbara Allen," sea songs like "The Dark-eyed Sailor," and "The Greenland Whale Fishery," a pack of Irish come-all-ye's, a bundle of the bawdiest ballads that ever burned a greenhorn's ears, as well as scores of occupational songs, dear to the lumberjack. So, these men without books, without contact with the outside world for many months, without any but self-made diversions, kept their hearts and their imaginations alive by feeding upon the world of balladry. If "The Jam on Gerry's Rocks" has served no other purpose, it should therefore stand among the greatest of American songs.

51. *A LUMBERMAN IN TOWN*

When the boys came to town after a winter in the lonesome woods and a wild ride down a foaming river on the back of the drive, they took the place over. Whether it was Bangor, Saginaw, Seney, Portland, or Seattle, the town shook with the wild yells of the timber tigers. Honest burghers locked their doors and shut their daughters in their bedrooms, but that didn't spoil the lumberjacks' fun. Down along the "skid rows" there were plenty of young ladies and bartenders to form a welcoming committee. The jacks smelled the rum in the air; they saw the light in the eyes of the barmaids; and, screaming like catawampuses, they retired behind the swinging doors for a little mild and peaceable diversion.

These timber beasts liked to show how tough they were. They'd jam their caulks into the floors, twist their ankles, and rip a whole board out of the floor. They also enjoyed kicking panels out of the bar, just to show their strength. They weren't afraid of anything that walked or crawled or flew and, if anyone resented their playfulness, a fight was on, a fight that included butting, kicking, gouging, biting, and stomping, a fight that might not end until an ear or two had been bitten off or the winner put his brand on his victim's chest with his sharp, steel caulks. Many an old jack today can show you the purple pockmarks on his face and chest gained in the battles of his young days.

Dr. Bohn, who practiced medicine in Seney, Wisconsin, one of the rowdiest towns the lumberjacks ever developed, writes of his first Christmas day there in 1890:

> I worked all day and all night treating the fighters who could find their way to my office by following the red trail in the snow that reddened and broadened as the day wore on. . . .
>
> The streets and the broad sidewalks of the town were literally swamped with fighting loggers. The Marquis of Queensberry would have been shocked. When a man was down, his opponent jumped upon him with both feet, kicking and tearing at him with the cruel caulks of his shoes. Yet no man interfered. There was no use. Until a man realized he was beaten, it was best to let them continue.

Meanwhile the prostitutes, the pimps, the bartenders, and the gamblers were taking the boys for everything they could grab. It was perfectly legitimate to blackjack your man, put a mickey finn in his drink, or throttle him while he was asleep, then rob him and dump him through a trapdoor. If he died, he was just a lone timber beast and nobody cared. But usually he lived. A real logger was almost impossible to kill. When he came to, he'd wake up with a head as big as a beerkeg and his pockets empty. Then he'd borrow enough money from the company to buy a new outfit and hit for the woods, walking the lonely trails of the pineries, on west into the uncut timber.

I'm a rambling wreck of poverty,
From Ogemaw I come,
My poverty compels me
To split wood in the rain.

But in all kinds of weather,
Bet it wet or dry,
I'm bound to gain an honest living
Or lay me down and die.

"The Lumberman in Town" is a Down-East ballad depicting a shanty-boy's trip to town in the spring of the year.

52. *THE BUFFALO SKINNERS*

One favorite among Maine woods' singers was a loggers' complaint that began:

It happened late one season in the fall of '53,
A preacher of the gospel one morning came to me.
Said he, "My jolly fellow, how would you like to go
To spend one pleasant winter up in Canada-I-O?"

The winter turned out to be not so pleasant:

To describe what we have suffered is past the art of man,
But to give a fair description, I will do the best I can;
Our food the dogs would snarl at, our beds were on the snow;
We suffered worse than murderers up in Canada-I-O.

Our hearts were made of iron and our souls were cased with steel,
The hardships of that winter could never make us yield. . . .

When the lumberjacks moved West, they used this acidulous ballad as the basis of a little ditty called "Michigan-I-O." Neither of these songs had anything special to recommend them among other lumbering ballads, and it was not until the old tune fell into the hands of a party of buffalo hunters that it achieved its real greatness. Compare "The Buffalo Skinners" with "Canada-I-O," stanza for stanza, and see for yourself what the alchemy of the Western plains and of wild adventure has wrought with the original, plodding song.

The buffalo skinner set out upon one of the most strange and savage enterprises that Americans have ever undertaken. When the white man reached the great plains, he found in the Plains Indian an antagonist he could not defeat. These Indians lived a nomadic life, following the buffalo herds, and, so long as these herds lasted, the mounted and hard-fighting aborigines could not be cornered and starved out. The plains were vast and the herds of buffalo were so large that they turned the prairie black for as far as a man could see. One frontiersman speaks of a herd that stretched for "seven miles from the Arkansas River to the foothills . . . a living mass of buffalo, pressing in countless thousands upon each other . . . a migration of millions of prime animals." Another plainsman tells of an even larger herd: "For five days we rode through and camped in a mobile sea of buffalo." Perhaps this was the same herd that was said to have drunk the Arkansas River dry. Every season these armies of bison migrated from the plains of Texas north to Hudson Bay and back, with the Indians always on their flanks, taking what they needed for their year's supply of meat.

The United States Government entered the picture by declaring a bounty on buffalo hides and the slaughter began. Parties of buffalo hunters—two to shoot, four to skin, one to cook—swarmed over the plains. The sluggish and stupid animals were easy to kill. Upwind, a man could lie at his ease on a hillock and knock over as many as seventy-five or a hundred with as many shots from his long range rifle.

Soon tens of thousands of raw and grisly bodies littered the plains and the arroyos, food for the wolves and the buzzards, but not for the Indians. The hides, hauled to the railroad and shipped East, began to command a good price as rugs and as women's coats. The slaughter continued, with exhibitionists like Buffalo Bill running the show and with the railroads taking trainloads of hunters out on the prairies to kill more thousands of the beasts for sport. Old-timers can remember places in the West where you could walk for a mile on the skeletons without ever having to step on the ground. Years later, these bones, bleached white by the wind and the rain, were sold for fertilizer, bringing more money to the bone-hunters than the buffalo skinners had ever obtained.

The toughest of old-time cowboys shunned the buffalo hunters and their Texas capital, the god-forsaken little town of Jacksboro. They claimed that "if them buffalo hunters don't kill ye for money, they'll try to kill ye for meanness." This ballad is a testament to their ruthlessness. A former buffalo hunter, who claims to have been in the party when old Crego got his, gave the senior editor the following account of the incident. . . .

It was a hell of a trip down Pease River, lasting several months. We fought sandstorms, flies, bedbugs, wolves, and Indians. At the end of the season old Crego announced he had lost money and could not pay us off. We argued the question with him.

He didn't see our side of things, so we shot him down and left his damned old bones to bleach where we had left so many stinking buffalo. On the way back to Jacksboro, one of the boys started up a song about the trip and the hard times and old Crego and we all set in to help him. Before we got back to Jacksboro we had shaped it up and the whole crowd could sing it.

Professor George Lyman Kittredge has called this the greatest of Western ballads, which indicates, perhaps, that it is only men "whose hearts are cased in buffalo hocks" who can speak epic language.

53. *SWEET BETSY FROM PIKE*

Among the first Americans to get a good look at the buffalo country were the '49ers who rumbled across the prairie in their covered-wagon trains. A vivid picture of this breed of American ballad-singers has been painted by A. B. Hulbert in his diary of the '49ers trail:

Independence, Mo., April 30, 1849. . . . Millions of stars are looking down on these rolling plains of Western Missouri where the many tracks of the California Trail curve out from this town of Independence into the Indian Territory beyond. On every side, as far as you can see tonight, earthly "stars"—the campfires of all this multitude of eager, restless Forty-Niners—twinkle on the ground, being fed by members of the most excited army that was ever assembled in the New World. . . . Across this vast, rolling bivouac you see the nation celebrating or lying in windrows under blankets in every posture of repose; or you hear the wail of fiddles, the strumming of banjos, or the snap of cards laid down vindictively on improvised, lantern-lighted "tables." . . . Our unquenchable songster continues his lyrical prophecy of finding gold in a land which would flow with something better, to his way of thinking, than milk and honey:

Instead of drinking pump water
Or even half and half, sir,
We all live like jolly souls
And Port and Sherry quaff, sir.
In spirits we will keep ourselves,—
The Mettle's coming in, sir.
And not a man will now be found
Who'll say he wants for "tin," sir.

In the light of a dying fire to the left, we see a sturdy family at their even-prayer, with a fine old patriarch, face uplifted to the starlight, describing an equal faith in future happiness, but in terms at variance with our singers.

Whither shall I go from thy Spirit?
Or whither shall I flee from thy presence?
If I ascend up into heaven, thou art there;
If I make my bed in hell, behold, thou art there.
If I take the wings of the morning, and dwell in the uttermost parts of the sea;
Even there shall thy hand lead me . . .

In a strange way the two voices blend in the evening breeze, expressive of different, but unconquerable philosophies:

(From the right)

Oh, the good time has come at last,
We need no more complain, sir.
The rich can live in luxury
And the poor can do the same, sir.
For the good time has come at last,
And as we all are told, sir,
We shall be rich at once now,
With California gold, sir.

(From the left)

. . . Thou hast possessed my reins. . . .
When I am awake I am still with thee.

No earlier cause ever called together in the New World such a strange medley of men, so curious a mass as this Golden Army. There they lie, amid their fading fires of prairie grass, of tepee poles, of cottonwood stumps, of chokecherry wood, of sagebrush, of greasewood—rich men, poor men, beggar men, thieves; farmers, lawyers, doctors, merchants, preachers, workmen; Republicans, Whigs, Federalists, Abolitionists; Baptists, Methodists, Transcendentalists, Campbellites, Millerites, Presbyterians, Mormons; white men, black men, yellow men, Germans, Russians, Poles, Chileans, Swiss, Spaniards; sailors, steamboat men, lumbermen, gamblers; the lame, squint-eyed, pock-marked, one-armed; the bearded, the beardless, the mustachioed, side-whiskered, and goateed; singing, cursing, weeping and laughing in their sleep; squaws in royal blankets, prostitutes in silk, brave women in knickerbockers, covered by knee-length skirts; the witty, nit-wits, and witless; pet cats, kittens, canaries, dogs, coons; cherished accordions, melodions, flutes, fiddles, banjos; fortune-tellers, phrenologists, mesmerists, harlots, card sharks, ventriloquists and evangelists from almost every state, nation, county, duchy, bishopric, island, peninsula, bay and isthmus in all the world—dreaming of gold, where those California trails zig-zag away over a hundred rough knolls where the Kansas and Missouri rivers have quarreled for centuries for the right of way. . . .

Among these thousands, described so magnificently by Mr. Hulbert, one night slept Sweet Betsy and her lover Ike. The ballad of their trip across the plains and the Sierras has come to represent the story of all the others who traveled that highway. Some waggish camp entertainer set their tale to the lively English air, "Villikins and His Dinah," and so has caused them to be remembered beyond all the rest who slept under those stars, dreaming dreams of gold.

54. *THE DAYS OF '49*

The hills were lined with gold, or so they said. Little mining communities sprang up along every gulch and creek. Goldseekers swarmed in from all over the world and lived lonely bachelor lives in tents and shacks in the wilderness, without diversion and with little to remind them that they were men who had once had homes.

The men were so hungry for the sight of a woman that in one little community they borrowed the hat of the only woman in camp (she was afraid to come to their fandango for fear of being torn to pieces) and solemnly promenaded around it, bowing and scraping as if she had been present. They were so starved for the sight of something that would remind them of home that, at a theatrical performance, when a baby began to cry in the audience, a huge, bearded miner arose with a pistol in each hand and roared, "Ring down that gol-durned curtain and let's hear that baby cry. It's the sweetest sound I've heard in two years."

Many miners struck it rich, some of them panning out as much as five hundred dollars of dust a day. Free spenders, they paid good gold for entertainment; and so, for a brief interval, the gold fields and San Francisco drew entertainers from all over the world—swarms of opera singers, fiddlers, acrobats, dancers, card sharks, fancy ladies, tragedians, song-and-dance acts, and their hangers-on.

Opera houses were hastily constructed in San Francisco and began to produce full-length plays and musical spectacles. Wagon shows struggled up and down the steep mountain roads into isolated camps offering blackface acts, wench dances, and magicians. Circuses, which could only boast a wild animal or two and some acrobats, made long and successful tours of the camps. One day Joe Taylor, a barnstorming performer of the days of '49, arrived at a lonely camp in the wilderness. The father of the house asked him why he didn't give a show there. Joe wondered about finding an audience, since this was the only house in sight. The old man asked him for a supply of handbills and sent his six sons out into the hills with them. For hours people streamed from every direction and that night Joe Taylor played to a crowded house.

Edwin Booth, II, rambled the Barbary Coast of San Francisco picking a five-string banjo. Well he might, since country fiddlers were making as much as sixteen dollars a night playing in barrooms. Soon theatrical companies began to tour, offering the latest melodramas from New York and full-length Shakespearean productions. The miners knew and loved their Shakespeare and, if an actor missed his lines, a chorus from the audience would yell corrections at him. If he turned out to be a ham, he might very well leave that camp in a dead run, with pistol balls whistling around his ears.

Naturally this was a good situation for the wandering ballad-maker and -singer. The miners, living out new lives in a strange country, seized avidly upon songs that told about their lives and their troubles. So in a few years a great number of extremely amusing '49er songs were composed, enough to make possible the publication before 1858 of two pocket songbooks—"Put's Original California Songster" and "Put's Golden Songster." These songsters contain the words to nearly all the folkish ballads of the period. About their author (perhaps editor would be a more accurate term, since we suspect that Old Put collected as many of the songs as he composed) we know little more than what he wrote in dedicating his first songster:

To the Miners of California, those hardy builders of California prosperity and greatness. . . .

Having been a miner himself for a number of years, he has had ample opportunities of observing, as he has equally shared, the many trials and hardships to which his brethren of the pick and shovel have been exposed, and to which, in general, they have so patiently, so cheerfully, and even heroically submitted. Hence, ever since the time of his crossing the plains, in the memorable year of '50, he has been in the habit of noting down a few of the leading items of his experience, and clothing them in the garb of humorous though not irreverent verse.

Many of his songs may show some hard edges, and he is free to confess that they may fail to please the more aristocratic portion of the community, who have but little sympathy with the details, hopes, trials or joys of the miner's life. . . .

After having sung them himself at various times and places, and latterly with the assistance of a few gentlemen, known by the name of the Sierra Nevada Rangers, the songs have been published at the request of a number of friends; and if the author should thereby succeed in contributing to the amusement of those he is anxious to please, enliven the long tedious hours of a miner's winter fireside, his pains will not be unrewarded.

Old Put's songs were as rough and ready as the audience that ate them up and howled for more, and none of them was better liked, or better portrayed the '49 audience than "The Days of '49." The tune for this song comes from "Yankee John Galusha," New York State lumberjack.

55. *THE OLD SETTLERS' SONG*

For many of the miners who came to the goldfields with little more than their hopes to sustain them, the search for Eldorado ended in dismal failure. One of Old Put's miners sings

I ha'nt got no home, nor nothin' else, I s'pose
Misfortune seems to follow me wherever I goes
I come to California with a heart both stout and
bold,

And have been to the diggin's, to get some lumps of gold.
But I'm a used up man, a perfect used up man,
And if I ever get home again, I'll stay there if I can.

The work was hard and the living harder:

I mine from break of day, but cannot make it pay,
Disheartened return to my cabin at night,
Where the rattlesnakes crawl round my bed made on the ground,
And, coiling up, lay ready to bite.

My boots are full of holes, like merchants have no soles,
My hands, once so soft, are harder than a stone;
My pants and woolen shirt are only rags and dirt
And must I live and die here all alone?

When he decided to change his luck by prospecting for new locations, he found the whole world there ahead of him:

When I got there, the mining ground
Was staked and claimed for miles around,
And not a bed was to be found,
When I went off to prospect.
The town was crowded full of folks,
Which made me think 'twas not a hoax,
At my expense they cracked their jokes
When I went off to prospect.

At Deadwood I got on a tight—
At Groundhog Glory I had a fight;
They drove me away from Hell's Delight,
When I went off to prospect.
From Bogus-Thunder I ran away—
At Devil's Basin I wouldn't stay;
My lousy shirt crawled off one day,
When I went off to prospect. . . .

Once bitten by the gold-bug, a man wandered on across the West from strike to strike—from California to Nevada, then on to the Black Hills of Montana:

The roundhouse at Cheyenne is filled every night,
With loafers and bummers of most every plight,
On their backs is no clothes, in their pockets no bills,
Each day they keep staring for the dreary Black Hills.

When I got to Cheyenne, no gold could I find,
I thought of the lunch route I'd left far behind,
Through rain, hail and snow, froze plumb up to my gills,
They call me the orphan of the Dreary Black Hills.

Don't go away, stay at home if you can,
Stay away from that city, they call it Cheyenne,
For Old Wallipee or Comanche Bill,
They will lift up your hair on those dreary Black Hills.

Yet, in spite of their disillusionment, prospectors kept following the new strikes across the West: south to Leadville and Cripple Creek, west to the new silver mines in the Southern California desert, east again into Nevada, south to Tombstone, Arizona. They grew stooped and grizzled, and many a man of them died alone in the desert where the coyotes picked their bones. Except for the lucky few, the men who prospered most were those who settled down in the new Western states and began to make stable communities of the shanty towns the miners had thrown together.

I've traveled the mountains all over,
And now to the valleys I'll go,
And live like a pig in the clover,
In sight of the mountains of snow.

I'll marry a rich senorita,
And live on a ranch in the west,
Have forty young greasers to greet her,
And fifty if put to the test.

These were exactly the sentiments of the unknown miner who composed "The Old Settlers' Song," the best ballad we know of from the Northwest. He put it to an old Irish air, "Rosin the Beau," which has been parodied by folk ballad-makers almost as frequently as "Yankee Doodle."

56. *DOWN, DOWN, DOWN*

A very different breed of singing miner was the lad who dug out the coal down beneath the smoke-grimed hills of Pennsylvania. Most of his ballads were grim accounts of fights for unionization, for better wages and shorter hours. His work was hard; his life in the shack towns of the coal companies was even harder. George Korson has put together two excellent volumes of these ballads under the aegis of the United Mine Workers of America—*Songs of the Anthracite Miners* and *Coal Dust on the Fiddle*. "Down, Down, Down" comes from the first of these collections. Its composer, an indestructible, bass-voiced, blue-eyed, dancing fool of a little Irish anthracite coal miner, by the name of William Keating, tells how he came to make his ballad:

The material for *Down, Down, Down* was picked up between gangway roof falls, put together on a mine car bumper, pencilled with car sprags, punctuated with mule kicks, tuned to the thunder and vibration of underground blasts and muted to the solitude of the mines, while this mule driver rhymster worked between drinks, traveling in and out of the third level of Oak Hill shaft at Buckley's Gap, Duncott, Pa. . . .

Me and the mule were the only living things in the gangway unless you count the rats. It got kinda lonesome, me sittin' there on the bumper with the cars rattlin' along the dark gangways and headin's. To break the loneliness and at the same time show Jerry, me mule, that I wasn't such a bad egg after all, I used to make up ditties out of me head and sing them as we rode along. One of them was *Down, Down, Down*. . . .

She was too long to sing straight through, so I broke her up into groups of verses, corresponding to the levels in a mine. When I got through singing one level, the boys alongside the bar would yell, "Time out for drinks." Then the drinks would go round. As the ballad has about forty verses, you can imagine in what condition the singer and the customers were by the time I got to the end. The barroom was me stage for thirty years and, bejabers, I done it up brown when I was at it.

This version gives you a sampling of ore from all the "levels" of Bill Keating's ditty.

48.

Once More a-Lumb'ring Go

Words and melody adapted and arranged by
E. C. Beck

Piano arrangement by
Charles and Ruth Seeger

CHORUS: And once more a-lumb'ring go,
And once more a-lumb'ring go,
And we'll range the wildwoods over,
And once more a-lumb'ring go.

1. Come all you sons of freedom
That run the Saginaw stream,
Come all you roving lumberjacks
And listen to my theme.
We'll cross the Tittabawassee,
Where the mighty waters flow,
And we'll range the wild woods over
And once more a-lumb'ring go.

2. When the white frost takes the valley
And the snow conceals the woods,
Each farmer has enough to do
To earn the family food,
With the week no better pasttime
Than to hunt the buck and doe
And we'll range the wild woods over
And once more a-lumb'ring go.

3. You may talk about your farms
Your houses and fine ways,
And pity us poor shanty boys
While dashing in our sleighs;
Around a good campfire at night
We'll sing while the wild winds blow,
And we'll range the wildwoods over
And once more a-lumb'ring go.

4. With our axes on our shoulders
We'll make the woods resound,
And many-a tall and stately tree
Will come tumbling to the ground.
With our axes on our shoulders,
To our boot tops deep in snow,
We'll range the wild woods over
And once more a-lumb'ring go.

5. When navigation opens,
And the waters run so free,
We'll drive our logs to Saginaw,
Then haste our girls to see.
They will welcome our return
And we'll in raptures flow;
And we'll stay with them through summer
And once more a-lumb'ring go.

6. When our youthful days are ended
And our jokes are getting long,
We'll take us each a little wife
And settle on a farm.
We'll have enough to eat and drink,
Contented we will go;
And we'll tell our wives of our hard times
And no more a-lumb'ring go.

49.

Blue Mountain Lake

Words and melody adapted and arranged by
Frank Warner

Piano arrangement by
Charles and Ruth Seeger

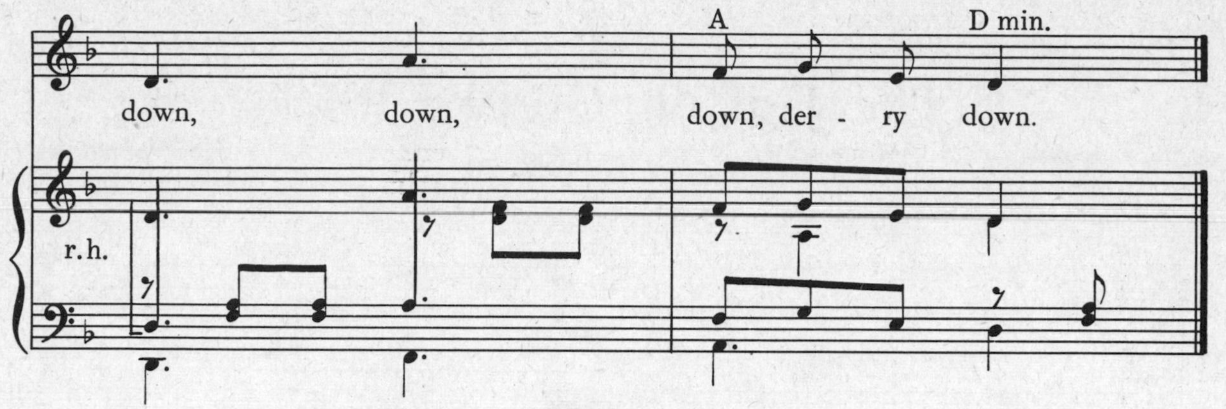

1. Come all you good fellers, wherever you be,
Come set down a-while and listen to me;
The truth I will tell you without a mistake
About the rackets we had around Blue Mountain Lake. *(Refrain)*

2. There's the Sullivan brothers and Big Jimmy Lou,
And old Mose Gilbert and Dandy Pat, too,
A good lot of fellers as ever were seen,
And they all worked for Griffin on township nineteen. *(Refrain)*

3. Bill Mitchell, you know, kept our shantee,
And as mean a damn man as you ever did see,
He'd lay round the shanty from morning till night,
And, if a *man* said a word, he was ready to fight. *(Refrain)*

4. One morning 'fore daylight Jim Lou, he got mad,
Knocked hell out of Mitchell and the boys was all glad,
And his wife, she stood there and, the truth I will tell,
She was *tickled* to death to see Mitchell catch hell. *(Refrain)*

5. Old Griffin stood there, the crabby old Drake,
A hand in the racket, we thought he would take,
When some of the boys came and took him away
"Be*cripes,*" said old Griffin, "I've nothing to say." *(Refrain)*

6. You can talk of your fashions and styles to be seen,
But there's none to compare with the cook of nineteen.
She's short, thick and stout, without a mistake,
And the boys call her Nellie, the belle of Long Lake. *(Refrain)*

7. And now, my good fellers, adieu to you all,
For Christmas is coming and I'm going to Glens Falls
And, when I get there, I'll go out on a spree,
For you know, when I've money, the divil's in me. *(Refrain)*

50.

The Jam on Gerry's Rocks

Words and melody adapted and arranged by
John A. and Alan Lomax

Piano arrangement by
Charles and Ruth Seeger

1. Come all you jolly fellows, wherever you may be,
I hope you'll pay attention and listen unto me,
It's all about some shanty boys, so manly and so brave,
'Twas on the jam on Gerry's Rock they met their watery grave.

2. 'Twas on one Sunday morning as you shall quickly hear,
Our logs were piled up mountain high, we could not keep them clear,
"Turn out, brave boys," the foreman cried, with a voice devoid of fear,
"And we'll break up the jam on Gerry's rock and for Eagletown we'll steer."

3. Some of us were willing, while others they were not,
For to work on jams on Sunday they did not think they'd ought;
But six American shanty-boys did volunteer to go
To break the jam on Gerry's rock with their foreman, young Monroe.

4. They had not rolled off many logs before the boss did say,
"I would you all be on your guard, for the jam will soon give way."
He had no more than spoke those words when the jam did break and go,
And carried away those six brave youths with their foreman, young Monroe.

5. We took him from the water, smoothed back his raven-black hair,
There was one fair form amongst them whose cries did rend the air,
There was one fair form amongst them, a girl from Saginaw town,
Whose mournful cries did rend the skies for her lover that was drowned.

6. She received their presents kindly and thanked them every one,
Though she did not survive him long, as you shall understand;
It was scarcely three weeks after and she was called to go,
And her last request was to be laid by her lover, young Monroe.

7. Come all of you brave young shanty-boys, I'd have you call and see
Two green graves by the river side where grows the hemlock tree;
The shanty-boys cut off the wood where lay those lovers low—
SPOKEN: 'Tis handsome Clara Clark and her true love, brave Monroe.

51.

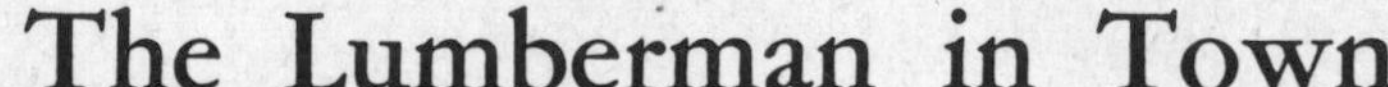

The Lumberman in Town

Words and melody adapted and arranged by
Philips Barry

Piano arrangement by
Charles and Ruth Seeger

Moderately fast

G D G D G D G A min. D7 G

mf

When the lum - ber-man comes down, ev' - 'ry pock - et bears a crown, And he wan - ders, some pret - ty girl to find; If — she is not too sly, with her dark and roll - ing eye, The — lum - ber-man is pleased in — his mind,

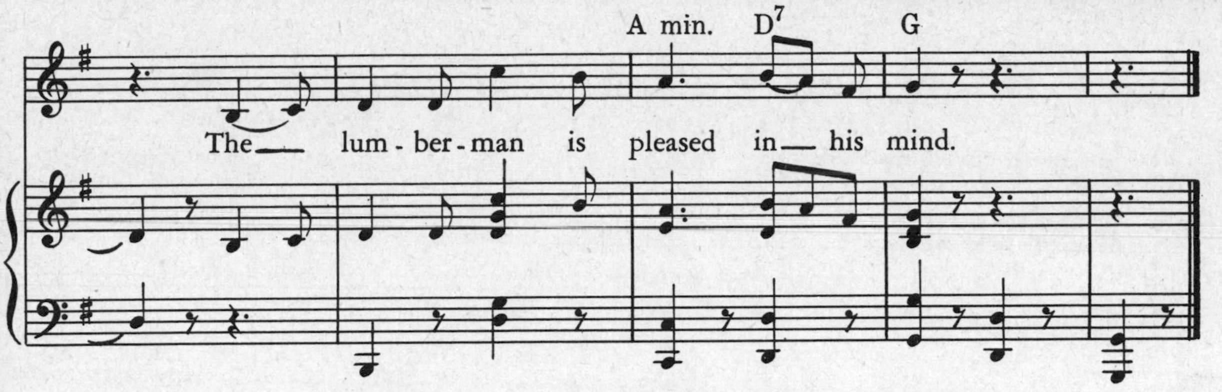

1. When the lumberman comes down, ev'ry pocket bears a crown,
And he wanders, some pretty girl to find;
If she is not too sly, with her dark and rolling eye,
The lumberman is pleased in his mind,
The lumberman is pleased in his mind.

2. The landlady comes in, she is dressed so neat and trim,
She looks just like an evenin' star;
She's ready to wait on him, if she finds him in good trim,
Chalk him down for two to one at the bar,
Chalk him down for two to one at the bar.

3. The lumberman goes on, till his money's spent and gone,
Then the landlady begins to frown;
With her dark and rolling eye, this will always be her cry,
"Lumberman, it's time that you were gone,
Lumberman, it's time that you were gone."

4. She gives him to understand there's a boat to be a-manned,
And away up the river he must go;
Good liquor and a song— "Go hitch your horses on,
Bid adieu to the girls of St. Johns'
Bid adieu to the girls of St. Johns."

5. To the woods he will go with his heart full of woe,
And he wanders from tree after tree;
Till six months have gone and past, and he forgets it all at last,
"It is time I should have another spree,
It is time I should have another spree."

6. When old age does him alarm, he will settle on a farm,
And he'll find some young girl to be his wife;
But to his sad mistake, she mock love to him will make,
And kind death will cut the tender threads of life,
SPOKEN: And kind death will cut the tender threads of life.

52.

The Buffalo Skinners

Words and melody adapted and arranged by
John A. and Alan Lomax

Piano arrangement by
Charles and Ruth Seeger

1. 'Twas in the town of Jacksboro in the year of '73,
When a man by the name of Crego came stepping up to me,
Saying. "How do you do, young fellow, and how would you like to go
And spend one summer pleasantly on the range of the buffalo?"

2. It's me being out of employment, boys, to old Crego I did say,
"This going out on the buffalo range depends upon the pay.
But if you will pay good wages, give transportation, too,
I think, sir, I will go with you to the range of the buffalo."

3. It's now our outfit was complete, seven able-bodied men,
With navy six and needle gun our troubles did begin;
Our way, it was a pleasant one, the route we had to go,
Until we crossed Pease River on the range of the buffalo.

4. It's now we've crossed Pease River, our troubles have begun,
The first damned tail I went to rip, it's how I cut my thumb!
The water was salty as hell-fire, the beef I could not go,
And the Indians waited to pick us off, while skinning the buffalo.

5. Our hearts were cased with buffalo hocks, our souls were cased with steel,
And the hardships of that summer would nearly make us reel.
While skinning the damned old stinkers, our lives they had no show,
For the Indians waited to pick us off on the hills of Mexico.

6. The season being near over, boys, old Crego, he did say
The crowd had been extravagant, was in debt to him that day.
We coaxed him and we begged him, but still it was no go—
So we left his damned old bones to bleach on the range of the buffalo.

7. Oh, it's now we've crossed Pease River and homeward we are bound,
No more in that hell-fired country shall ever we be found.
Go home to our wives and sweethearts, tell others not to go,
For God's forsaken the buffalo range and the damned old buffalo.

53.

Sweet Betsy from Pike

Words and melody adapted and arranged by
John A. and Alan Lomax

Piano arrangement by
Charles and Ruth Seeger

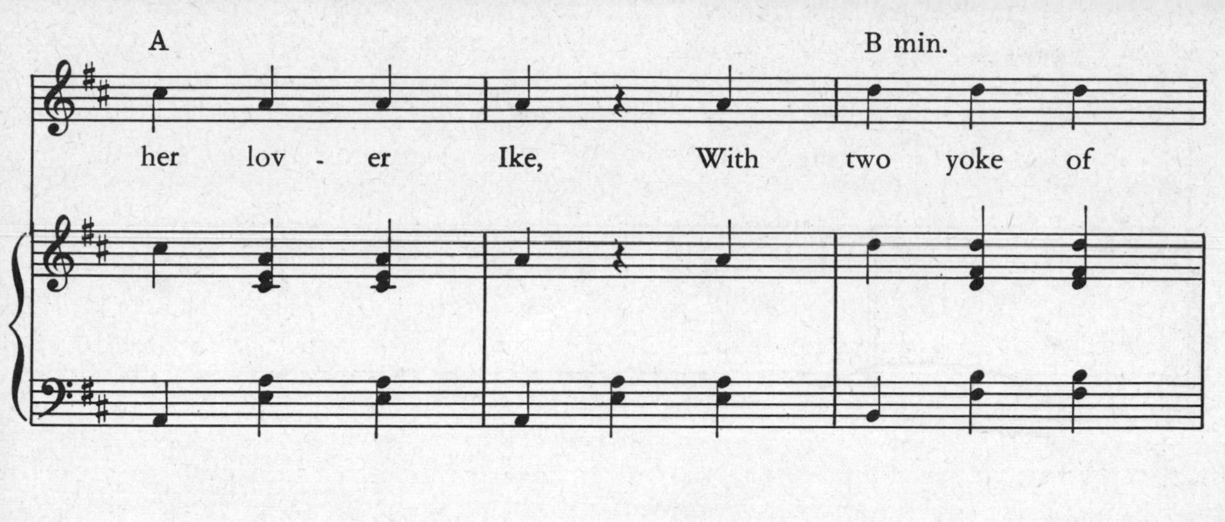
A
B min.
her lov - er Ike, With two yoke of

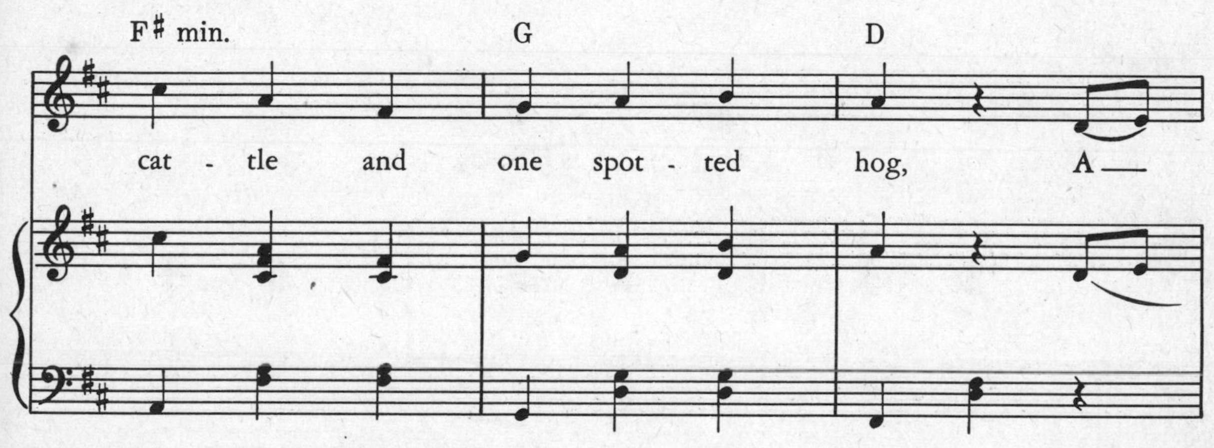
F♯ min.
G
D
cat - tle and one spot - ted hog, A—

A7
D
tall Shang - hai roost - er and an old yal - ler dog.

REFRAIN
A7
Hoo - dle dang fol - di dye - do, hoo - dle
f

D
dang fol - di day, Hoo - dle dang fol - di
8va bassa ad lib.

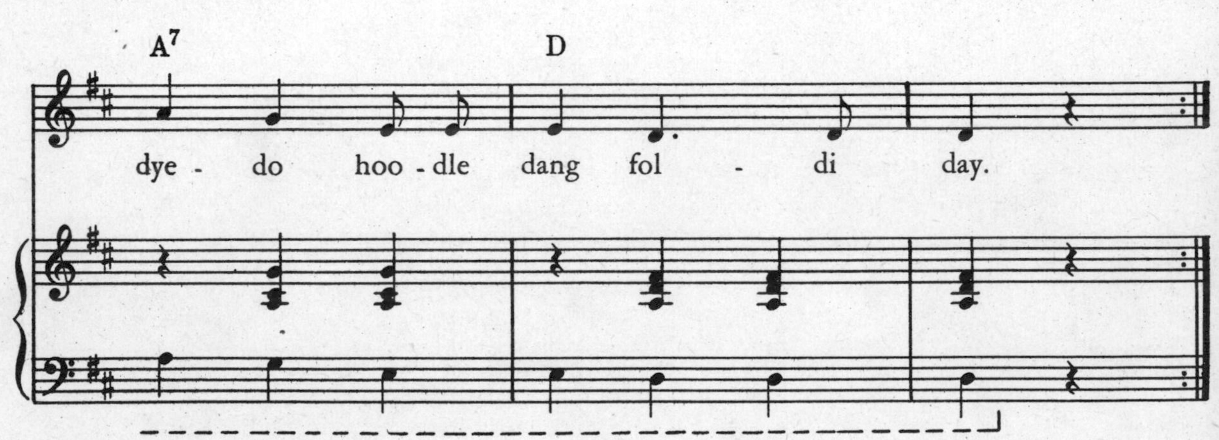
A7
D
dye - do hoo - dle dang fol - di day.

Refrain: Hoo-dle dang fol-di dye-do, hoo-dle dang fol-di day,
Hoo-dle dang fol-di dye-do, hoo-dle dang fol-di day.

2. One evening quite early they camped on the Platte,
Made down their blankets on a green shady flat;
Where Betsy, quite tired, lay down to repose,
While with wonder Ike gazed on his Pike County rose.

3. They swam the wide rivers and crossed the tall peaks,
And camped on the prairie for weeks upon weeks.
Starvation and cholera and hard work and slaughter,
They reached California spite of hell and high water.

4. Out on the prairie one bright starry night
They broke out the whisky and Betsy got tight;
She sang and she shouted and danced o'er the plain,
And made a great show for the whole wagon train.

5. The Injuns came down in a wild yelling horde,
And Betsy was skeered they would scalp her adored;
Behind the front wagon wheel Betsy did crawl,
And fought off the Injuns with musket and ball.

6. They soon reached the desert, where Betsy gave out,
And down in the sand she lay rolling about;
While Ike in great terror looked on in surprise,
Saying, "Get up now, Betsy, you'll get sand in your eyes."

7. The wagon tipped over with a terrible crash,
And out on the prairie rolled all sorts of trash;
A few little baby clothes done up with care
Looked rather suspicious — though 'twas all on the square.

8. The Shanghai ran off and the cattle all died,
The last piece of bacon that morning was fried;
Poor Ike got discouraged, and Betsy got mad,
The dog wagged his tail and looked wonderfully sad.

9. One morning they climbed up a very high hill,
And with wonder looked down into old Placerville;
Ike shouted and said, as he cast his eyes down,
"Sweet Betsy, my darling, we've got to Hangtown."

10. Long Ike and sweet Betsy attended a dance,
Where Ike wore a pair of his Pike County pants;
Sweet Betsy was covered with ribbons and rings.
Said Ike, "You're an angel, but where are your wings?"

11. A miner said, "Betsy, will you dance with me?"
"I will that, old hoss, if you don't make too free;
But don't dance me hard. Do you want to know why?
Doggone you, I'm chock-full of strong alkali."

12. Long Ike, and sweet Betsy got married of course,
But Ike, getting jealous, obtained a divorce;
And Betsy, well satisfied, said with a shout,
"Good-by, you big lummux, I'm glad you backed out."

Final Chorus: Saying, good-by, dear Isaac,
Farewell for a while,
But come back in time
To replenish my pile.

54.

The Days of '49

Words and melody adapted and arranged by
the Lomaxes and Frank Warner

Piano arrangement by
Charles and Ruth Seeger

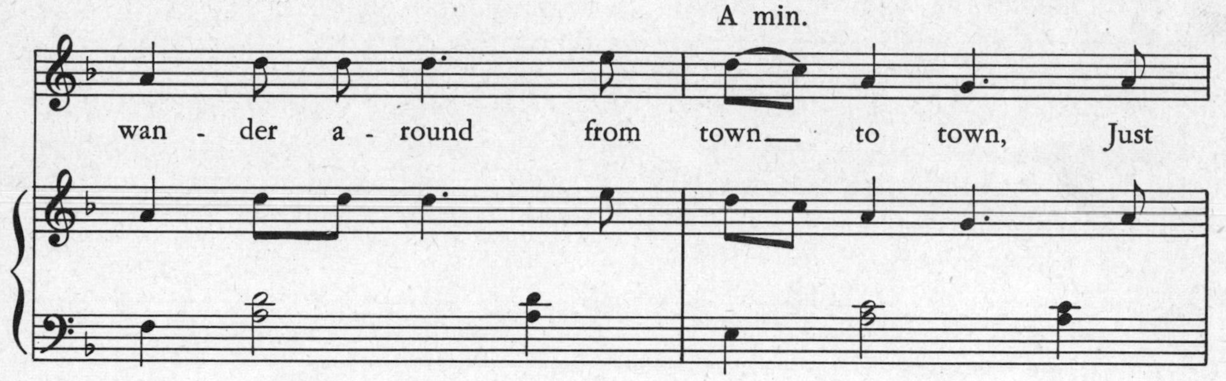
A min.
wan - der a - round from town — to town, Just

D min.
A min.
D min.
like a rov - ing sign, And the peo- ple all say, "There

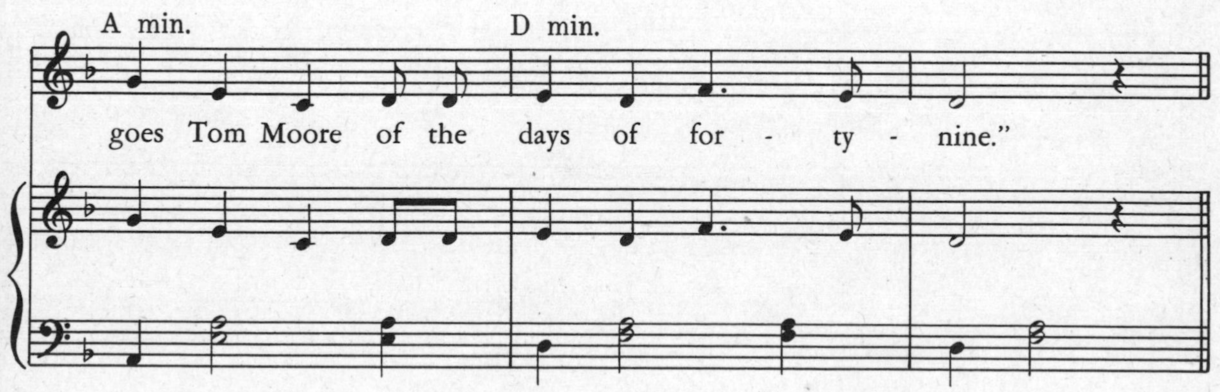
A min.
D min.
goes Tom Moore of the days of for - ty - nine."

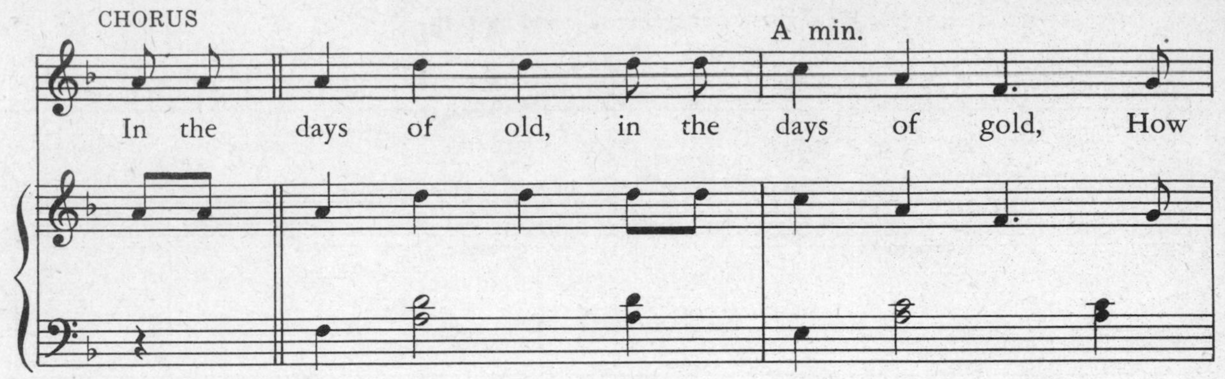
CHORUS
A min.
In the days of old, in the days of gold, How

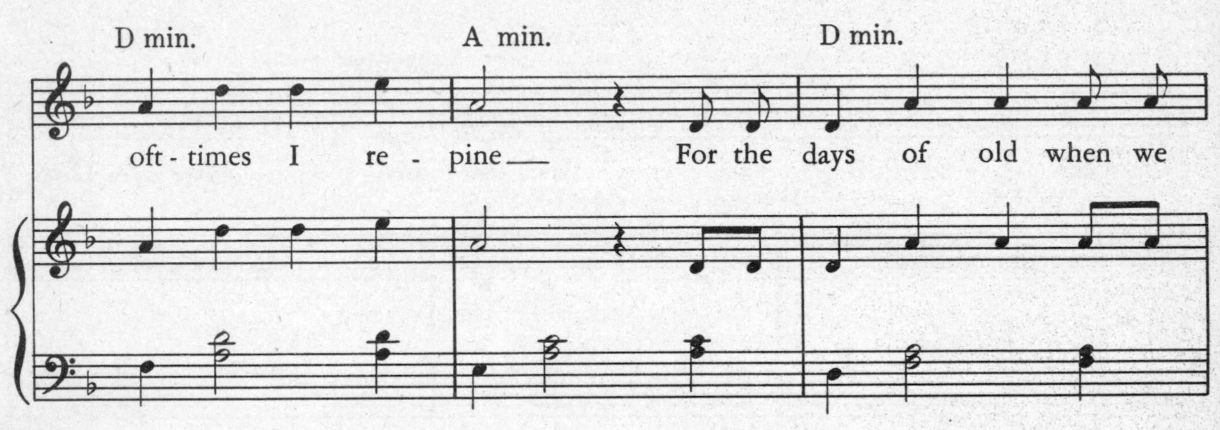
D min.
A min.
D min.
oft - times I re - pine___ For the days of old when we

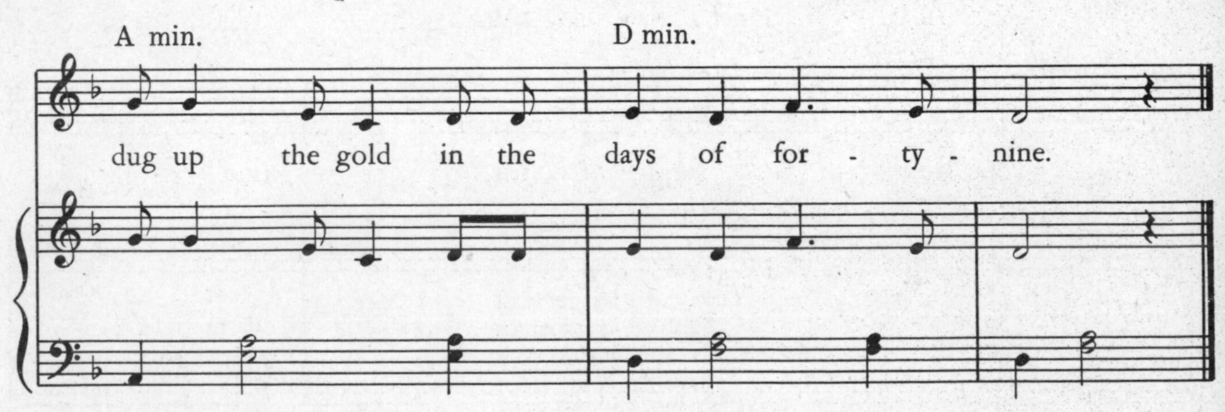
A min.
D min.
dug up the gold in the days of for - ty - nine.

2. My comrades, they all loved me well,
A jolly saucy crew,
A few hard cases I will admit,
Though they were brave and true;
Whatever the pinch they ne'er would flinch,
They never would fret or whine—
Like good old bricks, they stood the kicks
In the days of '49.

3. There was old Lame Jess, a hard old cuss,
Who never did repent;
He never was known to miss a drink
Or ever spend a cent;
But old Lame Jess, like all the rest,
To death he did resign
And in his bloom went up the flume
In the days of '49.

4. There was Poker Bill, one of the boys,
Who was always in for a game,
Whether he lost or whether he won,
To him it was all the same;
He would ante up and draw his cyards
He would go you a hatfull blind,
In the game with death Bill lost his breath
In the days of '49.

5. There was New York Jake, the butcher's boy,
He was always getting tight;
And every time that he'd get full
He was spoiling for a fight;
Then Jake ram*paged* against a knife
In the hands of old Bob Sine;
And over Jake they held a wake
In the days of '49.

6. There was Ragshag Bill from Buffalo,
I never will forget,
He would roar all day and roar all night
And I guess he's roaring yet;
One night he fell in a prospect hole
In a roaring bad design;
And in that hole he roared out his soul
In the days of '49.

7. Of all the comrades that I've had
There's none that's left to boast;
And I'm left alone in my misery
Like some poor wandering ghost;
And as I pass from town to town
They call me the rambling sign—
"There goes Tom Moore, a bummer shore,
Of the days of '49."

CHORUS: In the days of old, in the days of gold,
How oftimes I repine—
For the days of old when we dug up the gold
In the days of '49.

55.

The Old Settler's Song

Words and melody adapted and arranged by
John A. and Alan Lomax

Piano arrangement by
Charles and Ruth Seeger

Moderate

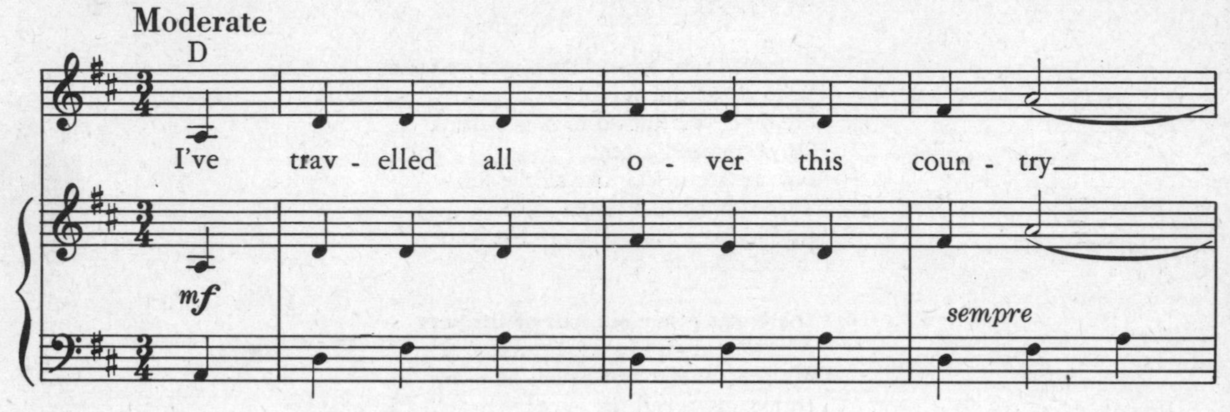

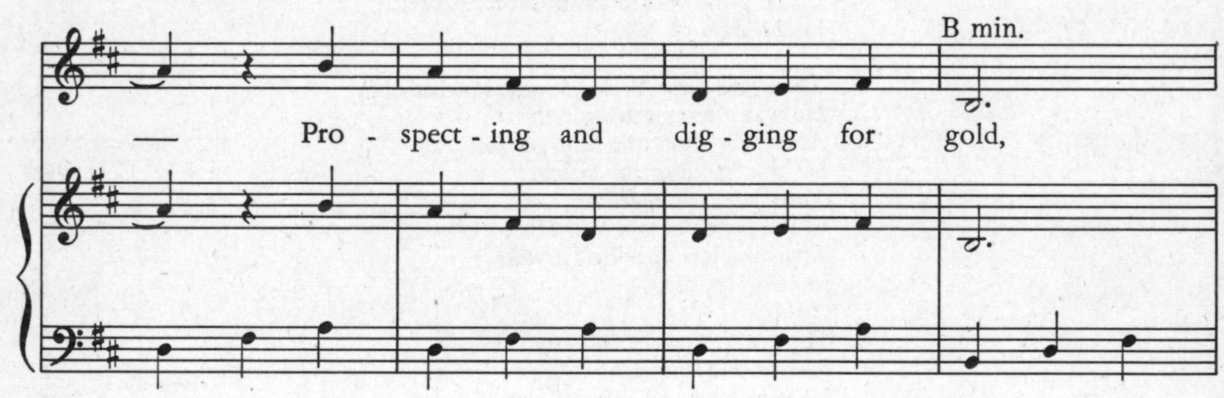

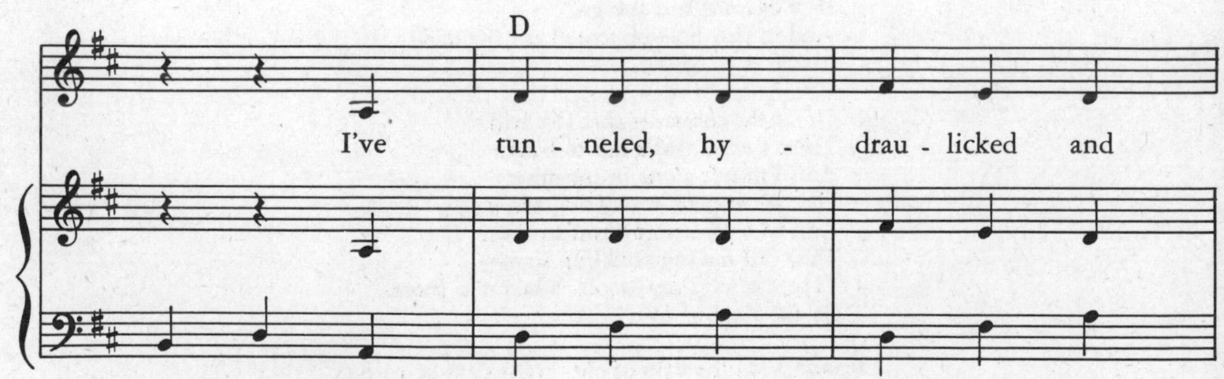

2. For each man who got rich by mining,
Perceiving that hundreds grew poor,
I made up my mind to try farming,
The only pursuit that was sure,

3. So, rolling my grub in my blanket,
I left all my tools on the ground,
I started one morning to shank it
For the country they call Puget Sound.

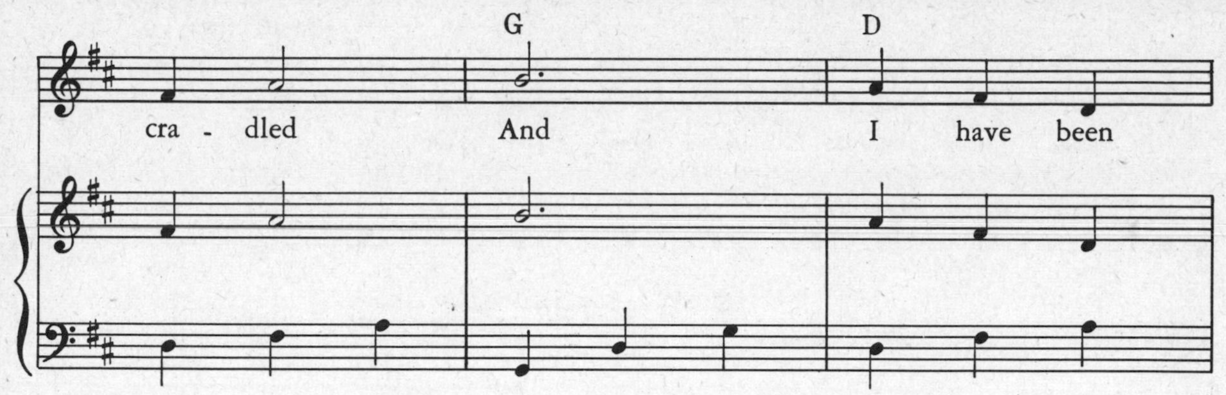

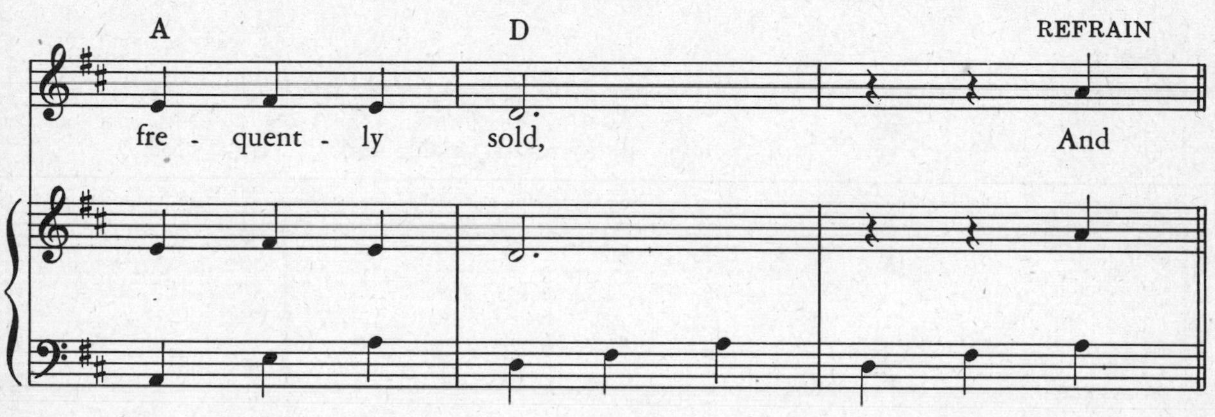

4. Arriving flat broke in midwinter,
I found it enveloped in fog,
And covered all over with timber,
Thick as the hair on the back of a dog.

5. When I looked on the prospects so gloomy,
The tears trickled over my face,
And I thought that my travels had brought me,
To the end of the jumping off place.

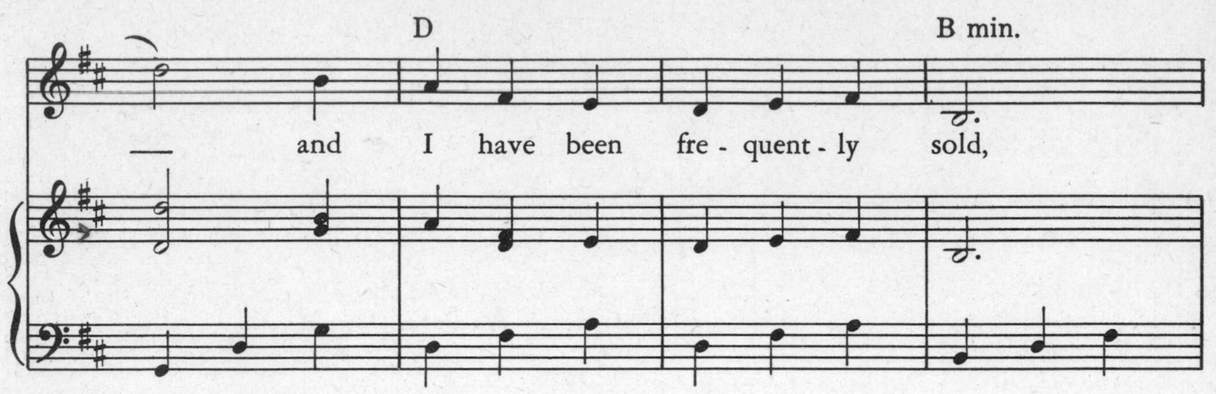

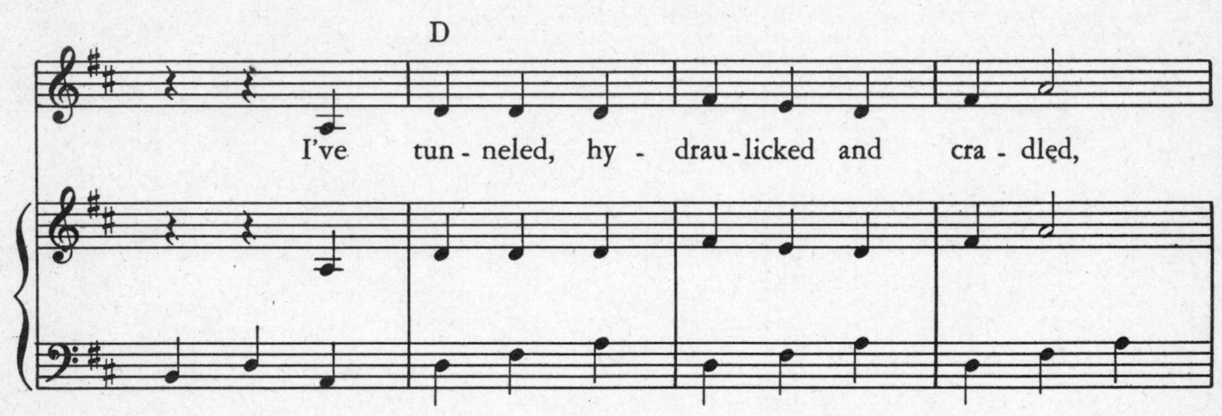

6. I staked me a claim in the forest
And sat myself down to hard toil,
For two years I chopped and I niggered,
But I never got down to the soil.

7. I tried to get out of the country,
But poverty forced me to stay,
Until I became an old settler,
Then nothing could drive me away.

1. I've traveled all over this country
Prospecting and digging for gold,
I've tunneled, hydraulicked and cradled
And I have been frequently sold,

REFRAIN: And I have been frequently so-o-old,
And I have been frequently sold,
I've tunneled, hydraulicked and cradled,
And I have been frequently sold.*

2. For each man who got rich by mining,
Perceiving that hundreds grew poor,
I made up my mind to try farming,
The only pursuit that was sure.

3. So, rolling my grub in my blanket,
I left all my tools on the ground,
I started one morning to shank it
For the country they call Puget Sound.

4. Arriving flat broke in midwinter,
I found it enveloped in fog,
And covered all over with timber,
Thick as hair on the back of a dog.

5. When I looked on the prospects so gloomy,
The tears trickled over my face,
And I thought that my travels had brought me,
To the end of the jumping off place.

6. I staked me a claim in the forest
And sat myself down to hard toil,
For two years I chopped and I niggered,
But I never got down to the soil.

7. I tried to get out of the country,
But poverty forced me to stay,
Until I became an old settler,
Then nothing could drive me away.

8. And now that I'm used to the climate
I think that if a man ever found
A place to live easy and happy,
That Eden is on Puget Sound.

9. No longer the slave of ambition,
I laugh at the world and its shams,
As I think of my pleasant condition,
Surrounded by acres of clams,

REFRAIN: Surrounded by acres of cla-a-ams,
Surrounded by acres of clams,
As I think of my happy condition,
Surrounded by acres of clams.

*The refrains of all subsequent stanzas are similarly formed by repetition of the fourth and third lines.

56.

Down, Down, Down

Words and melody by
William Keating

Piano arrangement by
Charles and Ruth Seeger

Moderate

1. With your kind attention a song I will trill,
All ye who must toil with the pick and the drill,
And sweat for your bread in that hole in Oak Hill,
That goes down, down, down.

2. When I was a boy, says my daddy to me:
"Stay out of Oak Hill, take my warning," says he,
"Or with dust you'll be choked and a pauper you'll be,
Broken down, down, down."

3. But I went to Oak Hill and I asked for a job,
A mule for to drive or a gangway to rob.
The boss said, "Come out,Bill, and follow the mob
That goes down, down, down."

4. On the strength of the job and the tune of this rhyme
I strolled into Tim's and drank twenty-five shines;
Reported next morning, half dead but on time
To go down, down, down.

5. Then into the office I sauntered to Boss Sam,
With a cheery "Good mornin'," says I, "Here I am,
With booze in me bottle and beer in me can
To go down, down, down."

6. I asked Sam what tools I would need in the place,
"Very few," said the boss with a grin on his face,
"One seven size scoop in a coop-stoopy space
Away down, down, down."

7. With a note from the boss to the shaft I made haste,
Saluted the topman and in line took me place
Sayin', "Gi' me a cage, for I've no time to waste,
Let me down, down, down."

8. "All aboard for the bottom;" the topman did yell,
We stepped on the cage, he ding-donged a bell;
Through that hole in Oak Hill, like a bat out of hell,
We went down, down, down.

9. In wet or dry weather that shaft always rains,
There's a trembling of timbers and clanking of chains,
Just off of a spree, it flip-flopped me few brains,
Going down, down, down.

Moderate
C
10. I've been on the out - side and in - side be - fore, I've
mf
G
fell in - to o - ceans and riv - ers ga - lore, But that
C
F
C
dip in that deep dir - ty sump made me sore A - way
G7
C
down, down, down.

10. I've been on the outside and inside before,
I've fell into oceans and rivers galore,
But that dip in that deep dirty sump made me sore
Away down, down, down.

11. She was blocked from the dish to the knuckle with smoke,
The dust was so thick I thought I would choke.
Says I to meself, "I guess here's where I croak
Away down, down, down."

12. Groped into a gangway and gave me a scoop,
The cut was just fired, muck heaped to the roof.
I scooped and I scooped till me back looped the loop.
Stoopin' down, down, down.

13. She was heaved on the bottom and cracked on the top,
Ne'er a pole, ne'er a slab, ne'er a laggin' nor prop,
Pretty soon I expect that Gap Mountain will drop
And come down, down, down.

14. That journey each morning, it near breaks my heart.
The steps in the mule-ways are ten feet apart,
You must watch your brogans, for if you get a start,
You'll roll down, down, down.

15. On pay-day I rave; Rube Lacey oft swore,
In fact 'twas enough to make both of us sore,
When our wives drag our wages all out in the store,
While we're down, down, down.

16. It's a most cruel fate, but continue we must,
Delvin' deep for black diamonds beneath the earth's crust,
Moil for mush and molasses and eating coal dust
Away down, down, down.

17. All I drew for a year was a dollar or three,
These company-store thieves made a pauper of me,
But for ballads like this, I'd have starved for a spree
In the town, town, town.

18. Toil, you put early-grey on my poor daddy's head,
While he slaved in Oak Hill to provide us with bread;
How I wish I had heeded the warning he plead:
Don't go down, down, down."

CHAPTER VII

Git Along, Little Dogies

It was a long and a lonesome go,
The herd rolled on to Mexico,
With laughter light and cowboy song
To Mexico we rolled along.

When the men with the long rifles and the buckskin breeches reached the desert of grass, they stopped and squatted down on their hunkers and stared for a long time. They had learned how to live in the woods; they knew how to fight Indians in the woods; but this treeless, almost waterless desert of grass stumped them. For a half century the Great Plains country had lain empty of settlers. Raftsmen moved along the Mississippi, the Missouri, and their tributaries; the '49ers organized their covered-wagon caravans and raced across the Great Plains, hardly daring to stop and bury their dead on the way; but the Great Plains still remained the free domain of the plains Indian, the coyote, the turkey buzzard, the buffalo, and the lobo wolf.

Two years after the Civil War the quiet of the plains was broken by the bawling of longhorn steers, the jingle of big bell spurs, and the wild yells of the Texas cowboys. The first herds began crossing the Red River and pushing North to meet the little spur of railroad that had pushed out into the Kansas flatland to Abilene. Next spring more herds crossed the Red River into Oklahoma and some of them rolled all the way to the Black Hills of South Dakota, where the cattle were kept for fattening. The Texans kept pushing more and more cattle into the plains, until by the 1890's ranches had sprangled out all over the Western prairies. Fifteen years later the trail-driving days had ended and the country was already being fenced off, and the Plains Indians and the cowboy rode off to Hollywood together. In this brief period of forty years, one million Texas ponies and twelve million Texas cattle had walked North to market.

The men, who thus opened this Western desert for settlement, came mostly from South Texas. They wore a costume named and designed by the Mexicans. They worked cattle of a wild Spanish stock. They rode "Spanish" ponies. They rounded up their tremendous half-wild herds on land they had taken from Mexicans only a generation earlier. Their horsemanship and their knowledge of how to live on the prairie they had learned from the Mexicans. They carried the first weapon that was superior to the plains Indian's bow and arrow—the six-shot, repeating Colt's revolver. Their food supply moved with them on the hoof. These mounted, lightly armed cattle-drovers finally wrested the Great Plains away from the buffalo-hunting Indians.

In the confused years of the Civil War, when the ranches of South Texas had gone to pieces, the longhorn cattle had multiplied by the hundreds of thousands in the mesquite brush country south of San Antonio. All a man had to do to own a herd was to ride into the thorny thickets along the Pecos River armed with a rope, a branding iron, and a whole lot of nerve. If he could survive the heat and the thorns and the hardships of the hunt, he'd soon be a rancher. The trouble was that the cattle weren't worth anything in Texas and good markets were practically unavailable. The route to New Orleans was almost impossibly swampy. The route to Illinois lay through the Arkansas hills where gangs of thieves were ready to break up the herd and kill the drovers.

Thus, when the railroad extended its line as far west as Abilene, Kansas, and an easy route north across level country opened up, the cowmen poured their cattle north by the millions and the plains were dotted with ranches almost overnight. In this period of trail-driving, cowboys created a whole literature of roughhewn verse that magnificently describes the West and the life of the wild buckaroos who tamed it. Although this homespun balladry was based directly on the folk-song stocks of the Northern lumberjacks and the Southern peckerwoods, it nevertheless had a quality of its own that is truly Western. So much so, that many of these Western ballads are sung by Eastern ballad-singers, who have forgotten the Eastern originals of these cowboy songs.

In the early years of the twentieth century John A. Lomax, senior editor of this volume, collected a great part of this oral literature that had grown up as quietly and as much unnoticed as the grass of the plains. Therefore, as explanatory material for this section, we have preferred to publish his accounts of his discovery of these now famous songs.

57. *THE OLD CHISHOLM TRAIL*

Of all songs, "The Old Chisholm Trail" was the most universally sung by the cowboys. They sang the song all the way up the cattle trail from San Antonio to Dodge City, Kansas, and then on into Montana and the Dakotas where herds were sometimes driven to be fattened and the meat sweetened by the richer grasses and cold winters of that region. Wrote one cowboy: "It was a dull day on the drive when one of the cowboys did not make a new verse to 'Old Chisholm Trail.' "

"It's as long as the cattle trail from Texas to Wyoming," said another cowboy to me after he had sung sixty-nine verses without stopping. Several hundred couplets are in my collection, a variety of refrains and a half dozen tunes. The words in their entirety would furnish a vivid picture of the experiences of a group of cowboys on the long drive to market, while the different rhythms and tunes reflect the various moods of the singers. For example, the stirring beat of the most common tune fits the rapid pace of a galloping horse in pursuit of a steer which has broken from the herd. (Version I.) When the cowboy was alone riding the fence-line or hunting the drifting cattle, the melody is soft, the time slow, reflecting the loneliness of the prairies, the vastness of the wide stretches of plain and sky. Moreover, the rattling chorus that follows each couplet sometimes provoked group singing around the campfire at the rare moments of rest in the life of the cowpuncher.

The cowboy has his troubles and he shouts them to the sky. Whenever the rain begins to fall, always the unlucky rider discovers that he has left his "damned old slicker in the wagon again"—the chuck wagon, far ahead of the herd, where the cook is getting the next meal of "bacon and beans" ready for the bunch of hungry men pushing the slowly drifting cattle along. Almost every stanza shows the reader a bright, informing picture of the life on the trail, of the types of men who made up that life:

Now, I've punched cattle from Texas to Maine,
And I've known some cowboys with their rightful name.

But only a few, only a few!

"Single men in barracks don't grow into plaster saints," wrote Kipling. Nor did the desperately hard life of the cowboy (sometimes he couldn't change clothes for a month and he took a bath only as he swam a swollen river on horseback) produce a model Sunday school laddie. At the end of the trail red liquor flowed freely; eager crimson-clad floozies and patooties swarmed for his attention. The complete "Chisholm Trail" frankly sets forth the gory details of these and other encounters far less innocent, in short, grim Anglo-Saxon words that are still rightfully excluded from the mails. But they are a part of the history of the times, and the record is carefully preserved.

58. *GIT ALONG, LITTLE DOGIES*

The old blind man shuffled along, clasping tight his guitar and his little tin cup, as I held his arm and guided him over the rough places. We were headed for the trees that fringed the Trinity West Fork near the cattle pens of the Fort Worth stockyards. Just a few minutes before I had found him sitting on the sidewalk twanging his guitar and listening for the ring of quarters in his tin cup.

"I don't know any cowboy songs," he said, "but lead me home to my wife. She knows 'em and can sing you a bookful." We found her dressed in a gypsy costume, seated out in front of a gaily colored tent. As we chatted the old man disappeared into the tent. When he came out, gone were the smoked glasses, the round, humped shoulders, the white hair, the tottering, shambling figure. Handsome, keen-eyed, alert, he stood before me, the perfect faker.

"My wife shakes down the saps who like to hold her hand as she tells their fortunes. The self-righteous fools who drop quarters into my tin cup go away happy. We aim to please our customers." He lay flat on his back on the mesquite grass, puffing a cigar, while his wife plucked the guitar strings and sang the songs of the road. I remember that she sang me the first blues I had ever heard, moving me almost to tears, and a pathetic ballad of a factory girl who got splinters in her toes. Many another ballad she sang that, unhappily, are gone with the Texas wind. At last came:

Whoopee-ti-ti-yo, git along, little dogies,
It's your misfortune and none of my own.

"To me," she said, "that's the loveliest of all cowboy songs. Its rhythm comes from the movement of a horse. It's not the boisterous hell-for-leather, wild gallop of 'Old Chisholm Trail,' nor the slow, easy canter of 'Goodby, Old Paint.' The dogies get nervous in crowds. You mustn't frighten 'em. Lope around them quietly in the darkness as you sing to them about their new home in Wyoming."

From her I heard the word *dogie,* and I think it was printed for the first time in the 1910 edition of my *Cowboy Songs.* A dogie, the gypsy lady told me, is a little calf who has lost his mammy and his daddy's run away with another cow. George W. Sanders of the San Antonio stockyards said that a motherless calf, forced to eat grass before it was old enough to digest it, developed a big stomach: "Nothing in your guts but dough," said his cowboy friends. These calves came to be called "doughguts," and that clumsy word, doughguts, was shortened and simplified into "dogies." Owen Wister in his personal letters to me always wrote it "doughies." But doughies or dogies, you hear the word daily nowadays—even hourly, if you listen to your radio.

59. *THE STREETS OF LAREDO*

After "The Chisholm Trail" the most popular Western ballad is this story of the young cowboy who rode the familiar road from rum to ruin. The hundred-odd examples of this ballad in my collection have located the scene of the cowboy's death in almost as many Western towns. As a matter of fact, the young man died in the British Isles, not of gunshot wounds, but of syphilis. Whereupon all the gay ladies of the town, grateful for his generosity to them, followed his coffin to the cemetery. We have one Irish version sung in Cork about the year 1790 which identifies the young man as a soldier and has him take his last journey with the ruffle of military drums:

My jewel, my joy, don't trouble me with the drums,
Sound the dead march as my corpse goes along;
And over my body throw handfuls of laurel,
And let them all know that I'm going to my rest.

An early English version discovers the "unfortunate lad down by Lock Hospital, wrapped in flannel, so hard was his fate." Here the balladeer goes into medical details:

Had she but told me when she disordered me,
Had she but told me of it in time,
I might have got salts and pills of white mercury,
But now I'm cut down in the height of my Prime.

Apparently the grim message of this ballad suited your moralizing folk-singer so well that a warning to young ladies was soon composed. This variant, current in England, is also known to United States singers and begins, in one form:

One morning, one morning, one morning in May,
I spied a young lady all clad in white linen,
All clad in white linen and cold as the clay.

When I was a young girl, I used to see pleasure,
When I was a young girl, I used to drink ale,
Right out of the ale-house, and into the jail-house,
Out of a barroom and down to my grave.

Go send for the preacher to come and pray for me,
Go send for the doctor to heal up my wounds,
My poor head is aching, my sad heart is breaking,
My body's salivated and Hell is my doom.

Here, too, as in the cowboy variant, the unhappy cause of the demise of the unfortunate sinner has been censored out by the folk. While the cowpunchers were making their Western forms of the ballad, Negro singers were also putting their impress upon the song. Thus emerged the well-known barrel-house piece, "St. James Infirmary Blues":

I was down in St. James Hospital,
My baby there she lay,
Out on a cold marble table
Well I looked and I turned away.
"What's my baby's chances?"
I asked old Dr. Tharp.
"By six o'clock this evenin'
She'll be playin' a golden harp."
Let her go, let her go, God bless her,
Wherever she may be,
She can hunt this wide world over,
But she'll never find a man like me."

60. *BURY ME NOT ON THE LONE PRAIRIE*

Many years ago an Englishman wrote a series of stanzas voicing the sailor's fear of being buried in the "deep, deep sea." Later a cowboy, name and time unknown, adopted a similar theme, weaving into his version some of the phases of his English cousin. The cowboy didn't want to be buried on the "lone prairie."

The plainsman says, "In this country you can look farther and see less than any other place in the world." The unbroken level miles of the western grassland possess the monotonous grandeur of the sea. Indeed, the prairie is a sea of grass. The wind moves it as it does the sea, sweeping the tall grass in peaceful summer swells, whipping and crackling through a dry sage in the winter with the sound of breakers curling up on a rocky beach. The cowboy rides lost and tiny across this illimitable land-sea, a mounted Magellan upon a pacific of prairie, and just as the sight of a single gull, far out to sea, diverts the lonely sailor, so the sudden flight of a yellow-breasted field lark startles the solitary rider out of the drowse of endless horizons.

Then the vasty silence of both plain and sea. The "dewdrops glow," the "butterflies rest," the "buzzard sails" on the far-stretching plains. Not much sound there. No sound at all in the dark stretches of the solemn sea. Don't bury us there in those dark voids of silence, plead both the sailor and the cowboy. And the pathos of this plea has touched the hearts of men.

A cowboy once told me in Haskell County, Texas, that he held a permanent grudge against the "Dying Cowboy" song. While visiting his sweetheart's home on a Sunday afternoon, he asked his lady love to sing, "Bury Me Not on the Lone Prairie." Custom compelled the young lover to stand by the organ, old-fashioned and squeaky, while his sweetheart went through the "whole damned twenty-nine verses and twenty-nine choruses. I liked to have died with all her relatives looking at me and making remarks. My legs wobbled and nearly wore out. I felt nearly as sorry for myself as for the dying cowboy."

61. *THE COWBOY'S DREAM*

"The Cowboy's Dream," fitted to the tune of "My Bonnie Lies Over the Ocean," was first made famous in Texas by a Methodist revival preacher, the Reverend Abe Mulkey. He was one of the many cowboy preachers who claimed to have a special message for the range riders while they rested up from the long, exhausting roundups and cattle drives. The stanzas of the song—the author or authors not certainly known—were fitted to the mood of the reflective cowboy alone with the herd as he rode about the sleeping cattle in the darkness with only the thud of his pony's hoofs and the "glittering stars" to bear him company. Among my informants about this song J. P. Skinner of Athens, Texas, wrote me: "Charley Hart of Carrolton, Mississippi, was under the necessity of living incognito on the Black Ranch in Clay County, Texas, soon after the War. He found surcease from sorrow in writing and composed this song." The song has "grown" since Charley Hart wrote the first group of stanzas.

The Reverend Mr. Mulkey, after he had preached his sermon, would sing the "Cowboy's Dream" as a solo, while between stanzas he would urge the listening cowboys to come forward, shake the minister's hand, and kneel at the "mourners' bench" for special prayer. This act of asking for prayer was accepted as a sign of repentance for the sins of the past and an indication that the cowboy proposed to change his ways—"quit his meanness," as Sam Jones was wont to phrase it. Following the prayers and more singing, the mourners were asked if they felt that their sins had been forgiven. Those that could rise and claim that the Lord had "fingered around their hearts with the finger of His love" were acclaimed as "saved" by the preacher and the congregation. They had been "washed in the blood of the Lamb."

Many and many a Texas cowboy abandoned the "broad road to perdition" and began to follow the "dim narrow trail" to that "bright happy region" while Abe Mulkey sang this beautiful song, which in cowboy lingo sketches an answer to the eternal question—What is beyond?

62. *HOME ON THE RANGE*

One day in 1908 I walked into the Buckhorn Saloon in San Antonio lugging a heavy Edison recording machine. It was the earliest, crudest type of dictaphone, requiring for its operation earphones and a large five-foot horn. The amazed German proprietor stared at my strange equipment and hastily put his hand under the counter where he was supposed to keep his arsenal of democracy. When I told him I was looking for cowboy songs, his face relaxed. He seemed to feel safe, though not entirely satisfied. He kept looking furtively at the unwieldly big-mouthed horn as though he feared it might be a gun. My friend, the proprietor, had two fads: it was said that festooned on the walls of his saloon hung the world's largest collection of horns; he was likewise interested in ballads. I had come to the right place.

He told me of a Negro singer who ran a beer saloon out beyond the Southern Pacific depot, in a scrubby mesquite grove. This Negro had been a chuck-wagon cook for years and had made the trip up the Chisholm Trail half a dozen times. He sang many cowboy songs. I found my man behind his saloon shack with his hat drawn down over his eyes, his head tilted back against a mesquite tree. When I shook him awake and told him what I wanted, he muttered as he looked at me with bloodshot eyes, "I'se drunk, I'se drunk, come back tomorrow and I'll sing for you."

I spent all the next day under the mesquite with this Negro. Among the songs he sang for me was "Home on the Range." From the recording I made that day down in the redlight district (they used stolen switch-lanterns to advertise the trade), Henry Leberman, a blind teacher of music, a few weeks afterward set down the music. This version, printed in the 1910 edition of *Cowboy Songs,* makes up the core of the tune that has become popular in this country and is sung throughout the English-speaking world. Mr. Leberman used earphones and played the old-fashioned cylinder records over and over again until he felt sure that he had captured the music as the Negro saloon-keeper had rendered it.

In 1925 Oscar J. Fox of San Antonio put the song into sheet-music form. Five years afterward, David Guion of Dallas followed with a slightly different arrangement. During the next six years eight other publishers of music issued the song with some variations. In 1933 the radio people took it up. For two or three years afterwards, "Home on the Range" was broadcast nightly by all of the big networks. It became known that it was President Franklin Delano Roosevelt's favorite song.

Suddenly radio stations in the United States were warned not to include "Home on the Range" on their programs. A suit for infringement of copyright had been filed in the courts of New York against thirty-five individuals and corporations for a cool half a million dollars. The claimants brought forth a copyright version of "Home on the Range," dated 1905, the music of which was similar to the current tune. A clever New York attorney, however, managed to locate in Smith Center, Kansas, eighty-six year old Clarence Harlan and his wife who made affidavit that in 1874 they had learned the song under the title of "The Western Home." The old couple recorded their early version of "Home on the Range" on phonograph records. The lawyer exhibited his new evidence to the plaintiff's attorney. The suit was dropped and the song was established in the public domain.

Homer Croy has gone further into the Kansas origin of "Home on the Range" in his book, "Corn Country." He tells of his visit to Smith Center, where old timers reminisced about Bruce Higley, the "writing doctor," who came out to Kansas from Indiana to escape a termagant wife and homesteaded in a little cabin on the banks of Beaver Creek. Higley farmed a little, doctored his sod-buster neighbors and wrote a lot of verse. One evening, as he waited for a deer to stick its head up along the breaks of the Beaver, an idea for a poem came to him and he scribbled down the first rough version of "Home on the Range."

O give me the gale of the Solomon Vale,
Where light streams with buoyancy flow;
On the banks of the Beaver, where seldom if ever,
Any poisonous herbage doth grow.

Time has dealt kindly with this crude poem. The folk have rubbed off its rough edges and improved the poesy. Time has turned the Higley cabin into a henhouse and filled the once-clear Beaver with sand and gravel. Higley, himself, moved to Shawnee, Oklahoma, where he died in 1911, a year after I published the Texas version of "Home on the Range" in my first book of cowboy songs.

When I read Mr. Croy's story, I turned to my files. A folklorist learns to be skeptical of any story of "ultimate origins." There I found a letter which stated that "Home on the Range" was sung in Texas in 1867. Where will the trail end? My guess is that it goes far back beyond Kansas and Texas, as well, into the big song-bag which the folk have held in common for centuries.

63. *GOODBY, OLD PAINT*

July Fourth in 1910 I sat in the grandstand at the Cheyenne, Wyoming, Frontier Day Wild West Show and watched the most thrilling bull-dogging and the wildest broncho-busting that can be found anywhere in the world. Teddy Roosevelt had put on the first act, dashing by a cheering crowd of 30,000 people, astride a snow-white horse and waving a ten-gallon hat. That night as I went into a saloon looking for frontier songs I came face to face with a University of Texas friend.

Boothe Merrill expressed surprise at meeting a former YMCA leader going into a saloon and I replied that I was downright astonished to find Boothe Merrill coming out of one. He joined me in one of the back rooms of the place to argue the question. There, later, he sang "Goodby Old Paint" (Version I), which he said had replaced "Home Sweet Home" as the last dance of the evening at cowboy shindigs in western Oklahoma. It was a slow waltz and told about the kind of horse variously described by the cowboy as paint, pinto, spotted, or calico—calico, not because of the color of the horse, but because, mounted on his paint pony, the cowboy rode to see his best girl, his calico.

Boothe Merrill scorned the clumsy horn of my Ediphone and I failed to record the song. However, he amiably sang it over and over until I held the tune safely in my mind. In my Austin home it became a family favorite. I passed it on to Oscar J. Fox of San Antonio, who issued "Goodby Old Paint" in sheet music. Only recently at a West Texas play-party on Orville Bullington's ranch in Wheeler County, I heard the song used as the farewell dance of the evening.

Carl Sandburg picked up a different melody for this song from Margaret Larkin (Version II). Perhaps better than any other cowboy creation, this song captures the bigness of the west and the love of the westerner for his wide horizons.

64. *RYE WHISKEY*

A herd of cattle on the trail often walked shrouded in a cloud of dust that was so thick "a buzzard would have to wear goggles and fly backward to keep from choking to death in it." The riders in the drag of the herd wore their bandannas across the lower parts of their faces and by the end of the day their bandannas would be coated and their eyebrows hung thick with dust. At such times blissful visions of the saloons at the end of the trail came rolling through a cowboy's mind; and the memories of the long, cool ones and the short fiery ones to be had at The Red Dog and The Last Chance and The Road to Ruin rose up to drive a man nearly crazy. Perhaps it is because a cowboy's job was the dustiest one in the world with dry spells that might last for several months that his drinking song, his ode to rye whiskey, is the best thing of its kind in American folklore.

American folk-singers, however, have had a good deal to say, pro and con, about our national alcoholic beverage. The seamen declare outright that:

Whiskey is the life of man,
Whiskey, Johnny,
I'll drink whiskey when I can,
Whiskey for my Johnny.

The mountain moonshiners, part of the same breed that staged the first armed rising against the American government, The Whiskey Rebellion of Pennsylvania, declare their independence in these lines:

I'll go on some mountain and set up my still,
I'll make you one gallon for a five-dollar bill.
With no wife to bother me, no babies to bawl,
A life without women is the best life of all.

Bully boys from coast to coast clink their glasses to the old Irish ditty, "Son of a Gambolier":

Like every honest fellow,
I drinks my lager beer,
Like every jolly fellow,
I takes my whiskey clear,
I'm a rambling rake of poverty,
The son of a son of a son of a son of a
gambolier.

And in the other camp, the teetotalers and the temperance legions darkly prophesy "The Drunkard's Doom":

The cup was filled at his command,
He drank of the poisoned bowl,
He drank, while wife and children starved,
And he ruined his own soul.

A year had passed, I went that way,
A hearse stood at the door:
I paused to ask, and one replied;
"The drunkard is no more."

Now, all young men, a warning take,
And shun the poisoned bowl;
'Twill lead you down to hell's dark gate,
And ruin your own soul.

The temperance songs often featured a child, pleading piteously with a gin-soaked parent:

Father, father leave off drinking,
Sign the temp'rance pledge today,
For our home it is so dreary,
While you at the dram-shop stay.

I remember when your footsteps,
When your footsteps made us glad;
Now I tremble at your footsteps
When the drink has made you ma-had.

No rusty-throated, saddle-weary cowboy, at the end of the trail, no desert rat at the close of a long prospecting trip over the scorched ribs of the Western badlands could fall in with such sentiments. His prayer would run:

O when I die, don't bury me at all,
Just pickle my bones in alcohol.
Put a bottle of booze at my head and feet
And then you know that I will keep.

Our present song grew, as a casual assemblage of stanzas, out of an old English song—"The Wagoner's Lad"—which was also the ancestor of "Old Smokey." Out West, where the boys ordered sulphuric acid flavored with rusty nails just to warm their boilers up, it grew wild and raucous. The drunken refrain, tacked on as the tail end of the tune, should sound like a combination of an Indian war-whoop, a panther scream, and a drunk just going into the d.t's.

65. *THE RED RIVER VALLEY*

This latter-day Western piece stands as proof of what folk-singers can do to refine and purify a song which comes to them from written sources. It has its origin in a ditty from New York State, "The Bright Mohawk Valley." Western singers not only changed the locale of the song, they cut away much of the original pretentiousness from both the melody and the lyrics. There emerges a chorus of great simplicity and a lazy little tune that drifts straight into your heart like smoke from a lonely cabin rising and disappearing into the prairie sky. Breathe this one softly through your harmonica or pump it gently out of your old concertina. You'll hear the summer wind swinging the tall grass. You'll see the sky of the West with its drifting herds of stars.

57.

The Old Chisholm Trail (I)

Words and melody adapted and arranged by
John A. and Alan Lomax

Piano arrangement by
Charles and Ruth Seeger

1. Come along, boys and listen to my tale,
I'll tell you of my troubles on the old Chisholm Trail.

REFRAIN: Coma ti yi youpy, youpy yea, youpy yea,
Coma ti yi youpy, youpy yea.

2. I started up the trail October twenty-third
I started up the trail with the 2-U herd.

3. O a ten-dollar hoss and a forty-dollar saddle,
And I'm goin' to punch in Texas cattle.

4. I woke up one morning on the old Chisholm trail,
Rope in my hand and a cow by the tail.

5. Stray in the herd and the boss said to kill it,
So I shot him in the rump with the handle of the skillet.

6. My hoss throwed me off at the creek called, Mud,
My hoss throwed me off round the 2-U herd.

7. Last time I saw him he was going 'cross the level
A-kicking up his heels and a-running like the devil.

8. It's cloudy in the west, a-looking like rain,
And my damned old slicker's in the wagon again.

9. The wind commenced to blow and the rain began to fall,
Hit looked, by grab, like we was goin' to lose 'em all.

10. I jumped in the saddle, grabbed holt of the horn,
Best damned cowpuncher ever was born.

11. I popped my foot in the stirrup and gave a litttle yell,
The tail cattle broke and the leaders went to hell.

12. Feet in the stirrups and seat in the saddle,
I hung and rattled with them goddam cattle.

13. I don't give a damn if they never do stop,
I'll ride as long as an eight-day clock.

14. We rounded 'em up and put 'em on the cars,
And that was the last of the old Two Bars.

15. Goin' to the boss to git my money.
Goin' back south to see my honey.

16. With my hand on the horn and my seat in the sky,
I'll quit herding cows in the sweet by-and-by.

The Old Chisholm Trail (II)

Words and melody adapted and arranged by
John A. and Alan Lomax

Piano arrangement by
Charles and Ruth Seeger

1. Come along, boys, and listen to my tale,
I'll tell you of my troubles on the old Chisholm Trail.

REFRAIN: Coma ti yi youpy, youpy yea, youpy yea,
Coma ti yi youpy, youpy yea.

2. We left the ranch on June twenty-third,
With a drove of Texas cattle, two thousand in the herd.

3. It's bacon and beans, most every day,
I'd as soon be a-eatin' prairie hay.

4. It's rainin' like hell and it's gettin' mighty cold,
These long-horn sonsaguns are gettin' hard to hold.

5. Saddle up, boys, and saddle up well,
For I think these cattle have scattered to hell.

6. I and Old Blue Dog* arrived at the spot,
We put them to millin' like the boilin' of a pot.

7. With lightnin' in his eye and thunder in his heels,
He went spinnin' round like a hoop on a reel.

8. "Make a circle, boys, don't lose no time,
I'm sure that they'll be easy to find."

9. It was over the hillside and over the draws,
And we soon brought in the old Two Bars.

10. We hit Caldwell and we hit her on the fly,
And we bedded down the cattle on the hill close by.

11. So I went to the boss to draw my roll,
He had it figgered out — nine dollars in the hole.

12. Me and my boss, we had a little chat,
And I slapped him in the face with my ten-gallon hat.

13. I hit the first train, it was the Cannon Ball,
I went rockin' home right early in the fall.

14. Hadn't been home but two days or three,
Till I put right out my gal for to see.

15. "If you've made up your mind to quit cowboy life,
I've fully decided to be your wife."

16. Farewell, old Blue Dog, I wish you no harm,
I have quit the business to go on the farm.

* Blue dog is the name of his horse.

58.

Git Along Little Dogies

Words and melody adapted and arranged by
John A. and Alan Lomax

Piano arrangement by
Charles and Ruth Seeger

1. As I was a-walking one morning for pleasure,
I spied a cow-puncher come riding along;
His hat was throwed back and his spurs were a-jinglin',
As he approached me a-singin' this song:

2. *Ear*ly in the springtime we'll round up the dogies,
Slap on their brands and bob off their tails;
Round up our horses, load up the chuck wagon,
Then throw those dogies *up* on the trail.

3. It's whooping and yelling and driving them dogies,
O, how I wish you would go on;
It's whooping and punching and go on, little dogies,
For you know Wyoming will be your new home.

4. *Some* boys goes up the trail for pleasure,
But that's where they git it most awfully wrong;
For you haven't any idea that trouble they give us
As we go driving those dogies along.

5. When night comes on and we hold them on the bed-ground,
Those little dogies that roll on so slow;
Roll up the herd and cut out the strays,
And roll the little dogies that never rolled before.

6. Your mother she was raised way down in Texas,
Where the jimson weed and sand-burrs grow;
Now we'll fill you up on prickly pear and cholla*
Till you're ready for the trail to Idaho.

7. Oh, you'll be soup for Uncle Sam's Injuns;
"It's beef, heap beef," I hear them cry.
Git along, git along, git along, little dogies,
You're going to be beef steers by and bye.

*Pronounced — "choy-ya", a form of cactus.

59.

The Streets of Laredo

Words and melody adapted and arranged by
John A. and Alan Lomax

Piano arrangement by
Charles and Ruth Seeger

1. As I walked out in the streets of Laredo,
As I walked out in Laredo one day,
I spied a dear cowboy wrapped up in white linen,
Wrapped up in white linen as cold as the clay.

2. "I see by your outfit that you are a cowboy"—
These words he did say as I boldly stepped by.
"Come sit down beside me and hear my sad story;
I am shot in the breast and I know I must die.

3. "It was once in the saddle I used to go dashing,
It was once in the saddle I used to go gay;
First to the dram-house and then to the card-house;
Got shot in the breast and I am dying today.

4. "Oh, beat the drum slowly and play the fife lowly,
Play the dead march as you carry me along;
Take me to the green valley, there lay the sod o'er me,
For I'm a young cowboy and I know I've done wrong.

5. "Get six jolly cowboys to carry my coffin;
Get six pretty maidens to bear up my pall.
Put bunches of roses all over my coffin,
Put roses to deaden the sods as they fall.

6. "Then swing your rope slowly and rattle your spurs lowly,
And give a wild whoop as you carry me along;
And in the grave throw me and roll the sod o'er me
For I'm a young cowboy and I know I've done wrong.

7. "Go bring me a cup, a cup of cold water,
To cool my parched lips," the cowboy then said;
Before I returned his soul had departed,
And gone to the round-up—the cowboy was dead.

8. We beat the drum slowly and played the fife lowly,
And bitterly wept as we bore him along;
For we all loved our comrade, so brave, young, and handsome,
We all loved our comrade although he'd done wrong.

4 Verses

60.

Bury Me Not on the Lone Prairie

Words and melody adapted and arranged by
John A. and Alan Lomax

Piano arrangement by
Charles and Ruth Seeger

(4)

1. "O bury me not on the lone prairie,"
These words came low and mournfully
From the pallid lips of a youth who lay
On his dying bed at the close of day.

2. He wailed in pain till o'er his brow
Death's shadows fast were gathering now;
He thought of his home and his loved ones nigh
As the cowboys gathered to see him die.

3. I've often wished to be laid, when I died,
In the little church on the green hillside;
By my father's grave there let mine be—
O bury me not on the lone prairie.

4. "O bury me not on the lone prairie,
Where the wild coyote will howl o'er me.
In a narrow grave just six by three,
O bury me not on the lone prairie.

5. "It matters not, so I've been told,
Where the body lies when the heart grows cold,
Yet grant, O grant this wish to me;
O bury me not on the lone prairie.

6. "These locks she has curled, shall the rattlesnake kiss?
This brow she has kissed, shall the cold grave press?
For the sake of the loved ones that will weep for me—
O bury me not on the lone prairie.

7. "O bury me not on the lone prairie
Where the buffalo paws o'er the prairie sea,
Where the buzzard sails and the wind goes free—
O bury me not on the lone prairie.

8. "O bury me not—," and his voice failed there;
But we took no heed of his dying prayer;
In a narrow grave just six by three,
We buried him there on the lone prairie.

9. ~~Yes~~ But, we buried him there on the lone prairie,
Where the owl all night hoots mournfully,
And the blizzard beats and the wind blows free
O'er his lonely grave in the lone prairie.

10. And the cowboys now as they roam the plain—
For they marked the spot where his bones were lain—
Fling a handful of roses o'er his grave
With a prayer to Him who his soul will save . . . .

61.

The Cowboy's Dream

Words and melody adapted and arranged by
John A. and Alan Lomax

Piano arrangement by
Charles and Ruth Seeger

1. Last night as I lay on the prairie
And looked at the stars in the sky,
I wondered if ever a cowboy
Would drift to that sweet by-and-by.

CHORUS: Roll on, roll on,
Roll on, little dogies, roll on, roll on.
Roll on, roll on,
Roll on, little dogies, roll on.

2. The road to the bright happy region
Is a dim narrow trail so they say;
But the bright one that leads to perdition
Is posted and blazed all the way.

3. They say there will be a great round-up,
And cowboys, like dogies, will stand
To be mavericked by the Riders of Judgment
Who are posted and know every brand.

4. I know there's many a stray cowboy
Who'll be lost at the great final sale,
When he might have gone in green pastures
Had he known of the dim narrow trail.

5. For they, like the cows that are locoed,
Stampede at the sight of a hand,
Are dragged with a rope to the round-up.
Or get marked with some crooked man's brand.

6. They tell of another big owner
Who's ne'er overstocked, so they say,
But who always makes room for the sinner
Who drifts from the straight narrow way.

7. They say he will never forget you,
That he knows every action and look;
So for safety you'd better get branded,
Have your name in his big Tally Book,

8. When I think of the last great round-up
On the eve of eternity's dawn;—
I think of the host of cowboys
That have been with us and gone.

62.

Home on the Range

Words and melody adapted and arranged by
John A. and Alan Lomax

Piano arrangement by
Charles and Ruth Seeger

CHORUS: Home, home on the range,
Where the deer and the antelope play,
Where seldom is heard a discouraging word
And the skies are not cloudy all day.

2. Where the air is so pure, the zephyrs so free,
The breezes so balmy and light,
That I would not exchange my home on the range
For all the cities so bright.

3. Oh, give me a land where the bright diamond sand
Flows leisurely down the stream;
Where the graceful white swan goes gliding along
Like a maid in a heavenly dream.

4. The red man was pressed from this part of the West,
He's likely no more to return
To the banks of Red River where seldom if ever
Their flickering campfires burn.

5. How often at night when the heavens are bright
With the light of the glittering stars,
Have I stood here amazed and asked as I gazed
If their glory exceeds that of ours.

6. Oh, I love these wild flowers in this dear land of ours;
The curlew I love to hear scream;
And I love the white rocks and the antelope flocks
That graze on the mountain-tops green.

7. Then I would not exchange my home on the range,
Where the deer and the antelope play;
Where seldom is heard a discouraging word
And the skies are not cloudy all day.

63.

Old Paint (I)

Words and melody adapted and arranged by
John A. and Alan Lomax

Piano arrangement by
Charles and Ruth Seeger

CHORUS: Good-by, old Paint, I'm a-leavin' Cheyenne,
Good-by, old Paint, I'm a-leavin' Cheyenne.

1. My foot's in my stirrup, my pony won't stan',
I'm a-leavin' Cheyenne, I'm off for Montan'.

2. I'm a-ridin' old Paint, I'm a-leadin' old Fan.
Good-by, little Annie, I'm off for Cheyenne.

3. Old Paint's a good pony, he paces when he can,
"Good morning, young lady, my hosses won't stand."

4. "Oh, hitch up your hosses and feed 'em some hay,
And seat yourself by me as long as you stay."

5. "My hosses ain't hungry, they'll not eat your hay,
My wagon is greasy and rolling away."

Old Paint (II)

Words and melody adapted and arranged by
John A. and Alan Lomax
Piano arrangement by
Charles and Ruth Seeger
Moderately slow
G D7
I ride an old paint I lead an old Dan, I'm goin' to Mon-
mf
G D7
tan' For to throw the hoo-li-han. They feed in the cou-lees, They
G D7 G
wa-ter in the draw, Their tails are all mat-ted, Their backs are all
CHORUS
D7 G
raw. Ride a-round, lit-tle do-gies, Ride a-round them

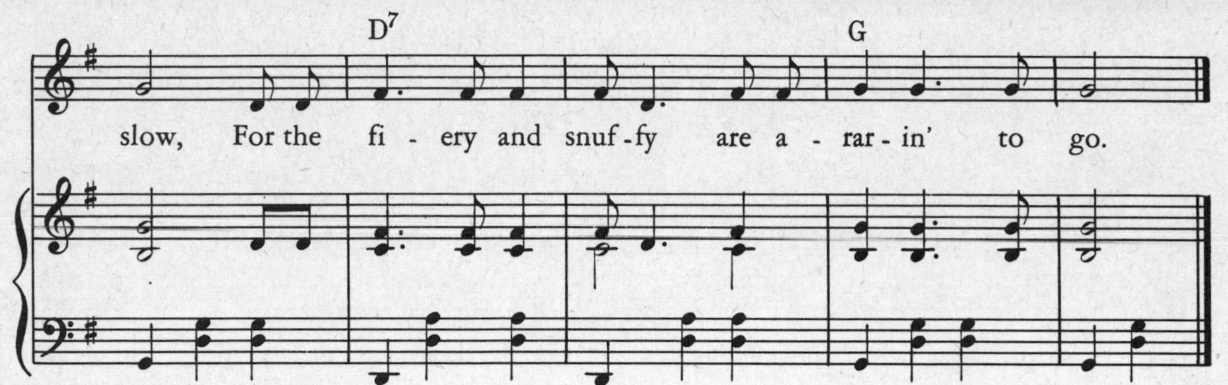

1. I ride an old paint
I lead an old Dan,
I'm goin' to Montan'
For to throw the hoolihan.
They feed in the coolies,
They water in the draw,
Their tails are all matted,
Their backs are all raw.

2. Old Bill Jones
Had two daughters and a song.
One went to Denver
And the other went wrong.
His wife she died
In a poolroom fight,
Still he sings
From morning till night.

3. O when I die,
Take my saddle from the wall,
Put it on my pony,
Lead him out of his stall,
Tie my bones to his back,
Turn our faces to the west,
And we'll ride the prairies
That we love the best.

CHORUS: Ride around, little dogies,
Ride around them slow,
For the fiery and snuffy are a-rarin' to go.

64.

Rye Whiskey

Words and melody adapted and arranged by
John A. and Alan Lomax

Piano arrangement by
Charles and Ruth Seeger

1. I'll eat when I'm hungry, I'll drink when I'm dry;
If the hard times don't kill me, I'll live till I die.

CHORUS: Rye whiskey, rye whiskey, rye whiskey, I cry,
If you don't give me rye whiskey, I surely will die.

2. Beefsteak when I'm hungry, red liquor when I'm dry,
Greenbacks when I'm hard up and religion when I die.

3. Jack o' diamonds, jack o' diamonds, I know you of old,
You've robbed my poor pockets of silver and gold.

4. Oh, whiskey, you villian, you've been my downfall;
You've kicked me, you've cuffed me, but I love you for all.

5. If the ocean was whiskey and I was a duck,
I'd dive to the bottom and get one sweet suck.

6. But the ocean ain't whiskey and I ain't a duck,
So we'll round up the cattle and then we'll get drunk.

7. I'll drink my own whiskey, I'll drink my own wine;
Ten thousands of bottles I've killed in my time.

8. O whiskey, you villian, you're no friend to me,
You killed my old daddy, gol darn ye, try me.

9. My foot's in my stirrup, my bridle's in my hand,
I'm leaving sweet Mollie, the fairest in the land.

10. Your parents don't like me, they say I'm too poor;
Just make me a pallet and I'll lie on the floor.

11. It's with the rabble army, O Mollie, I'll roam,
I'm an old rabble soldier and Dixie's my home.

12. I've no wife to quarrel, no babies to bawl;
The best way of living is no wife at all.

13. You may boast of your knowledge, and brag of your sense,
'Twill all be forgotten a hundred years hence.

65.

Red River Valley

Words and melody adapted and arranged by
John A. and Alan Lomax

Piano arrangement by
Charles and Ruth Seeger

1. From this valley they say you are going,
We will miss your bright eyes and sweet smile;
For they say you are taking the sunshine
That has brightened our pathways awhile.

CHORUS: Come and sit by my side, if you love me,
Do not hasten to bid me adieu,
Just remember the Red River Valley
And the cowboy who loved you so true.

2. I've been thinking a long time, my darling,
Of the sweet words you never would say,
Now, alas, must my fond hopes all vanish?
For they say you are going away.

3. Do you think of the valley you're leaving?
O how lonely and how dreary it will be.
Do you think of the kind hearts you're breaking?
And the pain you are causing to me?

4. They will bury me where you have wandered,
Near the hills where the daffodils grow,
When you're gone from the Red River Valley,
For I can't live without you I know.

CHAPTER VIII

The Farmer Is the Man

The farmer is the man, the farmer is the man,
The farmer is the man that feeds them all.

IF THE SONGS OF THIS CHAPTER SEEM TO BE melancholy or bitter, if they are a denial of the picture of—

The jolly farmer going whistling to the plow—

remember that here the farmer thinks of himself as a worker. His other moods are reflected in the ditties, dance tunes, and ballads elsewhere in this volume, most of which were made and sung by farm folk.

The job of a cowboy or a lumberjack or a raftsman had a good deal of change and variety and romance. The American pioneer farmer was tied to his little patch of ground—come hail, come drouth, come fire, come flood. He grubbed up the stumps the lumberjack left behind. He busted the tough prairie sod the cowboy rode freely across. He fought the pests and he waited on the weather. The task and the life of this man was truly onerous and bitter. He and his wife dug their knobby heels and their gnarled fingers into the harsh wilderness soil and tamed it for the rest of us. They pitted their bodies and souls against virgin forest humus and virgin prairie sod and so it is natural that their craft songs should be as tough as an oak handle and as harsh as a rusty plow point.

In her book, "God's Country," Martha Smith, pioneer Oklahoma farmwife, writes with irony as breezy and uninhibited as her spelling:

As time went on every thing went to rock bottem. Wheat, corn, cotton, hogs, cattle, and every thing. Things just was on the bedrock but we staid and fought it out and came out all right in the end. But it was a tough go. We raised thirty five bales of cotton that year and sold three bales early and had the rest jined and hauled hom. We piled it in the yard untell the next spring and then we sold it for three and a half cents a pound. It did not even pay for the picking. But we were in God's country, or so they said.

66. *THE YOUNG MAN WHO WOULDN'T HOE CORN*

There was a high, majestic fooling
Day before yesterday in the yellow corn.
The day after tomorrow in the yellow corn
There will be high, majestic fooling.

Always—I never knew it any other way—
The wind and corn talk things over together.
*And the rain and the corn and the sun and the corn talk things over together.**

* From the poem, *Laughing Corn,* in the collection entitled "Cornhuskers." Copyright, 1918, by Carl Sandburg, pub. by Henry Holt and Company.

They came from Europe, searching for the Gold of the Indies, and they found Indian corn. Corn kept them alive those first hard winters in Virginia and Massachusetts. The Pilgrims survived a winter on a daily ration of five kernels of corn per man. The Indians, who called corn "mother and father," taught them how to plant and cultivate and cook it. The dishes of the American folk are still made in the old Indian way and their names are still the Indian names: hominy, pone, succotash, tortillas, tacos, suppawn, samp, Indian pudding.

The Nebraska Farmer of 1862, after asserting that a dollar's worth of corn is more nourishing than two dollars' worth of wheat or four dollars' worth of potatoes, points out that there are thirty-three different ways of serving corn, mentioning: spoon bread, apple corn bread, corn bread, corn muffins, corn cake, hoe cake, corn on the cob, pumpkin, loaf, Indian dumplings, and corn whiskey. In the South, where whole generations were raised on a steady diet of corn bread, fat-back and bull-dog gravy, a controversy raged for a year over whether you dunked or crumbled your corn-pone in your pot-licker. Families were split between the dunkers and the crumblers.

America was a land that could really raise a crop of corn. There was enough land: the farms were so wide that about the time a man could pay his mortgage on the east side of his land it would come due on the west side. The land was rich and fertile: the earth groaned and shook because the crops were so heavy; the young potatoes fussed and the old ones grumbled because they were crowding each other; and the corn shot up so fast it drew its roots right out of the ground. One of Zora Hurston's Florida tale-tellers tops all tall corn tales thus:

> . . . I was droppin' and my brother was hillin' up behind me. We had done planted 'bout a dozen rows when I looked back and seen de corn comin' up. I didn't want it to grow too fast 'cause it would make all fodder and no roastin' ears, so I hollered to my brother to sit down on some of it to stunt de growth. So he did, and de next day he dropped me back a note—says: "Passed thru Heben yesterday at twelve o'clock sellin' roastin' ears to de angels."

A man that wouldn't hoe the weeds and crab grass out of his corn patch wasn't worth marrying, wasn't worth killing, wasn't worth burying, "wasn't worth nothin'." There is a lazy man of frontier folklore who lay around drunk all the time, did nothing to provide for his family, didn't even feed his hound dogs. So the neighbors got together and decided to bury him. The lazy man was agreeable. On the way to the graveyard in the wagon, a leading citizen stopped the procession and, when he heard the story, offered to give the lazy man a new start in life with the gift of a bushel of corn. The loafer raised up in his coffin when he heard that:

"Is it shelled?" he says.

"No, it ain't shelled," they told him.

The old rascal lay back in his coffin and waved his hand right lazy to the driver. "Drive on," he says, "drive on to the graveyard."

A man who wouldn't work at his corn crop that provided food for the family and fodder for the stock was just "plain no account," as much to be scorned as the lazy man of the foregoing pioneer lie. Frontier Americans, therefore, wagged their heads with pleasure over the moral of our present ballad and carried it westward with them from New England and the Southeastern states out into the corn belt of the Middle West.

67. *WHOA, BUCK!*

All along our song-hunting trail, from Texas east to Virginia, we have found so many versions of this ditty among rural Negroes that we have come to believe it is the best-liked of all Negro field songs. Every singer adds his own turns to the melody, letting the song come easy with his breathing; and one can always feel in these performances the uneven rhythm of the ploughman's steps, as he slogs along the furrow after his mule. It has a lively tune similar to "Old Joe Clark," and it is a ditty to make the long hot summer days of cultivating cotton go quicker. A comical little catch, warmed with gentle rural irony, it is spiced with many rib-ticklers which are a little too ribald to print.

This version of "Whoa, Buck!" is our own, a condensation of all the best stanzas and tunes we have heard. We dedicate it to that hardy American invention, the Missouri mule, famed for his great strength and his dynamite-loaded kicks, a central character in many a rural comedy and celebrated in this Florida Negro tale, "The Talking Mule."

Ole feller one time had uh mule. His name wuz Bill. Every mornin' de man go tuh ketch him, he say, "Come 'round, Bill!"

So one mornin' he slept late, so he decided while he wuz drinkin' some coffee he'd send his son tuh ketch Ole Bill. Told 'im say, "Go down dere, boy, and bring me dat mule up here."

Boy, he sich a fast Aleck, he grabbed de bridle and went on down tuh de lot tuh ketch Ole Bill.

He say, "Come 'round, Bill."

De mule looked 'round at 'im. He told de mule, " 'Taint no use you rollin' yo' eyes at me. Pa wants yuh dis mawnin'. Come on 'round and stick yo' head in dis bridle."

Mule kept on lookin' at 'im and said, "Every mornin' it's 'Come 'round, Bill! Come 'round, Bill!' Don't hardly git no rest befo' it's 'Come 'round, Bill!' "

De boy throwed down dat bridle and flew back to de house and told his Pa, "Dat mule is talkin'."

"Ah, g'wan, boy, tellin' yo' lies! G'wan ketch dat mule."

"Naw suh, Pa, dat mule's done gone tuh talkin'. You hatta ketch dat mule yo' ownself. Ah ain't gwine."

Ole man looked at ole lady and see, "See whut a lie dat boy is tellin'?"

So he gits out an' goes on down after de mule hisself. When he got down dere, he hollered, "Come 'round, Bill!"

Ole mule looked 'round and says, "Every mornin' it's 'Come 'round, Bill!"

De old man had uh little fice [feist] dog useter foller 'im everywhere he go, so he lit out wid de lil fice right behind 'im. So he told de ole lady, "De boy ain't told much of uh lie. Dat mule *is* talkin'. Ah never heard uh mule talk befo'."

Lil fice say, "Me neither."

De ole man got skeered agin. Right through de woods he went wid de fice right behind 'im. He nearly run hisself tuh death. He stopped an' commenced blowin' and says, "Ah'm so tired Ah don't know what tuh do." Lil dog run and set down in front of 'im and went to hasslin' [panting] and says, "Me, too."

Dat man is runnin' yet.

68. *PICK A BALE OF COTTON*

As a companion piece for "Whoa, Buck!," the Southern plowing song, try out this work song of the cotton pickers. Although Lead Belly claims that such a task is possible for some "double-jointed" men, we dare swear that no man or woman ever picked a whole bale of cotton in a day. If a man can bend over the cotton all day, shooting his fingers in among the thorny bolls and dragging his heavy cotton sack behind him, and then weigh up three hundred pounds at the end of a day's work, he's a cotton-picking fool. A bale of cotton weighs five hundred pounds and no man of record has picked so much in a day. The singers are just "carrying on" to give the folks a laugh, to help them forget the kinks in their backs, to encourage them to "snatch that cotton" as fast as they can.

We found this song only in Texas on the state prison farms. Lead Belly sung it with his big twelve-string guitar. Iron Head sung it in his sweet, nasal voice, the corners of his eyes and mouth creased with silent laughter. Quartets of black prisoners harmonized it, the "basers" taking their breaks and the "tribles" weaving in the top harmony with sweet, jazzy chords. Like other songs from the Brazos bottoms, we feel sure that this one has survived from "slav'y times" and is a genuine example of a slave work song.

In "de time befo' de war," all the work on the plantation was enlivened by such songs. The Negro slaves, fresh from their background of African work-singing, made special songs for corn-husking, cotton-picking, hoeing, plowing, pea-picking, rice-thrashing, raising and carrying, rowing, churning—for all their tasks. Their white masters knew that their chattels would work faster, more skilfully and more contentedly if they were encouraged to sing, just as the slave traders had discovered during the dreadful ocean voyages from the Ivory Coast that singing kept the death rate a little lower. Every day, when the weather was fine, they brought their human cargo up on deck out of the stinking holds, and drove them to sing and dance, drove them to it with whips if necessary. These New England captains, who sometimes lost half their cargo during the passage, recorded in their diaries the wonder that these black people could sometimes forget their miserable fate and dance with abandon and enjoyment when the music began.

So, in field gangs under slavery and in construction camps later, Negro song leaders have been privileged characters, paid more than the rest, given easier tasks, because their mother wit and their sense of rhythm led the men to sing together. The singing together made the work go easier; the singing together eased the aching backs and the aching hearts. In this ironic sense Negro work songs have served as a sort of spiritual speedup for the Negro workers.

Massa gimme one dram
To pick a bale of cotton,
Massa gimme one dram
To pick a bale a day.

On holidays, too, "Pick a Bale o' Cotton" served as a dance tune (see note on "Raise a Rukus"), the group shouting out the chorus and clapping a syncopated rhythm, while the young bucks danced the double-shuffle or cut the pigeon wing.

Just as this great cotton-picking song comes from Texas, so, too, did the best of the cotton-farmer's ballads—

69. *THE BOLL WEEVIL*

Sometime in the year of 1900 or thereabouts Texas suffered its second invasion from Mexico, not Santa Anna and his soldiers this time, but an innumerable army of tiny black bugs crossed the Rio Grande River. They were looking for a home. The boll weevil didn't stop in Texas. Marching forty miles a year, he moved steadily across the entire South, fording the Mississippi River in spite of state quarantine laws. Only the Atlantic Ocean stopped him.

My friend, Richard Amerson, a Negro well-digger in Alabama, sang a four-line stanza which sums up with amazing scientific accuracy the life history of Mr. Boll Weevil:

The cottonbush his shade,
Its root his cook-kitchen;
The boll his dining room
Where he do all his eatin'.

He doesn't like the hot sun. He is happiest in the river bottom where the cotton-stalk grows rank and the broad leaves shade the ground completely. The green cotton boll is his dining room where his grub feeds on the sweet liquid from which the cotton fiber is formed. But first his adult parent has punched a hole in the tender cotton square, from which the cotton boll grows, and deposited an egg. Again when winter comes, the boll weevil retreats to the roots of the cotton plant to hibernate. Further details of the history of the boll weevil are set out in the long "ballit" which we believe to be pure Negro creation.

More than a million boll weevils come from a single pair in one season. Sang the Negro, "I fus' saw a boll weevil settin' on the square" (the embryonic boll), "the next mornin' he had all his family there." To spur on the entomologists in their efforts to find a way to destroy the pest the Texas Legislature offered a reward of fifty thousand dollars. The Negro's song laughs hilariously: they put him in the ice; "it's mighty cool an' nice, it's jes' my home," counters the boll weevil. They fed him on Paris Green; "it's the best I ever seen," chortles the defiant insect. They put him in the fire; the valiant warrior wiggles his proboscis and chants, "Here I are, here I are." Indeed, the story goes that on one occasion red-hot weevils flew from the fire, landed on a farmer's wheat-stacks and burned up his entire crop.

Wherever the boll weevil traveled the cotton fields were left bare of fruit, the Southern farmers' one money crop was utterly destroyed. Government agriculture experts figure that in forty years the South has been damaged far in excess of a billion dollars. The Negro was the chief sufferer. He went to the groceryman for credit for meat and meal. "Nothin' doin'," says the merchant, "you got boll weevils in your field." Utter poverty followed in the wake of the little black bug, whose snout is as long as his body: "He got it in Texas, he got it in the Western hills," sang a blind guitar picker in Atlanta, Georgia. So out of his sufferings the Negro made a rare song, in which he sympathizes humorously with the boll weevil rather than with the white man's efforts to destroy him, just as in the Uncle Remus stories the Negro sympathizes with poor old Brer Rabbit against his natural enemies, Brer Wolf and Brer Bear. We found new stanzas in every state where cotton is grown.

In 1907 the senior editor first heard a blind Negro sing the boll-weevil song as he sat on a curbstone in Hearne, Texas, and thrummed his guitar. The records that I made then crumbled, but the song lived on in the singing of the Lomax family. The earliest printed story about the song, written by Mrs. Bess B. Lomax, was published in a Sunday *New York World*, probably in 1910.

Twenty years afterward, Carl Sandburg gave the song to the world along with its music. He writes in his *Songbag:* "John Lomax first sang this song for the present writer. . . . it never loses its strange overtones, with its smiling commentary on the bug that baffles the wit of man, with its whimsical point that while the boll weevil can make its home anywhere, the Negro, son of man, hath not where to lay his head, and with its intimation, perhaps, that in our mortal life neither the individual human creature nor the big human family shall ever find a lasting home on earth. It is a paradoxical blend of moods: quickstep and dirge, hilarious defiance and bowed resignation."

Still the farmer kept singing about his heavy load of troubles—in the South about the pests and the woes of a sharecropper's life and in the West about—

70. *STARVING TO DEATH ON A GOVERNMENT CLAIM*

In the 1860's there was a popular song which hopefully asserted:

Uncle Sam is rich enough
To give us all a farm . . .

Under the Homestead Act of 1862 great stretches of land in Kansas and Iowa and Nebraska became available for settlement. Any citizen, twenty-one years of age, who had not borne arms against the government, had a right to 160 acres of this land for a fee of eighteen dollars, provided he would make it his home for five years. The restless young veterans of the Civil War, the homeless immigrant from Europe, the kind of American who was forever looking for "God's country," and the kind who wanted elbow room poured into the Great Plains states. It was said to be the land of milk and honey, where the sky was the limit on the crops and the air was so pure "it would revive corpses." In 1871 an old settler of Adams County, Nebraska wrote: "One year ago this was a vast, homeless, uninhabited prairie, with no trace of approaching civilization to frighten the timid antelope or turn the buffalo from his course. Today I can see more than thirty dwellings from my door yard, aside from those in the village. . . ." In 1885 fifty thousand acres a day were being taken up in the Garden City, Kansas, land office.

Shelter was cheap. You could "dig yourself a hole in the side of a hill like a prairie dog" and make a dugout house for two dollars and eighty-seven and one half cents, which was the cost of the one window and one door required under the Homestead Act. Or, setting your plow into a half acre of tough prairie soil, you build a sod shanty in a half a day's work; your sod house would be cool in the summer and warm in the winter and next season your roof would blossom into a garden of huge prairie sunflowers. However, it took more "grit, grace and gumption" than some folks had to tough it out in a sod shanty on a government claim. In dry weather the sod roofs leaked straw and dirt; in wet, they leaked mud. One pioneer woman wrote: "The dugout was so full of centipeads that we had to sleep with a butcher knife under our pillows . . . we would whack them to pieces. Some nights we would kill as many as twenty."

Some years were blizzard years, when the storms that blew "right off the North Pole" killed the stock and snowed families in their shanties for days. Then it was dangerous to venture out of doors, because the dust ice penetrated your clothing, covered your face with a mask of ice and sealed your eyelids together with ice. Men froze to death in these blizzards, while they were trying to get to the barn to feed their stock.

Some years were drouth years. From June, 1859, to November, 1860, not a drop of rain fell in Nebraska. Even the prairie grass withered. The people ate acorns and the women dressed their families in gunnysacks and buffalo hide. Then, roaring down on the hot wind, came prairie fires, scorching the whole country black.

1874 was a grasshopper year. In Nebraska they remember a cloud of army hoppers 150 miles wide and one hundred miles long that swept the fields clean, chewed the bark off the trees and "the sound of their feeding was like a herd of cattle eating in a cornfield." They stopped trains, as they piled up on the tracks; they drowned by the millions in the creeks and turned the water brown and sour. They ate everything. They say the grasshoppers even stopped the children on their way to school and took their lunch boxes away.

Always the wind blew, "blew by ear and by note." Always the treeless plain stared back at you and the children asked, "Mama, do we always have to live here?" Some folks went broke and turned back East. Those who stayed and made the Western prairies into the bread basket of the world, cracked their brags in songs like "Starving to Death on a Government Claim." John A. Lomax first recorded this sod-shanty complaint in 1908 from that hardy old Western cowboy and homesteader, Tom Hight, who could sing ballads all night and never repeat.

71. *THE STATE OF ARKANSAS*

The people kept looking for "God's country." Some had the good fortune to try to "tough it out" on a farm of their own. Some worked on the land on shares. Others were hired hands, selling their strength and their knowledge of farm skills by the month or the year. One of these migratory farm workers left behind him the story of his trip to Arkansas. Today you can find it among folk-singers all over the South and the West. It fits in with the American taste for the comic, as Josh Billings has defined it:

> Americans luv caustic things; they would prefer turpentine to colone water, if they had to drink

either. So with the relish of humour; they must have it on the half-shell with cayenne.

It is in this sense that Americans have loved Arkansas. She has always been the target for their most cutting sarcasm. All of us have taken sides; either we boost her to the skies, or we throw slurs and slams at the state. Our laughter left the native Arkansawyer a mite sensitive, but it has piled up a whole mountain range of backwoods humor, from the famous frontier comedy, "The Arkansas Traveler," to Thomas W. Jackson's "On a Slow Train Through Arkansas."

It takes two to plant corn in Arkansas, one pries the rocks apart with a crowbar, the other fires the seed down the crack with a syringe. . . . The reason why ostrich raising is such a grand success in the state is because they can live on stones. The land is so poor, they have to put fertilizer around the telegraph poles to get the messages through. . . .

They raise thin hogs there, call 'em razorbacks. You have to shoot a razorback side ways on; because if you shot endways, it would be like aiming at the end of a splinter. They'll take an old sow and turn her over with her back to a sawlog and use her for a saw. When they get started you can hear the bark and splinters flying and the old hog squealing for three miles. . . .

And you talk about slow trains, they have them in Arkansas. I rode on one and it stopped at every house. When it came to a double house, it stopped twice. They made so many stops, I asked the conductor why and he said, "There are some cattle on the track." We ran a little ways further and stopped again. I said, "What's the matter now?" He said, "We have caught up with those cows again!"

Perhaps the best of all Arkansas booster stories is the famous comic speech which appeared during a now legendary debate in the Arkansas state legislature when it was proposed that "Arkansas" be spelled as it is pronounced —Arkansaw." A patriotic legislator, helping himself liberally to Mark Twain's "Life on the Mississippi," is purported to have bellowed:

Mr. Speaker: The man who would change the name of Arkansas is the original iron-jawed, brass-mounted, copper-bellied corpse-maker from the wilds of the Ozarks. Sired by a hurricane, dammed by an earthquake, half-brother to the cholera, nearly related to the small-pox on his mother's side, he is the man they call Sudden Death and General Desolation. Look at him! The man who would change the name of Arkansas would use the meridians of longitude and the parallels of latitude for a seine and drag the Atlantic Ocean for whales. He would scratch himself with lightning and purr himself to sleep with thunder. When he's cold he'd bile the Gulf of Mexico and bathe therein. He would massacre isolated communities as a pastime. He would destroy nationalities as a serious business. He would use the boundless vastness of the American desert for his private graveyard.

Hide the stars in a nail-keg, put the key to soak in a gourd, hang the Arkansas River on a clothesline, unbuckle the belly-band of time and turn the sun and moon out to pasture, but you will never change the name of Arkansas.

Gentlemen, you may tear down the honored pictures from the halls of the Senate, haul down the stars and stripes, desecrate the tomb of George Washington and rape the Statue of Liberty, but CHANGE THE NAME OF ARKANSAS, hell NO!"

The composer of the song falls into the category of an Arkansas slammer. It seems likely that he was an Irish migratory worker and that he came to Arkansas in the early days of its statehood, looking for a job. Having endured "swamp angels, canebrakes, chills and corn-dodgers as hard as any rock" for a month, he escaped back into America and went on his way spreading his "anti-Arkansas" propaganda. He must have traveled far and wide, because the song is known up and down the land and its variations are many. On one occasion, when a Texan cowboy sung it for the amusement of the boys at the chuck-wagon, a lanky Arkansawyer arose, unlimbered his six-foot-seven frame and beat upon the Texan until he admitted that the ballad was a "dadblamed lie."

72. *GOIN' DOWN THE ROAD FEELIN' BAD*

The people moved again. On one side of their covered wagons they wrote, "Oklahoma or bust." On the other side, "In God we trust." They one-cropped the land until. . . .

it got so poor it took nine partridges to holler "Bob White." The dogs had to lean against the fence to bark. It made the tears come into the kildee's eyes when he flew over the field.

Besides, it turned out that some of the country was just too dry for farming:

The cattle starved down and climbed through holes in the chicken wire and hid in among the chickens. . . . A drop of water hit a man, and they had to throw two buckets of dirt in his face to bring him to.

Out on the high plains in the Panhandle country of Texas, there was nothing to stop the wind but a barbed-wire fence. This barbed-wire fence had one barb on it and that barb was pointed North.

We kept track of the wind by hanging a log-chain to a post. If it stood out straight, that was a breeze; but when it got to whipping around and links snapped off, look out! It was likely to be windy by sundown.

When they plowed the grass off the plains, the winds picked up the soil and the big black dust-storms began to blow in from the North. The people were pinned down in their tiny houses, but they rubbed the dust out of their eyes and grinned: "Well, the wind blew the dirt away but we haven't lost everything. We still got the mortgage. . . ."

The banks moved in and took what was left of the farms. The tractors rolled in and tractored down their houses to make the little farms into bigger ones. The people loaded their stuff on their broken-down jalopies and trucks and headed down the road to nowhere—"busted, dusted, disgusted, and can't be trusted." They sang:

So long, it's been good to know you,
So long, it's been good to know you,
So long, it's been good to know you,
This dusty old dust is gittin' my home,
And I got to be driftin' along.

By the thousands they swarmed into the cotton fields and the fruit orchards of California, the beet fields of Michigan, the cherry orchards of Oregon, following the seasons and the crops, families learning to live in ditches by the side of the road—American gypsies, Okies, feeling themselves to be outsiders in American society. "Yeah, I'm from California. I've got relatives living under every railroad bridge in the state. . . .

I've picked in your orchards of peaches and prunes.
I've slept on your ground by the light of your moon,
At the edge of your cities you'll see me and then,
I come with the dust and I'm gone with the Wind."

The war and the shipyards provided a respite for these travelweary marginal Americans from marginal land. But now they are back with us again. Their guitar-picking poets follow them, rhyming up new songs as their problems worsen, but the old song, the song handed down from Negro singers, is still their best, their favorite, their most typical sentiment—

I'm blowing down this road, feelin' bad, Lord, Lord,
An' I ain't gonna be treated thisaway. . . .

66.

The Young Man Who Wouldn't Hoe Corn

Words and melody adapted and arranged by
John A. and Alan Lomax

Piano arrangement by
Charles and Ruth Seeger

1. I'll sing you a song and it's not very long,
It's about a young man who wouldn't hoe corn,
The reason why, I can't tell,—
This young man was always well.

2. In September his corn was knee high,
In October he laid it by,
In November there came a great frost
And all this young man's corn was lost.

3. He went to the field and there peeped in,
The jimpson weeds were up to his chin,
The careless weeds they grew so high,
Enough for to make this young man cry.

4. In the winter I was told
He went courting very bold,
When his courtship first begun—
"My kind sir, did you make any corn?"

5. "No, kind miss," was his reply,
"Long ago I've laid it by,
It wasn't worth while to strive in vain,
For I didn't expect to make one grain."

6. "Here you are, a-*want*in' me to wed,
And cannot make your own cornbread!
Single I am and single I'll remain
For a lazy man I won't maintain."

7. "Go down yonder to the pretty little widder,
And I hope, by heck, that you don't git her!"—
She gave him the mitten, shore as you're born,
All because he wouldn't hoe corn.

67.

Whoa Buck

Words and melody adapted and arranged by
John A. and Alan Lomax

Piano arrangement by
Charles and Ruth Seeger

1. Sometimes I plow my old grey horse,
   Other times I plow old muley,
   Soon's I get this cotton crop by,
   I'm gwine home to Juley.

REFRAIN: Tighten on the back-band, loosen on the bow,
An - a, whoa! quit pickin' that banjo so.

2. Last year was a very fine year
   For cotton, corn and tomatoes,
   Papa didn't raise no beans and greens
   But, Lawd Gawd, 'tatoes.

REFRAIN: 'Tatoes, 'tatoes,
But, Lawd Gawd, de 'tatoes.

3. My gal won't wear no button-up shoes,
   Her feet too big for gaiters.
   All she fit for—a dip of snuff
   And a yeller yam pertater.

REFRAIN: Jint ahead, center back,
Did you ever work on that railroad track?

4. Eighteen, nineteen, twenty years ago
   Taken my gal to de party-o,
   All dressed up in her calico,
   And I wouldn't let her dance but a set or so.

REFRAIN: Set or so, set or so,
Wouldn't let her dance but a set or so.

5. Takes four wheels to hold a load,
   Takes two mules to pull double,
   Take me back to Georgia land
   And I won't be no trouble.

REFRAIN: Rowdy-o! rowdy-o!
If you got the wagon loaded, lemme see you go.

68.

Pick a Bale of Cotton

Words and melody adapted and arranged by
John A. and Alan Lomax

Piano arrangement by
Charles and Ruth Seeger

1. You got to jump down, turn around,
Pick uh bale uh cotton,
Got to jump down, turn around
To pick uh bale uh day.

CHORUS: O—lawdy,
Pick uh bale uh cotton,
O—lawdy,
Pick uh bale uh day.

2. Me an' my pardner can
Pick uh bale uh cotton,
Me an' my pardner can
Pick uh bale uh day.

3. Me an' my wife can
Pick uh bale uh cotton,
Me an' my wife can
Pick uh bale uh day.

CHORUS: O— lawdy,
Pick uh bale uh cotton,
O— lawdy,
Pick uh bale uh day.

4. Had uh little woman could
Pick uh bale uh cotton,
Had uh little woman could
Pick uh bale uh day.

5. I b'lieve to my soul I can
Pick uh bale uh cotton,
I b'lieve to my soul I can
Pick uh bale uh day.

6. Went to Corsicana to
Pick uh bale uh cotton,
Went to Corsicana to
Pick uh bale uh day.

CHORUS: O— lawdy,
Pick uh bale uh cotton,
O— lawdy,
Pick uh bale uh day.

69.

The Boll Weevil

2. De boll weevil is a little black bug
F'um Mexico, dey say,
He come to try dis Texas soil
An' thought he'd better stay,
CHORUS: A-lookin' for a home,
Jes' a-lookin' for a home,
A-lookin' for a home,
Jes' a-lookin' for a home.

3. De fus' time I seen de boll weevil
He was settin' on de square,
De nex' time I saw de boll weevil
He had all his family dere—
CHORUS: Dey's lookin' for a home,
Jes' a-lookin' for a home,
Dey's lookin' for a home,
Jes' a-lookin' for a home.

4. De fus' time I seen de boll weevil
He was on the western plain,
Nex' time I seen de boll weevil,
He had hopped dat Memphis train,
CHORUS: Lookin' for a home,
Jes' a-lookin' for a home,
Lookin' for a home,
Jes' a-lookin' for a home.

5. De farmer took de boll weevil
An' buried him in hot sand;
De boll weevil say to de farmer,
"I'll stand it like a man,
CHORUS: For it is my home,
It is my home,
For it is my home,
It is my home."

6. Den de farmer took de boll weevil
An' lef' him on de ice;
De boll weevil say to de farmer,
"Dis is mighty cool an' nice.
CHORUS: O it is-a my home,
It is my home,
O it is-a my home,
It is my home."

7. Mr. Farmer took little weevil
An' fed him on paris green;
"Thank you, Mr. Farmer,
It's the best I ever seen.
CHORUS: It is my home,
It's jes' my home,
It is my home,
It's jes' my home."

8. De boll weevil say to de farmer,
"You better lemme 'lone,
I et up all yo' cotton,
An' now I'll begin on de co'n,
CHORUS: I'll have a home,
I'll have a home,
I'll have a home,
I'll have a home."

9. De Merchant got half de cotton,
De boll weevil got de rest;
Didn't leave de po' ol' farmer
But one old cotton dress;
CHORUS: An' it's full o' holes,
Oh, it's full o' holes,
An' it's full o' holes,
Oh, it's full o' holes.

10. De farmer say to de merchant,
"I ain't made but one bale,
But befo' I'll give you dat one
I'll fight an' go to jail,
CHORUS: I'll have a home,
I'll have a home,
I'll have a home,
I'll have a home."

11. Ef anybody axes you
Who wuz it writ dis song,
Tell 'em 'twas a dark-skinned farmer
Wid a pair o' blue duckin's on,
CHORUS: A-lookin' for a home,
Jes' a-lookin' for a home,
A-lookin' for a home,
Jes' a-lookin' for a home.

70.

Starving to Death on a Government Claim

Words and melody adapted and arranged by
John A. and Alan Lomax

Piano arrangement by
Charles and Ruth Seeger

1. My name is Tom Hight, an old bach'lor I am,
You'll find me out west in the country of fame,
You'll find me out west on an elegant plan,
A-starving to death on my government claim.

CHORUS: Hurrah for Greer County! the land of the free,
The land of the bedbug, grasshopper and flea;
I'll sing of its praises, I'll tell of its fame,
While starving to death on my government claim.*

2. My house, it is built out of national soil,
Its walls are erected according to Hoyle, (Edmond 1672-1769 Engl. authority - Whist
Its roof has no pitch, but is level and plain,
I always get wet if it happens to rain.

3. My clothes are all ragged, as my language is rough,
My bread is corndodgers, both solid and tough;
But yet I am happy and live at my ease
On sorghum molasses, bacon and cheese.

4. How happy am I when I crawl into bed,
A rattlesnake hisses a tune at my head,
A gay little centipede, all without fear,
Crawls over my pillow and into my ear.

5. Now all you claim holders, I hope you will stay
And chew your hardtack till you're toothless and grey,
But for myself I'll no longer remain
To starve like a dog on my government claim.

CHORUS: Goodbye to Greer County where blizzards arise,
Where the sun never sinks and the flea never dies,
And the wind never ceases but always remains
Till it starves us all out on our government claims.

6. Farewell to Greer County, farewell to the west,
I'll travel back east to the girl I love best,
I'll travel to Texas and marry me a wife
And quit corn dodgers the rest of my life.

71.

The State of Arkansas

Words and melody adapted and arranged by
John A. and Alan Lomax

Piano arrangement by
Charles and Ruth Seeger

1. My name is Stamford Barnes, I come from Nobleville town,
I've travelled this wide world over, I've travelled this wide world round;
I've met with ups and downs in life, and better days I've saw;
But I never knew what mis'ry were, till I came to Arkansas.

2. I landed in St. Louis with ten dollars and no more,
I read the daily papers until both my eyes were sore,
I read them evening papers until at last I saw,—
Ten thousand men were wanted in the state of Arkansas.

3. I wiped my eyes with great surprise when I read this grateful news,
And straightway off I started to see the agent, Billy Hughes;
He said, "Pitch me down five dollars and ticket you shall draw
To ride upon the railroad to the state of Arkansas.

4. I started off one morning at a quarter after five,
I started from St. Louis, half dead and half alive,
I bought me a quart of whiskey, my misery to thaw,
I got drunk as a biled owl when I left for old Arkansas.

5. 'Twas in the year of '82 in the merry month of June,
I landed in Ft. Smith one sultry afternoon;
Up stepped a walking skeleton and gave to me his paw
Invited me to his hotel, "The best in Arkansas."

6. I followed my conductor into his dwelling place,
Poverty were depictured in his melancholy face;
His bread it was corn dodger, his beef I could not chaw;
He charged me fifty cents for this in the state of Arkansas.

7. I started off next morning to catch the morning train,
He says to me, "You'd better work, I have some land to drain.
I'll pay you fifty cents a day, your board and wash and all,
You'll find yourself a different man when you leave old Arkansas."

8. I worked six weeks for this son-of-a-gun, Jesse Herring was his name,
He was six foot seven in his stocking feet and taller than any crane,
His hair hung down like rat tails on his long and lantern jaw,
He was the photygraph of all the gents who lived in Arkansas.

9. He fed me on corn dodgers, as hard as any rock,
Till my teeth began to loosen and my knees began to knock,
I got so thin on sassafras tea, I could hide behind a straw
And, indeed I was a different man, when I left old Arkansas.

10. Farewell to swamp-angels, canebrakes and chills,
Farewell to sage and sassafras and corn dodger pills,
If I ever see this land again, I'll give to you my paw,
It will be through a telescope—FROM HERE TO ARKANSAS.

72.

Goin' Down the Road Feelin' Bad

(4)

1. I'm goin' down this road feelin' bad,
Lord, I'm goin' down this road feelin' bad,
Well, I'm goin' down this road feelin' bad, Lord, Lord,
An' I ain't gonna be treated thisaway.

2. I ain't got but one old lousy dime,
Lord, I ain't got but one old lousy dime,
Well, I ain't got but one old lousy dime, Lord, Lord,
But I'll find me a new dollar some old day.

3. A two dollar shoe won't fit my feet,
Lord, a two dollar shoe won't fit my feet,
Well, a two dollar shoe won't fit my feet, Lord, Lord,
'Cause I ain't gonna be treated thisaway.

4. Takes a ten dollar shoe to fit my feet,
Lord, takes a ten dollar shoe to fit my feet,
Well, takes a ten dollar shoe to fit my feet, Lord, Lord,
'Cause I ain't gonna be treated thisaway.

5. I'm goin' where the climate suits my clothes,
Lord, I'm goin' where the climate suits my clothes,
Well, I'm goin' where the climate suits my clothes, Lord, Lord,
'Cause I ain't gonna be treated thisaway.

6. I'm goin' where the water tastes like wine,
Lord, I'm goin' where the water tastes like wine,
Well, I'm goin' where the water tastes like wine, Lord, Lord,
'Cause this water round here tastes like turpentine.

7. I'm tired of lyin' in this jail,
Lord, I'm tired of lyin' in this jail,
Well, I'm tired of lyin' in this jail, Lord, Lord,
An' I ain't gonna be treated thisaway.

8. Yes, they feed me on cornbread and beans,
Lord, they feed me on cornbread and beans,
Well, they feed me on cornbread and beans, Lord, Lord,
And I ain't gonna be treated thisaway.

9. Who'll stir your gravy when I'm gone?
Lord, who'll stir your gravy when I'm gone?
Well, who'll stir your gravy when I'm gone? Lord, Lord,
When I'm gone to my long, lonesome home—

CHAPTER IX

Lonesome Whistles

Lord, I hate to hear that lonesome whistle blow,
Lord, I hate to hear that lonesome whistle blow,
It blows so lonesome and it blows so low,
It blows like it never blowed before.

All through the strip of country that runs from Maryland, south and west to Oklahoma, which is the land of fiddlers, guitar players, banjo pickers and harp blowers, you can hear them making lonesome whistle tunes on their instruments. A fiddler will pull his bow in a long, minor moan across his top string and then start jerking it in quick, raspy strokes until you can close your eyes and hear a heavy freight train running down a steep grade. A harmonica player will blow out the high, hollering notes of a fast passenger engine, while the guitar player will make a rhythm on his bass strings like a train crossing a trestle. Together they'll play in the rhythm of car wheels clicking over sleepers; as counter-rhythm, they'll whip out the rattling bounce of a caboose as it shakes and jounces along a rough roadbed. Then they'll throw back their heads and holler—

Lord, Lord, I hate to hear that lonesome whistle blow.

These folk musicians and the people they're playing for listen to railroad whistles the way fisherfolk listen to bell-buoys and foghorns. Out in the country they tell time by the whistles of the trains that fly past their fields. The railroad whistles bring them good news and bad news. The whistles talk to them about the places they have never been, the women they've never seen, the fine clothes they have never worn.

Lord, I'm goin' where the water tastes like wine,
'Cause the water round here tastes like turpentine.

The whistles talk to them about the folks who have gone down that long, lonesome road and won't be back again.

Every time a freight train makes up in the yard,
Some po' woman got an achin' heart.

The whistles talk to them about the great big raw country they live in. The whistles remind them that every man is a traveler on a lonesome road.

I'm goin' lay my head on that lonesome railroad line,
Let the 219 ease my troubled mind.

Mostly the whistles talk to them about freedom. Before the railroads knit the whole country together in their shining web of steel, these folks were pinned down and forced to inch along across the big sea of the land in wagons. When the railroad whistles began to blow, these people found they could almost fly across their country anytime they paid their fare or caught a free ride on a freight.

Listen to the jingle, the jumble and the roar,
As she glides along the woodland, through the hills, and by the shore,
Hear the mighty rush of the engine and the merry hobo's squawl,
As he rides the rods and brake-beams of the Wabash Cannonball.

Restless by instinct, travelers by tradition, they began to move around more and more, taking in new towns, new jobs, and new sweethearts. Then, sometimes, when they were off somewhere in a new town, broke and hungry and out of a job, they'd hear that railroad whistle blow and then it meant "home" and all they'd left behind.

If that wheeler runs me right,
I'll be home tomorrow night,
'Cause I'm nine hundred miles from my home . . .
And I hate to hear that lonesome whistle blow.

The railroad has been for these people both villain and hero. Sometimes it was—

There's many a man been murdered by the railroad, railroad, railroad,
There's many a man been murdered by the railroad
And laid in his lonesome grave.

And sometimes it was—

Here she comes, look at her roll,
Ridin' those rails, eatin' that coal,
Like a hound waggin' its tail,
Dallas bound, bound, bound,
It's the fireball mail.

They made scores of ballads about wrecks and heroic engineers who stuck to their throttles till the end, just as their ancestors had heroized the gallant captains who stayed with their ships until they went down. The hoboes who rode the rods beneath the cars and the blinds between the cars made a whole literature of ballads and poems about their wandering lives. The blues blowers and the hillbilly yodelers have laid down a line of railroad ballads, which, strung together, would cover as much territory as the Santa Fe.

It is in the texture of our popular music, however, that the railroads have left their deepest impression. Listen to the blues, the stomps, the hot music of the last fifty years, since most Americans have come to live within the sound of the railroad. Listen to this music and you'll hear all the smashing, rattling, syncopated rhythms and counter-rhythms of trains of every size and speed. Listen to boogie-woogie with its various kinds of rolling basses. Listen to hot jazz with its steady beat. Listen to the blues with those hundreds of silvery breaks in the treble clef. What you hear back of the notes is the drive and thrust and moan of a locomotive. Of course, there's the African influence, the French influence in New Orleans, the Spanish influence from Cuba to account for the character of our hot music. These cultural elements have left their mark in our music, as they have elsewhere in this hemisphere, but, in our estimation, the distinctive feeling of American hot music comes from the railroad. In the minds and hearts of the people it is the surge and thunder of the steam engine, the ripple of the wheels along the tracks, and the shrill minor-keyed whistles that have colored this new American folk music.

73. *NINE HUNDRED MILES*

In its present form, this is a hillbilly blues. However, Woody Guthrie, the Okie balladeer and guitar-picker, learned it from a Negro shoeshine boy in his home town of Okemah, Oklahoma. The tune has appeared in many disguises and has relations all over the South. In the tidewater country of Virginia they call it the "Reuben Blues" and they sing:

When old Reuben left home, he wasn't but nine days old,
When he come back he was a full grown man,
When he come back he was a full grown man.

They got old Reuben down and they took his watch and charm,
It was everything that poor boy had,
It was everything that poor boy had.

In the backwoods, further west, the sharecroppers, white and black, dedicate the tune to a full belly, and sing:

I got the chickens in my sack and the hounds are on my track,
But I'll make it to my shanty 'fore day,
And I'll keep my skillet good and greasy all the time.

Up in Kentucky and Tennessee, they tell the story about a train that ran around a notorious coal mine, where convict labor was used in the old days:

The longest train that I ever seen,
Run around Joe Brown's coal mine,
The engine past at six o'clock,
And the last car passed by at nine.

Perhaps the oldest of all the versions is the Southern mountain song of the dark girl:

Black girl, black girl, don't lie to me,
Where did you stay last night?
In the pines, in the pines, where the sun never shines,
And I shivered when the cold wind blew.

Wherever this melody has turned up, it has been a vehicle for melancholy, for a yearning toward faraway places and toward things that are lost and irretrievable. In "Nine Hundred Miles" it has become the most haunting of railroad blues.

74. *JOHN HENRY (I AND II)*

It is fitting that America's greatest ballad should celebrate a railroad worker, a Negro named John Henry who met his death during the construction of the Big Bend Tunnel on the C. & O railroad sometime around 1873. John Henry was a steel driver. His hammer blows drove the drills into the rock to make holes for the blasting charges. They say he was quite a man:

> John Henry drove steel with a ten-pound sheepnose hammer with a regular-size switch handle four feet long, kept greased with tallow to keep it limber and flexible. He would stand from five and one half to six feet from his steel and strike with the full length of his hammer. He drove steel from his left shoulder and would make a stroke of more than nineteen and a half feet, making the hammer travel like lightning. And he could drive ten hours without turning a stroke. He was the steel-driving champion of the country and his record has never been equaled.

The Big Bend Tunnel was one of the longest and most difficult man had ever cut through a mountain. The C. & O. was pushing its line through the ruggedest part of the West Virginia mountains along the New River, when that country was a howling wilderness. During the two and a half years of drilling through the Big Bend, the section of the road along the New River was closed to the press and the public. The personnel files that cover that portion of the C. & O.'s history were destroyed in a fire—or that's the story. The names of many a man "who was murdered by the railroad" were in that file, how many we shall never know. Pete Sanders, who worked in the tunnel, says,

> . . . the Big Bend Tunnel was a terrible-like place, and many men got killed there. Mules, too. And they throwed the dead men and the mules all together there in that fill in between the mountains. The people in the tunnel didn't know where they went.

There were plenty of ways for a man to die in the Big Bend—silicosis, falling rock, cave-ins, and suffocation, to mention a few. In describing the work in such a tunnel, one writer says:

> One was almost smothered, so great was the heat; the smoke from the blasts became so thick that the light of the lamps was visible no farther than a few steps. As the work progressed, the temperature rose and the air became more vitiated, until visitors were rarely permitted to enter because of the sheer danger of being in such an atmosphere. And the horses on the job died at the rate of ten a month. The scene in the scantily lighted tunnel grew to resemble an inferno.

No one knows how many men were killed in the Big Bend Tunnel, but the *Kanawha Chronicle* of December 7, 1873, reported that in the Hoosac Tunnel, built in Massachusetts in the same period, "136 men have been killed by casualties."

Yes, you had to be a man to drive steel in the Big Bend. Louis Chappell in his fascinating study of the John Henry legend, describes the scene of John Henry's everyday work as follows:

> On the stage are hundreds of miners, mostly Negroes, and mostly naked. Here the miner wears a shirt, or a fragment of one, and the same may be said of his trousers and shoes, the other two parts of his wardrobe; but he has taken off his shirt, and I am not certain about his trousers in all cases. The heat is intense, the air filled with dust and smoke, and the lights from burning blackstrap are not at all adequate. Whatever the manner of turning steel in the heading may be, dozens of Negroes at least half-naked are sitting around on the bench holding with both hands a piece of steel upright between their legs, and the steel-drivers, two for each turner, are singing and driving. Now and then the turner does the singing, and the driller adds only a grunt as his hammer falls on the steel.

The steel-driving songs rise in the smoky air:

My old hammer
Rings like silver,
Shines like gold,
Shines like gold.

They sing with a grin on their faces, because of the lusty double meaning of their song. Here is the earthy beginning and the root significance of the John Henry ballad—men at work in the smoky bowels of the earth, thinking about their women and laughing with pleasure.

Into this setting comes the white boss with his steam-drill. Perhaps the question in the boss' mind was, "How many men can I lay off, how much money can I save, if the steam-drill is more efficient than my best man?" John Henry was asked if he would drive in a contest against the machine. The ballad gives him credit for the noblest lines in American folklore:

John Henry told his captain,
"A man ain't nothin' but a man,
And before I'd let that steam-drill beat
me down,
I'd die with this hammer in my hand."

That day in the Big Bend Tunnel, it was "the flesh agin the steam." John Henry drove the steam-drill down with his hammer "just hossin' in the wind" and proved for folksingers, for all men, that mankind is superior to his tools.

This old hammer,
Killed John Henry,
Can't kill me,
Can't kill me.

For the tunnel workers, to say that John Henry "had drove his poor fool self to death" was a Gargantuan bawdy joke. For the folk this was a proper time for their work hero to die, and so in the ballad he does, and is given a hero's burial.

Every locomotive come rollin' by,
Says—"There lies a steel-driving man!"

Dr. Chappell, who has followed John Henry's trail through the years, tells us, however, that John Henry did not actually die after the contest with the steam-drill. His death came later in familiar Big Bend style when a slab of rock fell from the ceiling and crushed him. Then the legend began to grow. Folks who live near the mouth of the Big Bend Tunnel won't go there at night because they see the ghost of John Henry driving steel in the shadows, "his hammer ringin' like a bell." Every state in the South claims him. You will find that he's distantly related to almost every good folk-singer that you meet. One informant will seriously swear that he was "a white man, who weighed 240 lbs. at the age of 22, with the muscle of his arm 22 inches around"; another that he was "short and brown-skinned, and weighed 150 lbs."; another that he was "a giant yellow Negro with one arm, with a thumb as large as an ordinary man's wrist. He could pick up a length of steel, straighten up, turn around, and then lower the rail back into place. . . ." Then there's the lady who says "he would lift a four-ton car so that his feet would go into the ground up to his ankles."

So the story has grown as it has traveled out from the gorges of the West Virginia mountains. John Henry is a roustabout, John Henry, as in our second version, is a spiker on a section gang. Yet the motive force in the legend is the John Henry ballad, a joint product of Negro and white singers. Its tune is rooted in a Scottish melody, its devices are those of medieval balladry, its content is the courage of the common man beating a raw country into shape. For good reason, therefore, has it become today the best-loved folk ballad among all Southern singers, black or white.

75. *CASEY JONES*

If John Henry is a legendary figure or a man whose real story has been overtopped by the folk legends that the people have built up around him, Casey Jones is a factual character, whose real story we know. The people have clothed him in their fancy, yet the facts and circumstances of his real life are still available.

He was born John Luther Jones, near the little town of Cayce, Kentucky. The men he worked with nicknamed him "Casey" after his home town. He stood six feet four and a half inches in his socks, had gray eyes and black hair and "an Irish heart almost as big as his body." He worked as an engineer on the Illinois Central, pushing the crack Cannonball Express from Memphis, Tennessee, south to Canton, Mississippi. He had a reputation among railroad men. Another engineer said of him: "He could perform feats with his famous engine that no other engineer could equal with locomotives of the same class." A conductor who punched tickets on Casey's run praised him thus:

> . . . a car roller, and in my estimation the prince of them all. We had a number of fast men, and since then I have had hundreds of good engineers pull me on different Western roads. But I have never met the equal of Casey Jones in rustling to get over the road. . . . The faster he could get his engine to roll, the happier he was. He would lean out of the cab window to watch his drivers and when he got her going so fast that the side rods looked solid, he would look at you and grin all over, happy as a boy with his first pair of red boots. Yet with all his fast running I never knew of him piling them up, of but a few derailments and never a rear-ender. He was either lucky or else his judgment was as nearly perfect as human judgment can be.

If we cannot quite share this conductor's enthusiasm for the judgment of the engineer who "piled them up" in the most famous wreck in history, remember that in Casey's day, because of inferior equipment and rather lackadaisical operating methods, wrecks were so frequent as to be normal. Casey's fatal collision, however, can be blamed not so much on his daredeviltry as his goodheartedness. He pulled into Memphis the night of April 29, 1906 at 10:00 P.M. He was ready to go home, when the engineer on the southern run turned up sick and Casey volunteered to take his place. He headed engine Number 638 out of the Memphis yards at eleven o'clock in the slow spring rain, and the switchmen "knew by the engine's moans that the man at the throttle was Casey Jones."

Casey's whistle was his trademark. Up and down the delta Negroes, standing in their shacks under the levee, would hear his sad Irish whistle and say to themselves, "That's ol' Casey makin' up time out there. Dat man can moan a whistle like a lonesome turtle dove." The romantic conductor we quoted earlier has described Casey's whistle as "a kind of long-drawn-out note, beginning softly, then rising, then dying away almost to a whisper." That night Casey's whistle sounded like the wail of a little lost child.

Down the track, ahead of Casey at Vaughn, Mississippi, there were two long freights stacked up on one siding. At the southern end of the switch the tail end of the second freight lapped out on the main line, but the crews figured that by the time the Cannonball had passed the head of the siding, they could move both their trains north and clear the mainline on through South. They figured without Casey Jones, coming down the line at a mile-a-minute clip. When Casey peered through the rain he saw the last of the boxcars moving off the main-line onto the siding, but only a hundred feet ahead. He knew that there was no way to stop in time. He hollered at Sim Webb, his Negro fireman, to jump and snatched at the brakes while No. 638 smacked into the boxcars. They found Casey in the wreck with one hand on the brakes and the other on his whistle cord. Sim Webb remembers that the last thing he heard as he jumped into the bushes was Casey giving one final scream of his beloved whistle.

For half a century Casey's ballad has stirred Americans just as the bluesy cadence of his whistle once stirred the Delta folk. The actual wreck was a familiar enough incident in those days and was soon forgotten by all but a handful of oldtimers on the I.C. It served only as the starting point of the ballad. Wallace Saunders, Negro engine wiper in the round-house down the line at Canton, made the difference. He, like so many other Negroes on the I.C. line, admired Casey and his whistle. When they hauled No. 638 into the round-house, he was the man who wiped Casey's blood off the cab and off the throttle handle. Perhaps then he hummed or turned over in his mind the first lines of the Casey ballad. Like a true ballad-maker, however, he did not attempt to make an "original" song. He took an old ballad and made it over, much in the manner of an old lady adding a new patch here and there to an old and beautiful quilt. His friend and fellow-worker in the engine house, Cornelius Steen, whom we interviewed in 1933, long after Saunders' death, told us what he remembered.

Steen said that he came back from a visit to Kansas City with a few verses that began:

On a Sunday morning it begins to rain,
Round the curve, spied a passenger train,
On the pilot lay po' Jimmie Jones,
He's a good old porter, but he's dead an' gone,
Dead an' gone, dead an' gone,
Kaze he's been on the cholly so long.

Wallace Saunders took a fancy to the song and, by changing "Jimmie" to "Casey," used most of it in making his Casey Jones ballad, which began, according to Cornelius Steen:

On a Sunday mornin' it began to rain,
'Round the curve spied a passenger train,
Under de cab lay po' Casey Jones,
He's a good engineer, but he's dead an' gone,
Dead an' gone, dead an' gone,
Kaze he's been on the cholly so long.

Apparently, Jimmie Jones' ballad was one of a family of Negro ballads current at that time. We have fragments that tell the story of Old John Brown (a fireman), Joseph Mickel (an engineer), Charley Snyder (an engineer), Jay Gould's daughter (who, from the stanzas the folk have made, was an unpleasant character). We have woven these stanzas together to make a composite ballad ("Casey Jones, I"), an archetype of the Casey Jones songs combining many of the best stanzas from the earlier ballads and ballad fragments. The refrain line—"Kaze he's been on the cholly so long"—means "He's been on the bum so long," or "He's been a rambling railroad worker so long."

The Casey Jones ballad familiar to most Americans, sprang from Wallis Saunders' song by way, curiously, of the vaudeville stage. Tallifero Lawrence Sibert (born June 4, 1877, in Bloomington, Indiana; died February 20, 1917, in Los Angeles) toured the vaudeville circuit in a five-character act. According to Elliot Shapiro (one of the pundits of popular song), Sibert "undoubtedly heard *Been on the Cholly So Long.* He wrote a sketch about the brave engineer and incorporated it in his act." Out on the pier in Venice, California, he bumped into a ragtime piano player, Eddie Walter Newton (born September 25, 1869, in Trenton, Missouri; died September 1, 1915, and his ashes were scattered under the pier cafe in Venice). Together they turned out a ragtime ballad about Casey, set him up as the main "hogger" on a Western railroad line, and published the song themselves in the Southern California Music Company. By 1909 the song had swept the country as a popular hit, retaining so many folk-song touches that folk-singers have since then created scores of variants and parodies based on the Newton-Sibert ballad.

Mrs. Jones and her friends have often expressed their indignation over the implication in the popular song that Mrs. Jones "had another papa on the Salt Lake Line." Memphis railroadmen have taken pokes at ignorant strangers who sung these lines in the barrooms down near the Memphis railroad yards. They knew Mrs. Jones well and they knew that she was a good and faithful wife to her gallant husband. What they did not know was that the boys who picked up the Negro song heard scandalous stanzas which Casey had inherited from the older "Been on the Cholly So Long" piece. These stanzas, which fit so well the Negro folk-singers' ironic view of life, are sometimes sung by barrelhouse blues-blowers:

When the women all heard that Casey was dead,
They went home and re-ragged in red,
Come a-slippin' an' slidin' up and down the street,
In their loose mother-hubbards and their stockin' feet.

Here come the biggest boy, comin' right from school,
Hollerin' and crying' like a doggone fool,
She say, "Quit cryin', boy, an' don't do that,
You got another papa on the same damn track."

76. *PADDY WORKS ON THE ERIE*

A big proportion of the laborers who laid down the railroads from the Eastern states clear to the Rockies bore names like O'Rourke, O'Riley, O'Sullivan, O'Casey, and O'Shane. They came from, as they said, "Erin's green shore" to seek their fortunes in the new land. They brought little beside their strength, their wit, and their singing tradition with them, but without them America, and especially the railways of America, would never have been built. In the years of the potato famine of 1840, when almost three million Irish men and women died of starvation, they flung themselves by the thousands on the immigrant boats, "bound for Amerikay." At that time their farewell parties were called "American wakes," so many of the boys were never heard from again, dying in the tightly packed holds of the "coffin ships" or in some lonely part of "wild Amerikay." Songs were made about this migration. Here an Irish girl speaks to her American-bound sweetheart:

"My curses attend that savage shore.
O, how came this to be?
That I should leave my parents
Who reared me tenderly?

For to follow you through woods and groves
Where savages wild do play,
That would devour both you and I
Gone to Amerikay."

Then he kissed her ruby lips
And embraced her tenderly,
"Will you come with me, my heart's delight
To the land of liberty?
When daylight peeps
No tribute we need not pay;
So forbear to spill those precious tears,
Come to Amerikay."

"Young man, your moving eloquence,
You've surely won my heart,
And it's from my old aged parents
I'm willing now to part."
He took his bonny lass on board
By the dawning of the day,
Crowded all sails to reach the shores
Of Rich Amerikay.

These Irish lads were the principal singers in the lumber camps and on the canals. We know that they sang as they built the Erie, the Pennsylvania, and the Union Pacific:

Damn be the President
My name's Mike.
I got a hand in it,
I drive the spike.

They sang on the section gangs:

"Give my rispicts to the Roadmas-ther,"
Poor Larry he did cry,
"And lave me up, that I may see
The ould hand-car-r before I die.
Then lay the spike-maul upon my chist,
The gauge an' the ould claw-bar-r,
And while the byes do be fillin' up the grave,
Oh, Jerry, go and ile that car-r-r!"

Up to this present writing most of their songs have been lost, except for one or two like "Paddy on the Erie." Let the twin strips of steel that link the Atlantic with the Pacific stand as their memorial.

77. *O LULA*

The Negro construction gangs who laid the mainline railroads of the South were always singing and all of their songs, distinct from the gang-labor chants of other laborers, bubble with fun or with a tender and ironic gaiety. It was as if they knew that the shining web of steel they spun across the land were freedom roads for them, escape routes to new jobs, new women, new towns where things might be better and people more friendly.

They sang while they cut the right-of-ways and levelled off the roadbeds. They hollered and whooped while they toted ties and unloaded the big steel rails, twelve men to every rail, and the steel-caller calling:

Be careful now, boys,
Don't git hurt,
I want you to go home,
Lookin' all right.

They chanted all together while they lined the track:

All I hate about linin' track
These old bars gonna break my back.

They chortled and chuckled while they tamped ties and the singing leader almost crooned to them:

When you git a section,
Lemme be yo' straw;
And when you git a daughter,
Lemme be yo' son-in-law.

In the heat of the day, while "the sweat ran down like water down a hill," he insinuated—

When you hear that blue-goose holler,
Gwine turn cold, cold, co-o-old,
Gwine turn cold.

And with the blood running warm in their veins, the hammers flashing rainbows 'round their shoulders, the men in pairs began to drive in the steel spikes that clinched the steel to the ties. Tapping the spike in a little, digging the balls of their feet into the gravel, getting set, the two men of the spiking team, threw back their heads and hollered, like the Cannonball express blowing its whistle, free and easy—

O—, Lu—la!
O—, La—awd, Gal!
I wanta see you so bad . . .

Then the two hammers began to whirl, falling in rhythm, smacking the head of the spike on alternate beats, so that it seemed to spurt into the tie in a continuous motion, the song accelerating with the hammers as the blows grew shorter and more rapid:

Gonna sée my lóng-haíred báby,
Gonna sée my lóng-haíred gál,
Wéll, I'm góin' 'cróss the cóuntry
Sée my lóng-haíred gál.

One spike down, one spike in there tight, hugging the rail to the tie against the shaking thunder of those heavy drive-wheels that will come soon. Twenty-two spikes to a rail, 324 rails to a mile, thousands of miles to go, but, man, think about old John Henry! "Didn't he drill all the way from Rome, Georgia, to Decatur, mo'n a hundred miles in one day? An' I ain' sure *that* was his best day. No, man, I ain' *sure!*"

78. *CAN'CHA LINE 'EM*

Up and down America's 404 thousand miles of railroad move the section gangs in their beetle-like handcars, watching the track, replacing a rotten tie here or a rusty spike there, straightening out the kinks that the sun, the rain, and the pounding trains put into the even rails. These are the men who live in the boxcar houses along the tracks. Theirs are the dusty faces that you have seen below your windows as the train flashed by, the little, dusty figures you have watched from the rear platform moving back on the tracks with their tools and dwindling into distant specks as your train speeds away.

Their big job is to straighten the track—"track-lining," they call it. The foreman spots the crooked section of track, directs the gang to it. The gang jam their heavy crowbars under the rail and shake their bars together or heave together against the rail in rhythm with their song, until the foreman calls a halt. Here is a report from Henry Truvillion, Negro section gang boss, on the job of track-lining in Louisiana.

> When the steel gits tight with the sun shinin' right warm on it, the track bucks and it looked as crooked as an old slavery-time fence row. Well, this day the sun was shining, the track was buckin', and I was walkin' and talkin'. The passenger train's due now, and I got to git out down there and line that track up straight. I holler and call six of my best men. I call 'em to git their linin' bars and git on down there and I tell 'em where to git it.

Turn to the song and follow Henry Truvillion and his gang through a track-lining job. We have written the whole operation down in dramatic form with the proper parts indicated for the foreman, the singing leader and the gang; for the Negroes have made track-lining into a work-drama, in which each man, every tool, the rails, and the approaching train, itself, are actors.

79. *THE BIG ROCK CANDY MOUNTAIN*

When a depression strikes America, men take to the railroads, riding the blinds, hanging precariously on the thin rods below the cars, clinging to the narrow catwalks on top of the freight cars, piling into the gondolas when the railroad bulls turn their heads aside. In the early years of this century, you could see ten to fifty tramps on every freight train. Some of these men began by looking for work and ended by preferring their wandering life, panhandling, doing odd jobs, sleeping in jails, holing up in the "jungles" alongside the tracks, and seeing America from coast to coast through the back door.

Oh, why don't you work like other men do?
How the hell can I work when the skies are so blue?
Hallelujah, I'm a bum,
Hallelujah, bum again,
Hallelujah, give us a handout,
And revive us again.

A famous tramp, whose moniker was A No. 1, advises in his hobo campfire tales, "to every young man and boy who reads this book—do not jump on moving trains or streetcars, even if only to ride to the next street crossing, because this might arouse the wander-lust! Wandering, once it becomes a habit is almost incurable."

Then I walked up to a kind miss,
And asked for a bite to eat,
A little piece of cornbread,
And a little piece of meat.

She took me in her kitchen,
She treated me nice and kind;
She got me in the notion
Of bumming all the time.

And as I left the kitchen,
And went down to the town,
I heard a double-header blow
And thought she was western bound.

My heart began to flutter,
And I began to sing,
"Ten thousand miles away from home
A-bumming a railroad train."

Many of the oldtime hoboes took along with them everywhere a "punk"—a younger tramp who, according to the rules of the road, had to wait on his master hand and foot, to die for him if required. Many of these boys were lured away from their farms and small towns by tales as fanciful as that told in this favorite hobo chantey, "The Big Rock Candy Mountain." The kids never found their "lakes of stew" and their "lemonade springs"; they ended by singing:

My pocket is empty,
My heart is full of pain,
Ten thousand miles away from home,
A-bumming an old freight train.

73.

900 Miles

Words and melody adapted and arranged by
the Lomaxes and Woody Guthrie

Piano arrangement by
Charles and Ruth Seeger

Moderately fast

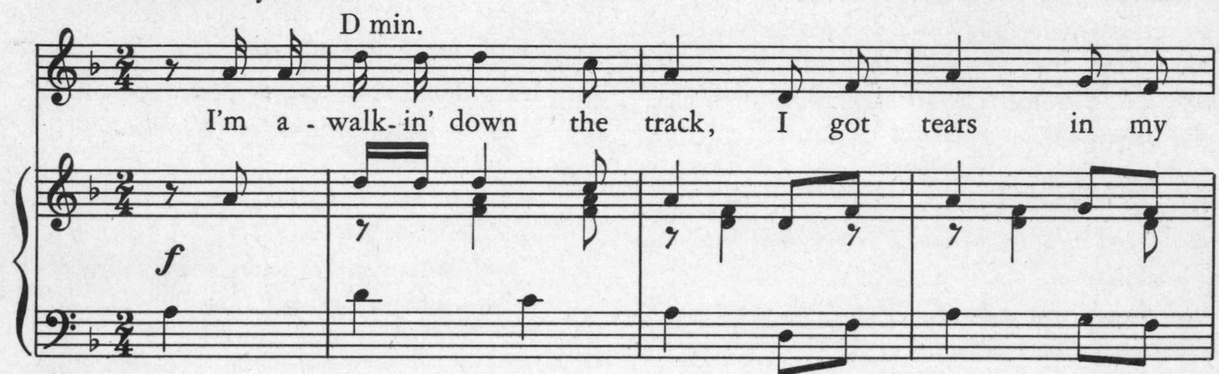

1. I'm a-walkin' down the track,
   I got tears in my eyes,
   Tryin' to read a letter from my home;
   If that train runs right,
   I'll be home tomorrow night,
   'Cause I'm nine hundred miles from my home . . .
   An' I hate to hear that lonesome whistle blow.

2. I will pawn you my watch
   And I'll pawn you my chain,
   I'll pawn you my gold diamond ring;
   If that train runs right,
   I'll be home tomorrow night,
   'Cause I'm nine hundred miles from my home . . .
   An' I hate to hear that lonesome whistle blow.

3. The train I ride on
   Is a hundred coaches long,
   You can hear the whistle blow a hundred miles.
   If that train runs right,
   I'll be home tomorrow night,
   'Cause I'm nine hundred miles from my home . . .
   An' I hate to hear that lonesome whistle blow.

*Sing stanza 3 to tune for first stanza, stanza 4 to tune for second stanza.

2. I'll pawn you my watch
And I'll pawn you my chain,
I'll pawn you my gold diamond ring;
If that train runs right,
I'll be home tomorrow night,
'Cause I'm nine hundred miles from my home . . .
An' I hate to hear that lonesome whistle blow.

3. The train I ride on
Is a hundred coaches long,
You can hear the whistle blow a hundred miles.
If that train runs right,
I'll be home tomorrow night,
'Cause I'm nine hundred miles from my home . . .
An' I hate to hear that lonesome whistle blow.

4. If my woman says so
I'll railroad no more,
But I'll sidetrack my train and go home.
If that wheeler runs me right,
I'll be home tomorrow night,
'Cause I'm nine hundred miles from my home . . .
An' I hate to hear that lonesome whistle blow.

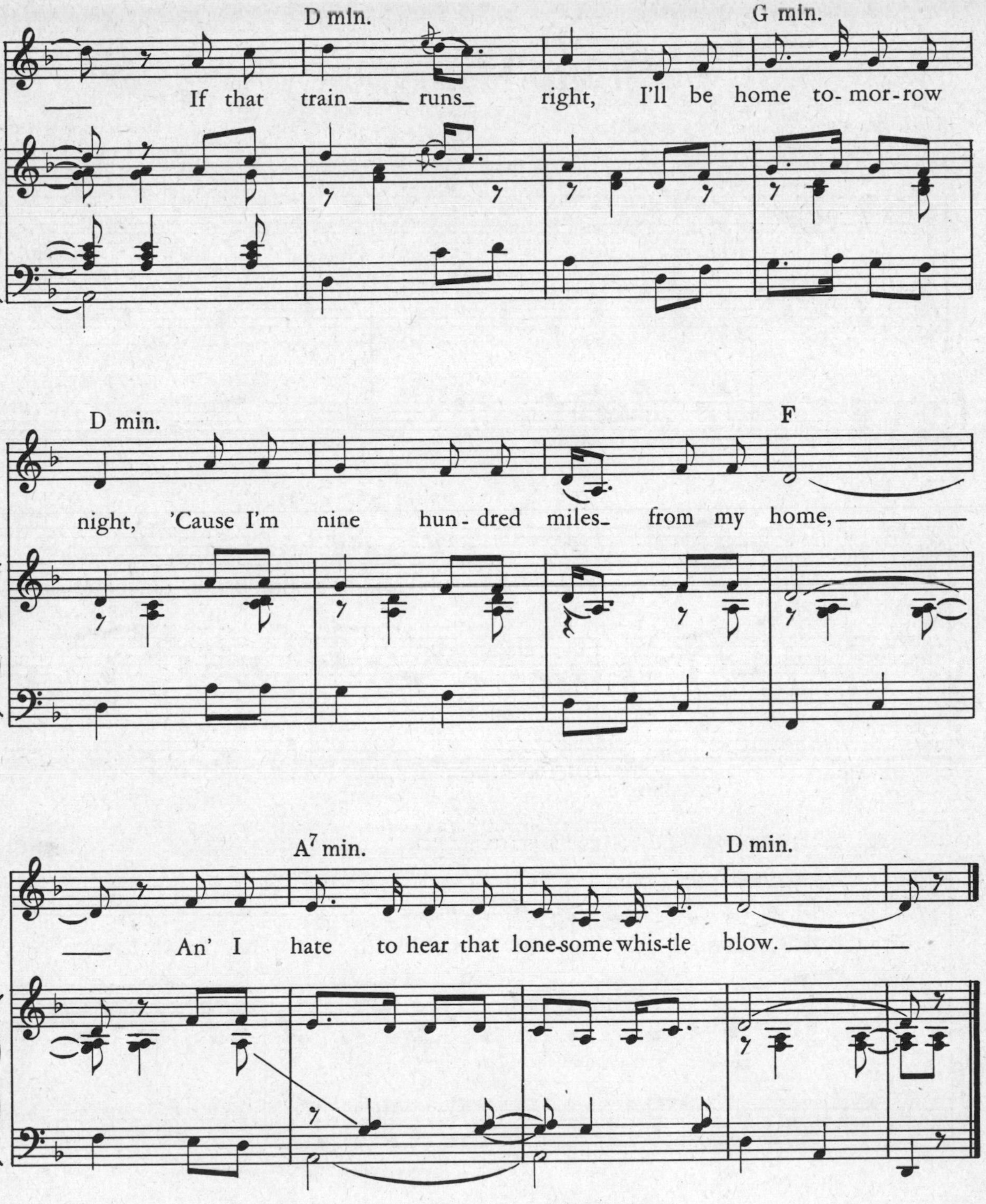

D min. G min.

If that train runs right, I'll be home to-mor-row

D min. F

night, 'Cause I'm nine hun-dred miles from my home,

74.

John Henry (I)

Words and melody adapted and arranged by
John A. and Alan Lomax

Piano arrangement by
Charles and Ruth Seeger

2. John Henry was a little baby,
Sittin' on his daddy's knee,
Point his finger at a little piece of steel,
"That's gonna be the death of me,
Lawd, Lawd, that's gonna be the death of me.

3. John Henry had a little woman
And her name was Mary Magdelene,
She would go to the tunnel and sing for John
Jes' to hear John Henry's hammer ring,
Lawd, Lawd, jes' to hear John Henry's hammer ring.

4. John Henry had a little woman
And her name was Polly Anne,
John Henry took sick and he had to go to bed,
Polly Anne drove steel like a man,
Lawd, Lawd, Polly Anne drove steel like a man.

5. Cap'n says to John Henry,
"Gonna bring me a steam drill 'round,
Gonna take that steam drill out on the job,
Gonna whop that steel on down,
Lawd, Lawd, gonna whop that steel on down."

6. John Henry told his cap'n,
Said, "A man ain't nothin' but a man,
And befo' I'd let that steam drill beat me down
I'd die with this hammer in my hand,
Lawd, Lawd, I'd die with the hammer in my hand."

7. Sun were hot and burnin',
Weren't no breeze atall,
Sweat ran down like water down a hill,
That day John let his hammer fall,
Lawd, Lawd, that day John let his hammer fall.

8. White man told John Henry,
"Nigger, damn yo' soul,
You may beat dis steam and drill of mine,—
When the rocks in the mountains turn to gold,
Lawd, Lawd, when the rocks in the mountains turn to gold."

9. John Henry said to his shaker,
"Shaker, why don't you sing?
I'm throwin' twelve pounds from my hips on down,
Jes' lissen to the cold steel ring,
Lawd, Lawd, jes' lissen to the cold steel ring."

John Henry (I)

Words and melody adapted and arranged by
John A. and Alan Lomax

Piano arrangement by
Charles and Ruth Seeger

Fast

A⁷ D A⁷

10. O the cap-'n told— John— Hen-ry, "I—

D G A⁷ D

b'lieve this moun-tain's sink-in' in," John Hen-ry said— to his

cap-'n, "O— my, It's my ham-mer just a-hos-sin in the wind, Lawd, Lawd, it's my

E min. A⁷ D

ham-mer just a-hos-sin in the wind."

10. O the cap'n told John Henry,
"I b'lieve this mountain's sinkin' in,"
John Henry said to his cap'n, "O my,
It's my hammer just a-hossin' in the wind,
Lawd, Lawd, it's my hammer just a-hossin' in the wind."

11. John Henry told his shaker,
"Shaker, you better pray,
For, if I miss this six-foot steel
Tomorrow be yo' buryin' day,
Lawd, Lawd, tomorrow be yo' buryin' day."

12. John Henry told his captain,
"Looky yonder what I see—
Yo' drill's done broke an' yo' hole's done choke,
An' you can't drive steel like me,
Lawd, Lawd, an' you can't drive steel like me."

13. John Henry was hammerin' on the mountain,
An' his hammer was strikin' fire,
He drove so hard till he broke his pore heart
An' he lied down his hammer an' he died,
Lawd, Lawd, he lied down his hammer an' he died.

14. They took John Henry to the graveyard
An' they buried him in the sand
An' ev'ry locomotive come roarin' by,
Says, "There lays a steel drivin' man,"
Lawd, Lawd, says, "There lays a steel drivin' man."

15. John Henry had a little woman,
An' the dress she wore was blue,
She went walkin' down the track and she never looked back,
Said, "John Henry, I've been true to you,
Lawd, Lawd, John Henry I've been true to you."

16. "Now who's gonna shoe your little feetses?
An' who's gonna glove your hands?
An' who's gonna kiss yo' red, rosy lips?
An' who's gonna be your man,
Lawd, Lawd, who's gonna be your man?"

17. "O my mama's gonna shoe my little feetses,
An' my papa's gonna glove my hands,
An' my sister's gonna kiss my red, rosy lips,
An' I don't need no man,
Lawd, Lawd, an' I don't need no man."

John Henry (II)

Words and melody adapted and arranged by
John A. and Alan Lomax

Piano arrangement by
Charles and Ruth Seeger

1. Well, ev'ry Monday mornin'
When the blue-birds begin to sing,
You can hear those hammers a mile or more,
You can hear John Henry's hammer ring, O Lordy!
Hear John Henry's hammer ring.

2. John Henry told his old lady,
"Will you fix my supper soon?
Got ninety miles o' track I've got to line,
Got to line it by the light of the moon, O Lordy!
Line it by the light of the moon."

3. John Henry had a little baby,
He could hold him out in his hand;
Well, the last word I heard that po' child say,
"My daddy is a steel-drivin' man, O Lordy!
Daddy is a steel-drivin' man."

4. John Henry told his old captain,
Said, "A man ain't nothin' but a man;
Before I let your steel gang down
I will die with the hammer in my hand, O Lordy!
Die with the hammer in my hand."

5. John Henry told his captain,
"Next time you go to town
Uh-jes' bring me back a ten-pound maul
For to beat your steel-drivin' down, O Lordy!
Beat your steel-drivin' down."

6. John Henry had a old lady,
And her name was Polly Ann.
John Henry tuck sick an' he had to go to bed,
Pauline drove steel like a man, O Lordy!
'Line* drove steel like a man.

7. John Henry had a old lady,
An' the dress she wore was red.
Well she started up the track and she never looked back,
"Goin' where my man fell dead, O Lordy!
Where my man fell dead."

8. Well some said-uh he's from England,
And some say he's from Spain;
But-uh I say he's nothin' but a Lou's'ana man
Just a leader of the steel-drivin' gang, O Lordy!
Leader of the steel-drivin' gang.

*" 'Line", pronounced "lean", is an abbreviation for Pauline.

Casey Jones (I)

1. On a Sunday mornin' it begins to rain,
Round the curve spied a passenger train,
Under de cab lay po' Casey Jones,
He's a good engineer, but he's dead an' gone,
Dead an' gone, dead an' gone,
Kaze he's been on the cholly so long.

2. Casey Jones was a good engineer,
Tol' his fireman not to have no fear,
"All I want's a li'l' water an' coal,
Peep out de cab and see de drivers roll,
See de drivers roll, see de drivers roll."
Kaze he's been on the cholly so long.

3. When we got within a mile of the place,
Old number four stared us right in the face,
Conductor pulled his watch, mumbled and said,
"We may make it, but we'll all be dead,
All be dead, all be dead."
Kaze he's been on the cholly so long.

4. O ain't it a pity and ain't it a shame?
A six wheel driver had to bear the blame. .
Some were crippled and some were lame,
And a six wheel driver had to bear the blame,
Bear the blame, bear the blame,—
Kaze he's been on the cholly so long.

5. When Casey's wife heard dat Casey was dead,
She was in de kitchen, makin' up bread,
She says "Go to bed, chillun and hol' yo' breath,
You'll all get a pension at yo' daddy's death,
At yo' daddy's death, at yo' daddy's death."
Kaze he's been on the cholly so long.

6. Jay Gould's daughter said before she died,
"Father, fix the blinds so the bums can't ride,
If ride they must, let 'em ride the rods,
Let them put their trust in the hands of God,
Hands of God, hands of God.—"
Kaze he's been on the cholly so long.

7. Hurry up, engine, and hurry up, train,
Missie gwine ride over the road again,
Swift as lightnin' and smooth as glass,
Darkey, take yo' hat off when the train goes past,
When the train goes past, when the train goes past,
Kaze he's been on the cholly so long.

Casey Jones (II)

Words and melody by
Newton and Siebert

Piano arrangement by
Charles and Ruth Seeger

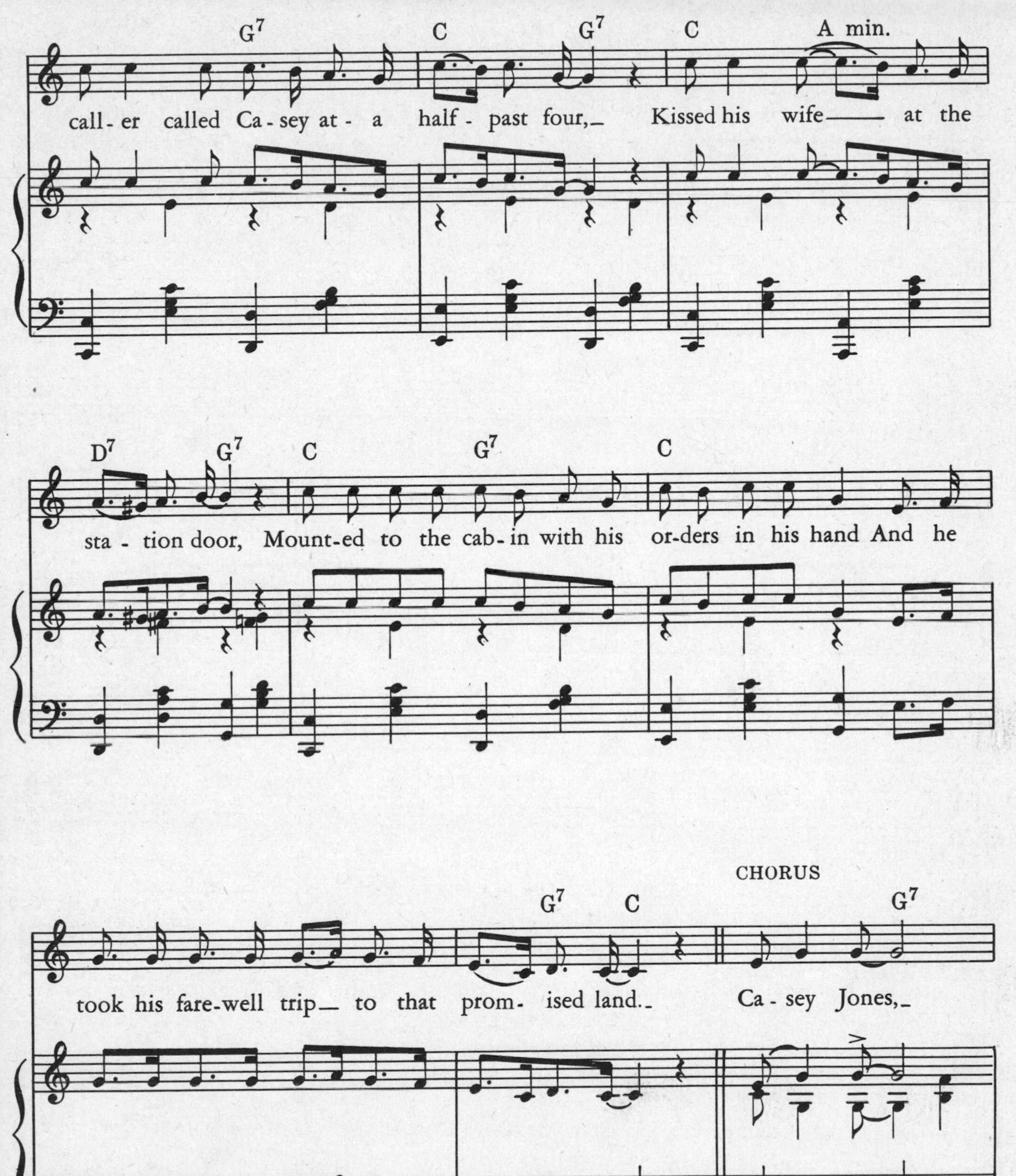

G7 C G7 C A min.
call-er called Ca-sey at-a half-past four,_ Kissed his wife___ at the
D7 G7 C G7 C
sta-tion door, Mount-ed to the cab-in with his or-ders in his hand And he
CHORUS
G7 C G7
took his fare-well trip_ to that prom- ised land._ Ca-sey Jones,_

C
F
C
G7
mount - ed to the cab - in,
Ca - sey Jones, with his

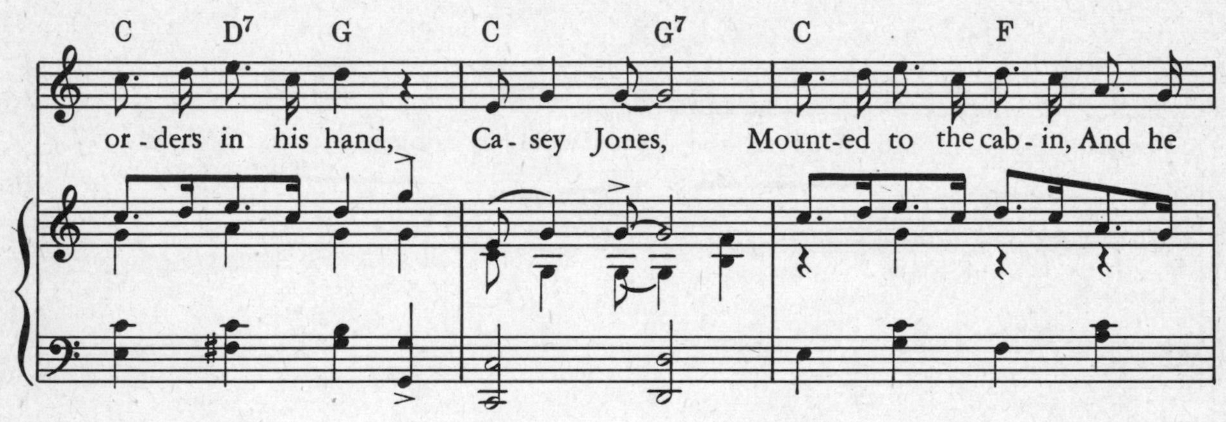
C
D7
G
C
G7
C
F
or - ders in his hand,
Ca - sey Jones,
Mount-ed to the cab - in, And he

C
A7
D min.
C
G7
C
took his fare - well trip to the prom - ised land.

1. Come, all you rounders, if you want to hear
A story 'bout a brave engineer.
Casey Jones was the rounder's name
On a six eight wheeler, boys, he won his fame.
The caller called Casey at-a half past four,
Kissed his wife at the station door,
Mounted to the cabin with his orders in his hand
And he took his farewell trip to that promised land:

CHORUS: Casey Jones, mounted to the cabin,
Casey Jones, with his orders in his hand,
Casey Jones, mounted to the cabin,
And he took his farewell trip to the promised land.

2. "Put in your water and shovel in your coal,
Put your head out the window, watch them drivers roll,
I'll run her till she leaves the rail
'Cause I'm eight hours late with that western mail."
He looked at his watch and his watch was slow,
He looked at the water and the water was low,
He turned to the fireman and then he said,
"We're goin' to reach Frisco but we'll all be dead:"
CHORUS: Casey Jones, goin' to reach Frisco,
Casey Jones, but we'll all be dead,
Casey Jones, goin' to reach Frisco,
"We're goin' to reach Frisco, but we'll all be dead."

3. Casey pulled up that Reno Hill,
He tooted for the crossing with an awful shrill,
The switchman knew by the engine's moan
That the man at the throttle was Casey Jones.
He pulled up within two miles of the place
Number Four stared him right in the face,
He turned to the fireman, said, "Boy, you better jump,
'Cause there's two locomotives that's a-goin' to bump:"
CHORUS: Casey Jones, two locomotives,
Casey Jones, that's a-goin'to bump,
Casey Jones, two locomotives,
"There's two locomotives that's a-goin' to bump."

4. Casey said just before he died,
"There's two more roads that I'd like to ride."
The fireman said what could they be?
"The Southern Pacific and the Sante Fe."
Mrs. Casey sat on her bed a-sighin',
Just received a message that Casey was dyin'.
Said, "Go to bed, children, and hush your cry'n,
Cause you got another papa on the Salt Lake Line:"
CHORUS: Mrs. Casey Jones, got another papa,
Mrs. Casey Jones, on that Salt Lake Line,
Mrs. Casey Jones, got another papa,
"And you've got another papa on the Salt Lake Line."

76.

Paddy Works On the Erie

Words and melody adapted and arranged by
John A. and Alan Lomax

Piano arrangement by
Charles and Ruth Seeger

1. In eighteen hundred and forty one,
I put me cord'roy breeches on,
I put me cord'roy breeches on
To work upon the railway.

2. In eighteen hundred and forty-two
I left the ould world for the new,
Bad cess to the luck that brought me through
To work upon the railroad.

3. When we left Ireland to come here,
And spend our latter days in cheer,
Our bosses, they did drink strong beer
And Pat worked on the railway.

4. Our boss's name, it was Tom King,
He kept a store to rob the men,
A Yankee clerk with ink and pen,
To cheat Pat on the railroad.

5. It's "Pat do this" and "Pat do that,"
Without a stocking or cravat,
And nothing but an old straw hat
While Pat works on the railroad.

6. One Monday morning to our surprise,
Just a half an hour before sunrise,
The dirty divil went to the skies
And Pat worked on the railroad.

7. And, when Pat lays him down to sleep,
The wirey bugs around him creep
And divil a bit can poor Pat sleep,
While he works on the railroad.

8. In eighteen hundred and forty-three
'Twas then I met Miss Biddy MacGhee
And an illygant wife she's been to me,
While workin' on the railway.

9. In eighteen hundred an forty-seven,
Sweet Biddy MacGhee, she went to heaven,
If she left one child, she left eleven,
To work upon the railway.

10. In eighteen hundred and forty-eight,
I learned to take my whiskey straight,
'Tis an illygant drink and can't be bate
For working on the railway.

O, Lula!

Words and melody adapted and arranged by
Zora Neale Huston and the Lomaxes

Piano arrangement by
Charles and Ruth Seeger

1. Oh Lula, Oh Lord, gal:
   I want to see you so bad.

CHORUS: Gonna see my long-haired baby,
Gonna see my long-haired gal,
Well, I'm goin' 'cross the country,
To see my long-haired gal.

2. What you reckon Mr. Treadwell said to Mr. Goff?*
   Lawd, I b'lieve I'll go South, pay them poor boys off.

CHORUS: Gonna see my long-haired baby,
Gonna see my long-haired gal,
Well, I'm goin' 'cross the country,
To see my long-haired gal.

3. Lawd, I ast that woman, lemme be her kid,
   And she looked at me and began to smile.

CHORUS: Gonna see my long-haired baby,
Gonna see my long-haired gal,
Well, I'm goin' 'cross the country,
To see my long-haired gal.

*You may have difficulty in singing the second and third stanzas of the melody given. This is no problem for a steel-driver, however; he simply lets his voice play freely with the melody, expanding it to encompass any number of syllables.

78.

Can'cha Line 'Em

FOREMAN: (Shouting to the section gang)*

Go down yonder to the third joint ahead
And touch it NORTH
So the track be runnin' east and west,
Touch it NORTH!

(When the men have come to the third joint ahead and jammed their bars under the rail and are getting set to heave together.)

INTRODUCTION

LEADER: *Ho, boys, is you right?**

GANG: *Done got right.*

LEADER: *If I could, I sho'ly would*
Stand on the rock where Moses stood.

ALL: (As they heave)
Ho, boys, can'cha line 'em?
Ho, boys, can'cha line 'em?
Ho, boys, can'cha line 'em?
See Eloise go linin' track.

LEADER: (While the men get ready to heave again)
Mary, Marthy, Luke and John,
All them 'ciples dead and gone.

ALL: *Ho, boys, can'cha line 'em?*
Ho, boys, can'cha line 'em?
Ho, boys, can'cha line 'em?
See Eloise go linin' track.

FOREMAN: All right, now boys, you got that one straight now.
I want you to run down to the second joint ahead
And touch it easy. Quick, make haste, I hear the train a-comin',

LEADER: (Chanting while they walk)
Run, boys, run,
You not too old to run.
(While the men are getting set again)
All right, boys, I'm gonna tell you 'bout my woman this time now..

LEADER: *I got a woman on Jennielee square,*
If you want to die easy, lemme catch you there.

ALL: *Ho, boys, can'cha line 'em?*
Ho, boys, can'cha line 'em?
Ho, boys, can'cha line 'em?
See Eloise go linin' track.

*Only lines in italics should be sung, the remainder should be chanted in a sing-song fashion.

STANZA (Leader)
B min. D G D A7 D A D
Lit-tle Ev-a- line, set-tin' in the shade, Fig-urin' on the mon-ey I ain't made.
All
D7
Ho, boys, can' cha line 'em? Ho, boys, can' cha line 'em?
D
A7 D
Ho, boys, can' cha line 'em? See El - o-ise go lin-in' track.

LEADER: *Little Evaline, settin' in the shade,*
Figurin' on the money I ain't made.

ALL: *Ho, boys, can'cha . . . etc . . . .*

FOREMAN: Now, wait a minute, you stop right there.
Put your guns on your shoulders
And come walkin' back.
Go on to the next one and touch it just a fraction.
I want you to just barely move it.
Touch it just a little bit.

LEADER: *Jack de Rabbit, jack de Bear,*
Can'cha move it just a hair?

ALL: *Ho, boys, can'cha . . . etc . . . .*

FOREMAN: Now, put yo' guns on your shoulders and come by me.
Come in a hurry.
Come trottin'.
Come laughin'.
Come like you gon' git paid for it.
Get a *move* on you.
Down yere to the third joint ahead and
Git yo' back breakin' holts and throw it North!
Train's a-comin'.

LEADER: *All I hate about linin' track,*
These old bars about to break my back.

ALL: *Ho, boys, can'cha . . . etc . . . .*

LEADER: *You keep on talkin' 'bout joint ahead,*
Never said nothin' 'bout my hog and bread. . . . *Ho, boys, can'cha . . . etc . . . .*

(And so they work and sing on until sundown, the leader keeping the men grinning, sometimes dreamy with stanzas like these . . .)

LEADER: *Way down yonder in the holler of the field,*
Angels workin' on the chariot wheel.

The reason I stay with my cap'n so long,
He give me biscuits to rear back on.

Jes' lemme tell you what the captain done,
Looked at his watch and he looked at the sun.

ALL: *Ho, boys, it ain't time,*
Ho, boys, you cain't quit.
Ho, boys, it ain't time,
Sun ain't gone down yit.

79.

The Big Rock Candy Mountains

Piano arrangement by
Charles and Ruth Seeger

D G D G D
turn-ing. I'm head-ed for a land that's far a-way Be-
G A D A7
side the crys-tal foun-tains. I'll see you all this
D A7 D A7 D
com-ing fall In the Big Rock Can-dy Moun-tains.

STANZAS
G
D
In the Big Rock Can - dy Moun-tains There's a land that's fair and bright, Where the
G
D
G
A
hand-outs grow on bush-es— And you sleep out ev - 'ry night, Where the
D
G
D
box-cars all are emp-ty And the sun shines ev - 'ry day — O the
G
D
G
D
G
D
birds and the bees and the cig - a - rette trees, The rock - rye springs where the

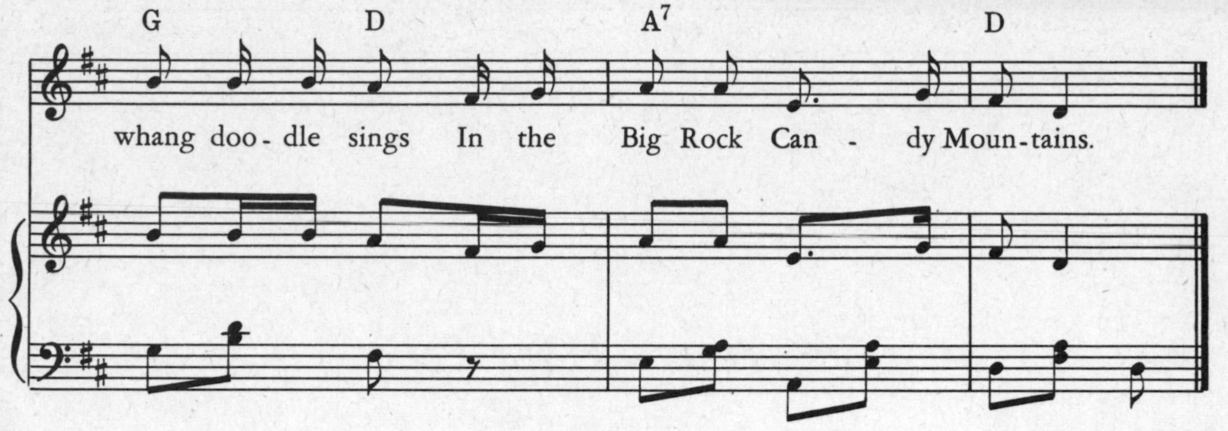

2. In the Big Rock Candy Mountains,
All the cops have wooden legs,
And the bulldogs all have rubber teeth
And the hens lay softboiled eggs.
The farmer's trees are full of fruit
And the barns are full of hay.
O I'm bound to go, where there ain't no snow,
Where the sleet don't fall and the wind don't blow
In the Big Rock Candy Mountains.

3. In the Big Rock Candy Mountains,
You never change your socks,
And the little streams of alkyhol
Come trickling down the rocks.
The shacks all have to tip their hats
And the railroad bulls are blind,
There's a lake of stew and of whiskey, too,
And you can paddle all around in a big canoe
In the Big Rock Candy Mountains.

4. In the Big Rock Candy Mountains,
The jails are made of tin,
And you can bust right out again,
As soon as they put you in.
There ain't no shorthandled shovels
No axes, saws or picks—
I'm a-going to stay, where you sleep all day,
Where they boiled in oil the inventor of toil
In the Big Rock Candy Mountains.

CHAPTER X

Heroes and Hard Cases

BLOODY TRAGEDY AND VIOLENCE HAVE been the favored subjects for ballad-makers and their folk audience for centuries, just as they are today the bread and butter of the daily press. The longest-lived of the classical British ballads dealt with shocking tragedy. "Lord Thomas and Fair Eleanor":

Lord Thomas he had a sword by his side,
As he walked about the hall;
He cut his bride's head from her shoulders
And kicked it against the wall.

"Earl Brand" or "The Douglas Tragedy":

She held his steed in her milk-white hand,
And never shed one tear,
Until she saw her seven brethren fall,
And her father who loved her so dear.

American folk-singers treasured these medieval tales of passion and violence, but left them largely to the women to sing, calling them with unconscious scorn "old-time *love*-songs." The bear hunters, Indian fighters, six-gun artists, and eye-gougers who flourished on the frontier found these old tales rather tame in comparison with their own lives. They preferred a language that reeked with gore:

I was raised on six-shooters till I got big enough to eat ground shotguns.
The music of widders and orphans is music to me melancholy soul.
I'll snatch you bald-headed and spit on the place where the hair come off.
I'll take a leg off you and beat you over the head with the bloody end of it.
I'll slap your head up to a peak and then knock the peak off.
Take your eye out and eat it for a grape. . . .

The counterparts and opponents of these "ring-tailed roarers," these "half-man-half-horse-and-half-alligator" boys were the frontier peace officers, hard-eyed, quiet, and deadly. Of one of these it is told that he went after three bad men in a distant town with instructions to bring them back dead or alive. In a few days he wired home: "FOUND THEM. SEND TWO COFFINS AND A DOCTOR. JAKE." The American peace officer has always had a problem on his hands, since there seems to be a real ornery streak in the American character that inclines us to acts of "crime and disgrace." Some Kentucky mountaineer has left us a verse that describes and defines this American trait. "Hit comes natural to you," he indicates, "to be mean and lowdown when you are raised to hit."

Rattlesnake, rattlesnake,
What makes yore teeth so white?
Why I've been in the bottom all of my life
And I ain't done nothin' but bite, bite,
I ain't done nothin' but bite.

Those of us who do not indulge in violence certainly enjoy hearing about such behavior and its consequences. At any rate, there is no question that stabbings, poisonings, floggings, beheadings, dismemberments, drownings, and gunplay have produced more American ballads than any other kind of subject. Little Frankie, Billy the Kid, Railroad Bill, Stagalee, John Dillinger, Pretty Boy Floyd, the Knoxville Boy, the Hatfields and the Coys, Jesse James, John Hardy—these outlaws and coldblooded killers make proper ballad heroes. Alongside these desperadoes stand the passion-murderer, whining his confession, and the prisoner, moaning out his agony and loneliness in the "hard-rock hotel,"—both everlasting folk-song heroes and creators.

80. *JESSE JAMES*

The best-known and most singable of all our outlaw ballads is the story of Jesse James. Its creator, an anonymous people's poet said to have been a Negro convict, signed himself Billy Gashade in the final stanza—probably a pseudonym. Whatever the author's name, his song has carried the legend of Jesse James all over America and into a dozen ballad versions, Negro and white. Like outlaw heroes in the great tradition from Robin Hood to Pretty Boy Floyd, the Missouri train robber is portrayed as—

. . . a man, friend to the poor,
He never could see a man suffer pain,
He robbed from the rich and he gave to the poor
He'd a hand and a heart and a brain.

One of the classic stories in the James legend is the tale of the outlaw and the widow woman. They say that Jesse and his gang stopped at a widow woman's farm for dinner, and, as they ate their victuals, they noticed that she was crying.

Jesse kept asking questions. The woman said there was a mortgage due on her farm for $1400; it was overdue and this was her last day of grace. The man who held the mortgage was a hardhearted old miser and would be sure to turn her out. After they finished eating, Jesse produced a sack and counted out $1400 on the table. "Here, lady," said Jesse, "you take this money and pay off your mortgage."

The widow said she couldn't believe it was anything but a dream—things never happened that way—, but Jesse assured her it was good money and for her use.

They rode some distance from the house and hid in the bushes beside the rocky road along which the mortgage man was to come in his buggy. Presently they saw him driving toward the widow's house, and pretty soon, driving back, looking prosperous. He was humming "Ol Dan Tucker was a fine old feller" as he came opposite. The boys stepped out into the road, held him up, and recovered the $1400.

Just as this exploit of Jesse James fits the folklore pattern of the trickster hero, so the story of his death falls into the ancient tradition of hero-death, a tradition that embraces both Baldur and the carpenter of Nazareth. This story appeared in the St. Joseph, Missouri, *Evening News,* April 3, 1882, the day after Jesse "tumbled from the wall," showing that before the ballad-singers began their James saga, the newspaper stories had taken on the ballad flavor in their account of his death.

Between eight and nine o'clock yesterday morning Jesse James, the Missouri outlaw, before whom the deeds of Fra Diavolo, Dick Turpin and Schinderhannes dwindled into insignificance, was instantly killed by a boy twenty years old, named Robert Ford, at temporary residence on the corner of Thirteenth and Lafayette Streets, in this city.

In the light of all moral reasoning the shooting

was unjustifiable; but the law was vindicated, and the $10,000 reward offered by the state for the body of the brigand will doubtless go to the man who had the courage to draw a revolver on the notorious outlaw even when his back was turned, as in this case.

There is little doubt that the killing was the result of a premeditated plan formed by Robert and Charles Ford several months ago. Charles had been an accomplice of Jesse James since the 3rd of last November and entirely possessed his confidence. Robert Ford, his brother, joined Jesse last Friday a week ago and accompanied Jesse and Charles to this city Sunday, March 23.

The opportunity they had long wished for came this morning. Breakfast was over. Charlie Ford and Jesse James been in the stable currying the horses preparatory to their night ride. On returning to the room where Robert Ford was, Jesse said:

"It's an awfully hot day. I guess I'll take off my pistols for fear somebody will see them if I walk in the yard."

He unbuckled the belt in which he carried two .45 calibre revolvers and laid them on the bed with his coat and vest. He then picked up a dusting brush with the intention of dusting some pictures which hung on the wall. To do this he got on a chair. His back was now turned to the brothers, who silently stepped between James and his revolvers.

At a motion from Charlie both drew their guns. Robert was the quicker of the two and in one motion he had the long weapon to a level of his eye, and with the muzzle not more than four feet from the back of the outlaw's head . . . Even in that motion, quick as thought, there was something which did not escape the acute ears of the hunted man. He made a motion as if to turn his head to ascertain the cause of that suspicious sound, but too late. A nervous pressure on the trigger, a quick flash, a sharp report, and the well-directed ball crashed through the outlaw's skull. . . . The shot had been fatal, and all the bullets in Charlie's revolver, still directed at Jesse's head could not more effectively have determined the fate of the greatest bandit and freebooter that ever figured in the pages of a country's history.

So, in the minds of folk-singers and, to some degree, for us all, Jesse James, train robber and gunman lives as a hero and his betrayer as another Judas Iscariot.

81. *SAM BASS*

Whatever ranges Jesse James is riding today, it is certain that Sam Bass lopes close to his side. Sam was a cowboy, "light-hearted, gay, and free." At the end of the trail in Kansas, he and his companions added to their bankrolls by sticking up the Union Pacific mail train. Then they fled south, robbing banks, living on the jump, riding high, wide, and handsome. A lot of otherwise respectable citizens of Texas helped Sam along when he was on the prod, sashaying silently in the cross-timbers region of Texas.

He met his fate in the little town of Round Rock, Texas in 1878. The squealer, Jim Murphy, had tipped off the sheriff that Sam would try to open up the Round Rock bank on July the nineteenth. When Sam and his boys rode into town, the shooting started. Seaborn Bass, his brother, fell fatally wounded. Sam got away, but died the next day from his wounds. He was buried in the Round Rock cemetery. Today the path between Sam and the gate runs straight across the other graves, worn by the hundreds that have come to see the resting place of the young outlaw, who died with his boots on at the age of twenty-seven. The souvenir hunters have completely destroyed Sam's first tombstone and are chipping away at the second. The people keep mementos of Sam: shoes from his horses, saddles he is supposed to have ridden on, six-guns he is supposed to have carried.

John Denton, an old-time cowpuncher of Gainesville, Texas, is said to have made up this typical come-all-ye-style ballad; and his opening stanza is as good as anything in ballad literature. In four easy-running lines he packs in information about Sam's birthplace, his reason for leaving home, his profession, and his character. The entire ballad is graceful and well-constructed and will probably cause Sam to be remembered long after many a history-book hero has been forgotten.

82. *TOM DOOLEY*

Wars help to make killers and outlaws. The Civil War turned some men like Jesse James and the Younger Boys into bushwhackers and, after the war, into professional gunmen. The Civil War brought out the ornery streak in Tom Dula, too. After it was over, he came riding home into the North Carolina mountains, a wornout, badly whipped, and bitter Rebel soldier. He'd fought through the war with Zeb Vance's cavalry. He'd seen Gettysburg. He was feeling as mean as a nestful of hornets, but at least he was looking forward to a warm welcome from his sweetheart, "the prettiest little gal in the county-o."

His welcome scarcely matched his expectations. The young lady was cordial but cool, friendly but tentative. Tom soon smelled trouble. He had several rivals, and, as if specially to gall him, one of them was a dad-burned impudent Yankee schoolteacher. The more Tom sulled up about that, the cooler his lady grew.

One day he invited her to go for a walk in the hills, and that night she didn't turn up for supper. Nobody knew what had become of her, least of all Tom Dula. The Yankee schoolteacher kept looking around and asking questions. Then one morning, after a rain, as he was moping along through a lonely mountain cove, he noticed a gleam of red against the rocks. He climbed the hill and clawed away the earth. There in a shallow grave lay his sweetheart, white and still, wrapped in her scarlet cloak and the cloak all muddy.

When Tom Dula heard about this, he saddled up the same old nag he'd ridden home from the war and took off for the Tennessee line. His brother, in order to throw the posse off the track, galloped off in the opposite direction. Hours later, as Tom was heading his winded animal up through the pass which led into Tennessee and freedom, a quiet voice spoke out of the laurel bushes. Tom pulled up. The Yankee schoolteacher stood there at the side of the path, his rifle lying across his mule's neck. Right there Tom gave up. A dad-burned Yankee had outfoxed him again.

While he was lying in the county jail, waiting his hanging day, Tom Dula made himself up a ballad, a confession of his crime. They say that he sat up in the cart on the way to his hanging ground and sang it in his sour baritone, playing the tune over on his fiddle between every verse. Among real ballad-singers there are some who never forget a song if they hear it through one time. Some folks never forgot Tom Dula's confession song and so his stark verses have lived on among the people of the Great Smokies as a ballad epitaph of a bitter returned veteran of the Civil War. . . . Since *Dooley* sings much more easily than *Dula,* that's the way the song has come to us from that flavorsome North Carolina singer, Frank Warner.

83. *DOWN IN THE WILLOW GARDEN*

The ballad of Tom Dooley, one of thousands of such criminal confessions in the history of English balladry, omits the moral customary in such songs. Tom seems to have been an unregenerate character, very much like Sam Hall, who swore just before he swung:

And I hate you one and all,
God damn your eyes!

Ordinarily the conventions of confession ballads have required the condemned man to turn pious, to apologize for his misdeeds, and to point a moral to his audience. James Munks, who in pioneer days in Ohio—

. . . shot Reuben Guile, who I never saw before,
And left him lie waldring all in his bloody gore.

begins his confession in the approved fashion. Thus:

O come all ye good people, it's now I've come to view
The sad and unhappy fate which now I come unto;
I pray you all take warning by my unhappy fate
And shun vice and folly before it is too late,
And alas, I am undone.

Again, John McAfee, another of Ohio's ballad heroes, starts off with a long, pious moan:

Come all young men and learn of me
My sad and mournful history,
And may you ne'er forgetful be
Of all this day I tell to thee.

Then McAfee proceeds with relish to describe just how he did his wife in, offering her poison in the place of medicine.

She gave to me a tender look,
Then in her mouth the poison took;
Then with her baby on her bed
Down to her last long sleep she laid.
But fearing she was not yet dead,
Upon her throat my hands I laid
And they such deep impression made
Her soul soon from her body fled.

"Down in the Willow Garden" is the modern descendant of just such an original, and has to do with a rather strange murder of a young lady named Rose Connelly. The murderer gives Rose Connelly some wine, which is variously described as "merkly," "burglar's," and "burgling," and apparently *was* Burgundy. One wonders whether the wine was really poisoned or whether the old-fashioned singers conceived this sinister liquid as poisonous enough, since the young man felt it was necessary to run his dagger or "skeever" through her to finish the job. Because of the wailing melody which rolls the murderer to his final execution, the ballad is still quite popular with "hillbilly" singers on the air and, curiously enough, is one of the songs that young lady folk-singers in New York seem especially to relish.

When you try this poisoner's confession, sing it with the slow swing of a veteran rocking chair rocker, rocking easy on the front porch on a cool evening, accenting the words every time your feet hit the porch.

84. *PRETTY POLLY*

The people, in passing their songs on by word of mouth through the years, make frequent changes that are especially notable in the texts. Some critics seem to feel when lines are lost, proper names garbled or plot details omitted, that the song has decayed. "Changed" is a fairer term; such alterations can be judged only as they affect the life of a song. In America the old ballads have tended to become lyric songs. For instance, "The Lass of Roch Royal," which in the Child volume runs to thirty-five stanzas, has contributed three stanzas only to the broad American tradition.* These stanzas appeared in a couple of ballads, but recently emerged with additional material as the basis of a hillbilly song. One can only say that the people do what they need to with their folklore and have *forgetteries* as good as their memories. This process of folk editing by simplification has transformed a rather theatrical British come-all-ye into the best and most effective of all American murder ballads. In the British original, sometimes known as "The Gosport Tragedy," the murderer tries to make his escape on board ship. The ship will not sail and the captain is therefore convinced that a murderer is on board. All the sailors, including the murderer, deny any guilt, and then the ghost of Pretty Polly appears with Willie's baby in her arms:

Away from his Captain he turn-ed with speed
And met his dearest Polly, which made his heart to bleed.

* See the "Who Will Shoe Your Feet" stanzas in "John Henry."

She rent him, she stripped him, she tore him
all in three:
Because he had murdered her and her baby.

Kentucky mountain singers were not impressed by the sailor's superstition. They exorcised the ghost, censored the baby, and thus cut the ballad down to a hard-hitting description of a brutal crime. They sing "Pretty Polly" without visible irony or sentimentality, flat-voiced and pokerfaced, a swift and rippling banjo accompaniment contrasting with the long somber line of the melody. Sung in this fashion, with real seriousness and objectivity, the ballad acquires the feeling of inevitability and horror common to the great tragic ballads.

Dreiser based his best-known novel upon a theme essentially the same as that of "Pretty Polly," calling it *An American Tragedy.* He might well have called it "*The* American Tragedy," if our ballads are a good index to our mores. There are literally scores of local ballads that tell the story of the young man who murders his sweetheart instead of marrying her, when "she gets in a family way." Such ballads pull no punches, when they come to describe the dirty deed.

In "Oma Wise" or "Pretty Romey," the murderer . . .

. . . kicked her and he cuffed her
Till she hardly could stand,
Then he drowned pretty Omie
Just below the mill dam.

In "The Knoxville Girl," derived from the British "Wexford Girl" and probably the most commonly known of these passion-murder ballads . . .

I picked a stick up from the ground
I beat her more and more,
I beat her till the ground around
Was covered all over with gore.

I took her by her long black hair
I slung her round and round,
I threw her into the still water deep
That flows through Knoxville town.

In "Pearl Bryan," another Ohio tragedy, but of recent date, the two young medical students cut off Pearl's head and threw her body into the Ohio River. To this day no one has found her head. The ballad describes an affecting scene at the trial . . .

In come Pearl Bryan's sister,
And falling on her knees,
Begging to Scott Jackson—
"My sister's head, O please!"

All these songs were sung, according to the many old ladies questioned about the matter, "as warnings to young women, how they should beware of men and their false, lying tongues." They served, thus, to bulwark the sex mores of frontier America.

85. *JOHN HARDY*

This ballad of a West Virginia Negro murderer is often a companion piece to "Pretty Polly." Like "Pretty Polly," it is ordinarily sung by white singers in the Southern Appalachians, sung in the same pokerfaced style with a hard-hitting, fast-moving five-string banjo accompaniment. Despite its recent origin, it has many of the stylistic qualities of the ancient tragic ballads, yet, because of its recent vintage, we know a good deal about John Hardy's story. There follows an excerpt from the court record of his trial . . .

STATE OF WEST VIRGINIA VS. JOHN HARDY

This day came again the State by her attorney and the prisoner who stands convicted of murder in the first degree was again brought to the bar of the Court in custody of the sheriff of this County; and thereupon the prisoner being asked by the court if anything he had or could say why the Court should not proceed to pass sentence of the law upon him . . . and the prisoner saying nothing . . . it is therefore considered by the Court that the prisoner John Hardy is guilty as found by the verdict of the jury herein and that the said John Hardy be hanged by the neck until he is dead . . . on Friday, the 19th day of January 1894 . . . and the prisoner is remanded to jail.

Standing before the court was John Hardy, a steel-driver, over six feet tall and two hundred pounds of muscle, "black as the kittle of hell." (For this and other reasons John Hardy has been often and wrongly confused with John Henry, Negro work hero.) Anyhow, they say that this John Hardy came to the gambling table one night, slapped down his forty-five and said, "Now I want you to lay here and the first man who steals my money, I mean to kill him." Along toward midnight he began to lose. He accused a Negro (in our version a "Chinaman") of taking twenty-five cents, and, although the man returned his money, he grabbed up his pistol and shot him dead, saying, "Man, don't you know I wouldn't lie to my gun?"

John Hardy hid out in the Negro shanties in the mountains until one day they caught him asleep, took his two guns, and slipped the cuffs on him. On his way to the county jail he jumped off the open vestibule of the train, taking the sheriff with him, but the sheriff pistol-whipped him and held him. In jail he watched the men building the scaffold where he was to be hung and he told all the boys, "I ain't never gonna be hung on that scaffold." Yes, John Hardy was like the bad man in the song:

In come a man name Billy Gessef,
He was so bad till he was scared of hissef.

But no matter how bad he was, John Hardy knew he had to die. So he called for a preacher, confessed his sins, and spent his last days praying and singing hymns. The white Baptist preacher gave him a new suit of clothes, took him down to the river, and baptized him "like a white man." On the scaffold he "confessed he had done wrong in killing a man under the influence of whiskey and advised all young men to avoid gambling and drink."

86. *PO' LAZ'US*

The Negro balladist, like the white folk-singer, heroized the desperado. To match Sam Bass and Jesse James and Billy the Kid, the Negro sings of "Railroad Bill":

Railroad Bill, he was a mighty bad coon,
Shot the sheriff by the light of the moon.

He had a .38 special as long as his arm—
"Gonna kill everybody ever done me wrong."

He sings of "Brady," who went to Hell for killing Duncan:

Heard a mighty rumbling way under the ground,
Must have been King Brady going down.

"Mama, mama what was that?"
"Mister Brady's in Hell with his Stetson hat."

He sings of "Stackerlee," the Memphis badman, who killed Billy Lyons over a milk-white Stetson hat and then took charge of Hell—

Stackerlee he told the devil,
Say, "Come on, let's have some fun,
You stick me with your pitchfork,
I'll shoot you with my 41."

"Take your pitchfork, Tom Devil,
And lay it on the shelf,
I'm that bad man, Stackerlee,
And I'm gon' rule Hell by myself."

We have chosen to print "Po' Laz'us," because it tells the most poignant and moving story and is the most widely sung of all these ballads. It is said that Laz'us (short for Lazarus) worked on the levee camps, in the days when "you worked from can to can't (from when you can see in the mornin' till you can't see at night) and maybe they paid you and maybe they didn't." Laz'us got tired of finding meat (worms) in his greens, so he decided to walk the table. You had to be really disgusted and really tough to walk the table in a levee camp, tromping right down the middle of the mess table and slapping your big muddy shoes right in everybody's plates. Po' Laz'us walked the table that day with a blue-steel revolver in each hand. He knew the white boss would give him a whipping for what he had done, so he decided to go all the way. He walked over to the commissary, introduced himself by poking his pistols in the pay-clerk's window and then took off with the payroll.

The ballad takes up the story at this point describing the death of this tough guy with obvious sympathy and in powerfully tragic lines. You cannot fail to know, when you hear a gang of men on the road shouting out this ballad-work-song in rhythm with their picks, that they had often wished to do what Po' Laz'us had done, never mind the consequences. The song has no end, just as the troubles of the Negro working man have no end. Sometimes, however, when the singers have come to the lines about Laz'us' death, they pause. The picks fall all together in concert for a few moments. Then they sing:

Captain, did you hear about all your men gonna
leave you,
Next pay-day, Lawd, Lawd, next pay-day.

87. *DARLIN' COREY*

In an ancient riddling ballad, still known to American singers, the devil asks a girl, among other questions, what is "meaner than womankind." She gives the right answer in the song, when she observes that only . . .

The devil is meaner than womankind.

So, for toughness, for heroism, for pure cussedness, there are women in American folklore who can keep right up with their men. There were some with hearts as hard as "marble-stones,"—Belle Starr, Stacko'dollars, Bonny Parker, and Little Frankie. Then there was the frontier type, the breed from which darling Corey, as a Kentucky mountain moonshining gal, is derived. Here is a portrait of this style of frontier hellcat from the Davy Crockett *Almanacs,* written in the days when, apparently, the American language was all purple.

It's most likely that my reeders has heered of Colonel Coon's wife, Judy. She used to brag that she war a streak of litenin set up edgeways and buttered with quicksilver. She wore a bearskin petticoat, an alligator's hide for an overcoat, an eagle's nest for a hat, with a wildcat's tail for a feather. When she sung a psalm, you'd-a thought all the trees in creation war organ pipes and a harrycane war blowin' the bellows.

When she was fourteen years old, she wrung off a snapping turtle's neck and made a comb of its shell, which she wears to this day. When she was sixteen years old, she run down a four year old colt and chased a bear three miles through the snow, because she wanted his hair to make a tooth brush. She outscreamed a catamount on a wager when she was just come of age, and sucked forty rattlesnakes' eggs to give her a sweet breath the night she was married.

When she had got her growth, she could scalp an Indian, skin a bear, laugh the bark off a pine tree, swim stark up a cataract, gouge out alligators' eyes, dance a rock to pieces, sink a steamboat, blow out the moonlight, ride a painter bareback, sing a wolf to sleep and scratch his eyes out. It is told on her that she carried twenty eyes in her work bag at one time, eyes that she had picked out of the heads of certain gals of her acquaintance. She always made them into a string of beads when she went to church and wore 'em round her neck. Being out one evening to a tea squall, about ten mile from home, in coming home through the woods she found a nest of young wildcats in the stump of a tree. She said nothing about it, but let her toe nails grow till they were an inch long. Then she started out all alone one morning, and went to the nest, and, jumping in upon the wildcats, stamped them to death with her feet. . . . Finely she cotch'd her death by standing two days up to her chin in the Maississippy to hail the steambotes as they past by.

Keep Mrs. Judy Coon in mind when you sing about darling Corey. A mountain banjo picker performs it "like all the trees in creation war organ pipes and a harrycane wind war blowin' the bellows."

88. *FRANKIE AND ALBERT*

Far better known than darling Corey is her Negro sister, Frankie, who "kilt her man for doin' her wrong." There is much precedent for Frankie's deed in antique balladry. Lady Margaret, for instance, disposed of Young Hunting without a moment's hesitation or a quiver of remorse when he told her that he had found another sweetheart.

He bended over her soft pillow
And gave her a kiss so sweet,
But with a penknife in her right hand,
She wounded him full deep.

She took him by his long, yellow locks
And also round the feet;
She plunged him into that doleful well
Full sixty fathoms deep.

The ballad of little Frankie is the modern counterpart of the same old story. Like most things in folklore, the facts of Frankie's case are somewhat obscure.

Sometime between 1849 and 1890 a sporting woman, probably named Frankie, shot or stabbed to death her fancy man, named Allen, Albert, or Johnnie, having found him *in flagrante delictu* with a woman named Alice Fly, Alice Bly, Alice Swan, Nellie Bly, Katie Fly, Ella Fry, Sara Siles, or, most colorfully, Alkali. According to one well-documented account, probably too well documented to be seriously regarded, the famous lady, one Frankie Baker, still lives in Portland, Oregon. The *St. Louis Post Dispatch* of October 20, 1899, carried a news story which connects this living and real Frankie Baker with the incident and the ballad:

> Allen Britt's brief experience in the art of love cost him his life. He died at the City Hospital Wednesday night from knife wounds inflicted by Frankie Baker, an ebony-hued cake-walker. Britt was also colored. He was seventeen years old. He met Frankie at the Orange Blossom's ball and was smitten with her. Frankie reciprocated and invited him to call upon her. Thereafter they were lovers.
>
> In the rear of 212 Targee St. lived Britt. There his sweetheart wended her way a few nights ago and lectured Britt for his alleged duplicity. Allen's reply was not intended to cheer the dusky damsel and a glint of steel gleamed in the darkness. An instant later the boy fell mortally wounded. Frankie Baker is locked up at the police force courts.

The *Post Dispatch* story probably does not describe the incident on which the Frankie and Johnnie ballad is based. Emerson Hough maintains that he heard the song in St. Louis before 1850. Many informants are yet alive who say they had heard it long before 1890. To add to the confusion a woman named Frankie Baker came to St. Louis from Oregon not long ago and prosecuted a suit for slander against those she thought had defamed her!

The tragedy of the jealous sporting woman who dropped her man "as a hunter drops his bird" has become an American classic. Mae West has made it her very own on the stage and in the movies. Joe Cook and many another American have crooned it, slapstickled it, and sung it for thousands of audiences. Negro honkytonk piano players, soldiers in foxholes, and Americans of all varieties have intoned this American litany. The version we print here is not the tongue-in-cheek college-boy "Frankie and Johnny," but a deeply felt Negro melody collected before 1910, combined with a cross-country pooling of the stanzas.

89. *TAKE A WHIFF ON ME*

Like the ballad of Frankie and her two-timing man, this merry and convivial chant of the "snowbirds" comes from the city. A city folk song from the redlight district, from the skid-rows, from the gambling hells and "dens of vice" of the turn of this century, it followed the cocaine habit out into the levee camps and the country barrelhouses of the Deep South. Old-timers remember the day in New Orleans when you could buy cocaine and opium at the corner drugstore and when the men in the levee camps used to bum a "tab of cocaine" just as free and easy as they do a chew of tobacco today. That these tough guys thought of "the snow" as no more dangerous than hard liquor is evidenced in an old couplet that advises:

Why don't you be like me?
Why don't you be like me?
Quit your high tension whiskey, boy,
And let your cocaine be.

A surprising number of songs and ballads and tunes have come from the hopheads and snowbirds in the past two generations. Some of them, like "Willie the Weeper" and his sister "Minnie the Moocher," are nationally known. "Take a Whiff on Me," with stanzas we have collected in Louisiana, Texas, and New York, tops them all. It could have been made only by true snowbirds like Cocaine Lil. Of her it is sung:

She had cocaine hair on her cocaine head.
She wore a snowbird hat and sleigh-riding clothes.
She had a cocaine dress that was poppy red.
On her coat she wore a cocaine crimson rose. . . .

They laid her out in her cocaine clothes
In her snowbird hat with its crimson rose;
On her headstone you'll find this refrain:
"She died as she lived, sniffing cocaine."

For the best of all our songs about one of our national beverages, turn to "Rye Whiskey."

90. *HARD TIMES, POOR BOY*

Desperadoes, tough Annies, hopheads and gunsels, they all end up in jail before they're through. There they have made a lingo all their own; there they have stirred up a batch of songs all their own. The national jailbird ballad, however, the same from coast to coast, with only minor variations as between Mount Holley, New Jersey, and Portland, Oregon, is this song with its scores of stanzas about low-down sheriffs and ravenous bedbugs. In the following paragraphs we give you an impression of how it feels to board in the hard-rock hotel, an impression gleaned from talks with a number of singing jailbirds:

When they take your money and your knife and your watch away from you and march you down that damp, smelly corridor past the big door, when you hear that big door clang behind you and then the small cell door slams in your face, when you ask the jailer for a match and you hear no reply but his footsteps dying away down the corridor, man, it looks like cold chills run all through your heart, and you get those old lonesome jailhouse blues. Your heart begins to turn as hard as a marble stone.

The chuck they give, well, you may be able to eat it, but the way they throw it at you, it can't ever taste good. The bed they give you, well, you may be able to sleep on it, but, if your blanket is thin and buggy, certainly your jailers won't care. Their job is to hold you, brother, hold you with guns and concrete and steel bars and locks, just hold you as long as the twelve men tell them to.

Out in the bull pen, the cell-block compound, where you get your exercise, the older prisoners try you in the kangaroo court and sentence you to a fine or a licking for breaking in the jailhouse without their permission. Don't look to these old birds for sympathy; they've got troubles of their own—one year, ten years, twenty years, natural life.

Some got six months, some got a solid year,
But my old buddy, boys, he's got lifetime here.

The first trick you throw may not be so bad, but by your second or third trip behind those cold, iron bars, your heart turns solid like a rock cast down in the sea. A policeman can spot you a block away. He can tell you're a jailbird by the way you walk. He can see "jailbird" for certain in your face, when he asks you where you're from and what you do for a living. He knows. And he won't take any of your talk, as he walks you down to the city jail as a suspect in the latest holdup or dime-store robbery.

Now, you think and talk the language of the "hard-rock hotel." You're a member of the big brotherhood that includes Sam Hall and Clyde Barrow and Flip the Jip and Al Capone. You know the jails from coast to coast, and this is your song—

For lying and stealing, I never shall fail,
But I don't give a damn for lyin' in jail,
And it's hard times, poor boys.

Our version of America's national jailhouse complaint comes from an old boy who had done time in Durant, Oklahoma.

91. *DE MIDNIGHT SPECIAL*

This is the Negro jailbird's ballad to match "Hard Times, Poor Boy." Like so many American folk songs, its hero is not a man but a train—the Midnight Special that crashes by in the darkness, its headlight cracking the lonesome night apart, its whistle talking about the open, free country up ahead. We have been told that the Midnight Special, about which the song was made, is the Golden Gate Limited that pulls out of the Southern Pacific Depot at Houston, Texas, sharp at midnight, headed for San Antonio, El Paso, San Francisco, and "any other place you want to go." Thirty miles farther along the Midnight Special shines its "ever-lovin' light" through the barred windows of the Texas State Prison farm at Sugarland. The Negro convicts, who lie awake in the dormitory, send their dreams of the "free world" along with the train.

The Midnight Special runs free through the night; iron bars hold us to our rusty, dusty monotony. Every morning, when the "ding-dong rings" we "get the same damn thing" for breakfast. "Yes, we have a doctor who gives us tablets when we're sick, but "ain't no one can cure de fever on a convict man." Man, an' it's so easy to get in trouble. Just start a little squabble in the street, and Bud Russell will be carrying you on down to the pen. "Say, I believe, that's my gal, Rosie, coming down the road. It really looks like her. See that umbrella. I'd know it anywhere. She's got that pardon in her hand, too. . . ."

But this, like the Midnight Special, is only a convict's dream. There's no little Rosie coming to tell the captain, "I wants my man." That was just another con dragging his feet in the dust. There's no pardon. There's just a long stretch of years ahead, "before the man gonna call me an' I'm goin' home. Even when that day comes, I'll have to ride the rods to get home. They can't send me no money."

So this song from behind the prison bars expresses in the most poignant, tender, and melancholy way the prisoner's longing for freedom. "Mister," said one convict after he'd finished his song, "can't you help me get out of this place? I just nacherly don't like it."

92. *AIN' NO MO' CANE ON DIS BRAZIS*

When floods deluge the Brazos plains region, the big Brazos River washes down off the Panhandle, past Graham, Palo Pinto, and Waco, turning from adobe red to coffee color, getting bigger, cutting deeper into the rich Texas plain, till it sends out a wide skirt of silty water into the blue of the Mexican Sea. The big red Brazos cuts soil out of many elbows of land all along its thousand-mile track. If you live along the river you can hear the soil slipping down into the water when the Brazos is on its springtime rise.

West of Houston, the Brazos and Colorado Rivers have washed the plains for centuries. They have helped to make the land fat; the soil is deep and rich and mucky, like Mississippi Valley soil. The land is good for corn and cotton and cane. Before the Civil War the plantations on the lower-river ranches were broad and rich like the plantations in the Mississippi Delta. And right there in the middle of this fat farming section in the Brazos bottoms is a place called Sugarland.

In slavery time there were big plantations. We don't know just what the slaves sung in the long hot days back yonder, but we know they had plenty of trouble and we are sure they sung. After slavery was formally abolished, the big plantations kept on, only they got their cheap Negro labor from the state of Texas—leased convicts. The men who ran these plantations under the "lease system" drove their men mighty hard. The old songs clung to the land like the mists over the old red Brazos in the early mornings, songs of trouble and anguish. The Negroes called that time the "Red Heifer Time," because the whips that were used to punish them were made from raw cowhide with the red hair still on the hide.

You oughta been here in nineteen fo',
You could find a dead man on every turn row.

The cane at Sugarland grows jungle-thick, arching over the rows so that the workers move in continual twilight. And in "Red Heifer Times" leased convict labor was so plentiful at Sugarland that if a man fell out with sunstroke, or if a rebellious man fought back and was beaten down, if a man just plain wore out and dropped in the field, the state could always furnish another. So the convicts made their songs out of the things they saw.

In the late fall, when the frost stripes the sugar cane with red and purple, when the cane gets so sweet you can eat a stalk like a rich, twelve-foot candy bar, chewing up the pulp and spitting it out, sucking up the sweet, sugary cane juice, the men go into the fields with their cane knives. They slog painfully down the rows in the cold and soggy muck between the hills where the ripe cane pushes up against the pale winter sky. The Texas norther cuts them to the bone. The razor-edged cane leaves slash at their faces and at their hands. Yet the knives of the cane-cutters sing against the crisp cane and up from the muck and across the matted green jungle, the old song of the sweet Brazos land rises into the chilly wind over the ringing rhythm of the knives.

This song has clung to the fat Brazos land for a long time, from slavery, through the "Red Heifer Times," to these days when the men who cut the cane are state convicts, working and living under better conditions—but still cheap labor, still guarded, still men with plenty of troubles. And so every year—for how long?—almost a hundred years—this song has been sung at cane-cutting time in the Brazos bottoms near Sugarland in Texas. "Ol' Hannah" is the sun.

93. *TAKE THIS HAMMER*

. . . once was sung on all sorts of jobs, but now is mainly current on the Southern prison farms. Hand labor is cheap in the pen.

Where "Ain' No Mo' Cane on Dis Brazis" has a free rhythm, a slow rock, *leading* the cane-cutters to strike together, "Take This Hammer" *drives* the men to keep to a swift and steady work tempo. Both songs have their real roots in Africa, which was and is a land of work-songs. Thence the Negro slaves brought their work-song tradition with them and the land of the South was cleared and the crops harvested, as the black slaves chanted their communal songs. The roads were built, the levees raised, the railroads laid down, the cotton baled, the steamboats loaded—the work of the post-Civil War South has been done in harmony and rhythm, with satire and with overtones of sorrow—to song, the work-songs of the Negroes. Even aboard the clipper ships, the Negro was recognized as the best of all chantey singers.

It is impudence to present one of these songs in print. Only a sound film can adequately represent them. The hot Southern sun shines down on the brown and glossy muscles of the work gang. The picks make whirling rainbow arcs around the shoulders of the singers. As the picks dig into the rock, the men give a deep, guttural grunt; their pent-up strength flows through the pick handle and they relax their bodies and prepare for the next blow.

The song leader now begins—pick handle twirling in his palms, the pickhead flashing in the sun:

Take this hammo— Huh!

The men grunt as the picks bite in together. They join the leader on his line, trailing in, one in harmony, one talking the words, another grunting them out between clenched teeth, another throwing out a high, thin falsetto cry above the rest. On the final syllable, the picks are descending and again they bite a chip out of the rock and again there is a grunted exhalation of breath:

Carry it to my captain—Huh!

The picks whirl up together in the sunlight and down again, they ring on the earth together, with maybe one or two bouncing a couple of times in a sort of syncopation. When the leader comes to the third—

Carry it to my captain—

he holds on to the word "captain" as long as he can, looks around at the boss and grins; his buddies chuckle and relax for a moment, knowing that he is giving them a little rest; then, "wham" the steel bites at the rock and the whole gang roars out the final line, so that the hill gives back the sound and the white boss trembles a bit where he sits watching in the shade.

Scores of songs, thousands of stanzas:—food, women, mean boss-man, good buddy; you can't work me down, I'm like John Henry, I'm burning down; where's the water boy; don't call me a nappy-headed devil, that ain't my name—a catalogue of the life and reflections of the Southern Negro worker. . . . We've sat for hours and days listening, recording, taking them down. We know this is one thing that can't be captured on the printed page. The way of singing is unique, the way of using the voice and attacking the tones of the melody have to be heard to be understood. The delicate irony that comes with the pronunciation of a word or the double meaning that steals in with an inflection and a smile—all this is the stuff of drama. And the drama, itself, has its roots in strength and sweat and sorrow and strong laughter that no singer can quite capture unless he's been there, unless he knows . . .

Man, if you don't sing, you sho git worried!

94. *ALMOST DONE*

"Take This Hammer" is the most common Southern work-song in one variant or another. "Almost Done" we found only in Alabama, sung by the prisoners on the Birmingham County Farm. These men slept chained by one leg while they slept, each man's chain linked to a huge anchor chain that ran down the center of the dormitory. It is another work-song with a regular rhythm, good for all sorts of gang labor, very syncopated and rather gay, but wistful at the same time. By way of introduction listen to what Left Wing Gordon, an itinerant Negro worker, a singer who has been on several county farms in the old days, has to say.

I had a hard time, same as any other fellow, in the chain gang on the roads. Had to work very hard. Sometime I would be so sick I felt like I could hardly hold up my head, but I had to keep on working. Sometime when I close my eyes, I could see them heat waves shimmering like little red fires in my head. But we had to keep on. Maybe cuttin' a new road, big rocks to move. It would strain your muscles; it would work a fellow down to nothin' in less'n ten years. Sometime I say to the road boss that I'm sick.

"Well, dammit, die an' prove it," he would say.

"Well, cap'n, jes' let me res' a little bit."

"Lissen, if you'd paid yo' fine, you wouldn' be here. The jedge didn't show you no mercy, I can't give you none."

Plow up the gravel, boys, dig up the rocks,
Ain't no need to hurry, got six long months.

I told my captain my feet was cold—
"God damn yore feet, let the wheelers roll."

Run here, water boy, bring your water round,
I need me some water, I sho am burning down . . .

I lived in a shack 'bout ten or fifteen men in the same room, two or three bunks high for sleepin'. All of us tied to one chain, chain tied to one fellow. Bed made out of old sacks full of straw, never made up. Rainy days, boys work a little while, come in all muddy and wet and flop down an' go to sleep, sleep till nex' mornin'. Sometimes on road we sleep in boxcar cage crowded up same as shacks. Don't remember how I got along. Don' remember much about it. Always thinkin' 'bout sumpin else, goin' somewhere or seein' my baby. Just took things as they come.

Don't talk about it,
'Bout it, if you do, I'll cry.
Don't crowd around me,
Round me, if you do, I'll die.

95. *ANOTHER MAN DONE GONE*

Some of them are chained. Some of them work under the eye of a riding boss with a Winchester across the pommel of his saddle. There is always a pack of bloodhounds ready to strike out on their trail. But still they keep running, zigzagging till they're out of range of the rifle, laying a crooked trail through the bottoms for the hounds. They're brought back, whipped, put in solitary, deprived of their few privileges and then, once back in the field or on the road, they'll make a break as soon as they get a chance. Some men are built like that.

Long John—they sing about him in Texas —had a pair of shoes:

With a heel in front and a heel behind,
Till you couldn't tell where that boy was gwine.

Then there was Riley, another Texas escape artist, who made it to the river, when it was on a rise and the water was boiling with whirlpools and floating timber. Riley swam that river, when the captain said no man could. Now the convicts tell how Riley "walked the water like Jesus." A prisoner named Lightning told us, proudly, in the presence of the guards, that he could leave Darrington State Farm anytime he got ready to go. There was no horse on the place that could outrun him nor dog that could follow his trail.

Like every underprivileged Negro in the South, Vera Hall knew all about the county farm and the state pen. She had heard about them from people who were close to her. Although Vera Hall was a peaceloving cook and washerwoman and the pillar of the choir in her Baptist church, she knew about these things and she knew, as well, a song from the prison, a song about escape. Her song, "Another Man Done Gone," can be a blues or a work-song, but mostly it is enigmatic, full of silent spaces, speaking of the night and of a man slipping by in the night. You see his face, you know him, but at the same time you put him out of your mind, so that when the white man asks after him, you can say:

I didn't know his name,
I didn't know his name.

I don' know where he's gone,
I don' know where he's gone.

80.

Jesse James

Words and melody adapted and arranged by
John A. and Alan Lomax

Piano arrangement by
Charles and Ruth Seeger

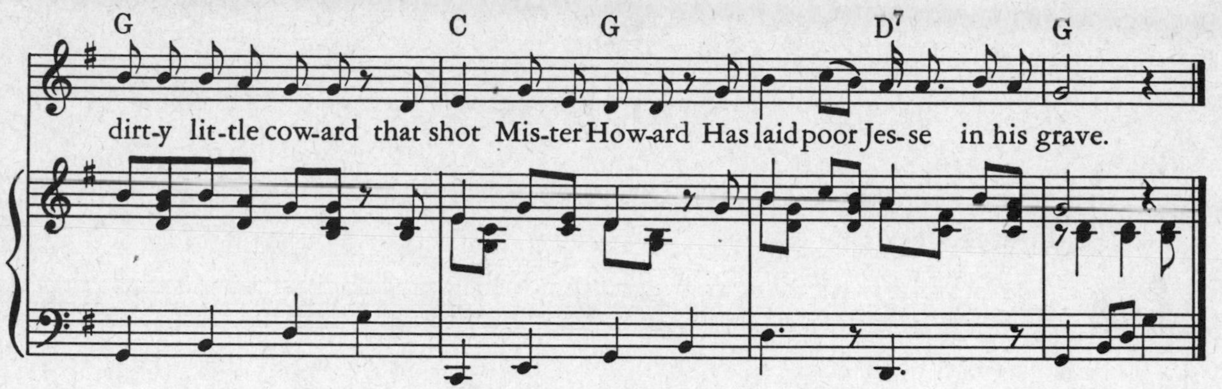

CHORUS: Poor Jesse had a wife to mourn for his life,
Three children, they were brave,
But that dirty little coward that shot Mister Howard
Has laid poor Jesse in his grave.

2. It was Robert Ford, that dirty little coward,
I wonder how does he feel?
For he ate of Jesse's bread and he slept in Jesse's bed
And laid poor Jesse in his grave.

3. It was his brother, Frank who robbed the Gallatin bank
And carried the money from the town;
It was in this very place that they had a little race
For they shot Captain Sheets to the ground.

4. They went to the crossing not very far from there
And there they did the same;
With the agent on his knees, he delivered up the keys
To the outlaws, Frank and Jesse James.

5. It was on a Wednesday night, the moon was shining bright,
They robbed the Glendale train;
The people they did say for many miles away,
It was robbed by Frank and Jesse James.

6. It was on a Saturday night, Jesse was at home,
Talking to his family brave,
Robert Ford came along like a thief in the night
And laid poor Jesse in his grave.

7. The people held their breath, when they heard of Jesse's death
And wondered how he ever came to die;
It was one of the gang, called little Robert Ford,
He shot poor Jesse on the sly.

8. Jesse went to his rest with his hand on his breast;
The devil will be upon his knee.
He was born one day in the country of Clay
And came from a solitary race.

9. This song was made by Billy Gashade,
As soon as the news did arrive;
He said there was no man with the law in his hand,
Who could take Jesse James when alive.

81.

Sam Bass

Words and melody adapted and arranged by
John A. and Alan Lomax
Piano arrangement by
Charles and Ruth Seeger
Moderately slow
F
C
Sam Bass was born in In - di - an - a, it was his na - tive
mf
F
home, And at the age of sev - en - teen, young Sam be - gan to
C
B♭
F
roam. Sam first came out to Tex - as a cow - boy for to

2. Sam used to deal in race stock, one called the Denton mare;
He matched her in scrub races and took her to the fair.
Sam used to coin the money and spent it just as free,
He always drank good whisky, wherever he might be.

3. Sam left the Collins ranch in the merry month of May
With a herd of Texas cattle the Black Hills for to see,
Sold out in Custer City and then got on a spree—
A harder set of cowboys you seldom ever see.

4. On their way back to Texas they robbed the U. P. train,
And then split up in couples and started out again.
Joe Collins and his partner were overtaken soon,
With all their hard earned money they had to meet their doom.

5. Sam made it back to Texas, all right side up with care;
Rode into the town of Denton with all his friends to share.
Sam's life was short in Texas; three robberies did he do:
He robbed all the passenger, mail, and express cars, too.

6. Sam met his fate at Round Rock, July the twenty-first,
They pierced poor Sam with rifle balls and emptied out his purse.
Poor Sam, he is a corpse and six foot under clay,
And Jackson's in the bushes trying to get away.

7. Jim had borrowed Sam's good gold and didn't want to pay,
The only shot he saw was to give poor Sam away.
He sold out Sam and Barnes and left their friends to mourn—
Oh, what a scorching Jim will get when Gabriel blows his horn!

8. And so he sold out Sam and Barnes and left their friends to mourn.
Oh, what a scorching Jim will get when Gabriel blows his horn!
Perhaps he's got to heaven, there's none of us can say,
But if I'm right in my surmise he's gone the other way.

82.

Tom Dooley

Words and melody adapted and arranged by
Frank Warner

Piano arrangement by
Charles and Ruth Seeger

CHORUS:
Hang down your head, Tom Dooley,
Hang down your head and cry,
Hang down your head, Tom Dooley,
Poor boy, you're bound to die.

1. I met her on the mountain
And there I tuck her life;
I met her on the mountain
And stobbed her with my knife.

CHORUS:
Hang down your head, Tom Dooley,
Hang down your head and cry,
Hang down your head, Tom Dooley,
Poor boy, you're bound to die.

2. This time tomorrer,
Reckon where I'll be?—
If it hadn'-a been for Grayson
I'd-a been in Tennessee.

CHORUS:
Hang down your head, Tom Dooley,
Hang down your head and cry,
Hang down your head, Tom Dooley,
Poor boy, you're bound to die.

3. This time tomorrer,
Reckon where I'll be?—
In some lonesome valley
A-hangin' on a white oak tree.

CHORUS:
Hang down your head, Tom Dooley,
Hang down your head and cry,
Hang down your head, Tom Dooley,
Poor boy, you're bound to die.

83.

Down in the Willow Garden

Words and melody adapted and arranged by
John A. and Alan Lomax

Piano arrangement by
Charles and Ruth Seeger

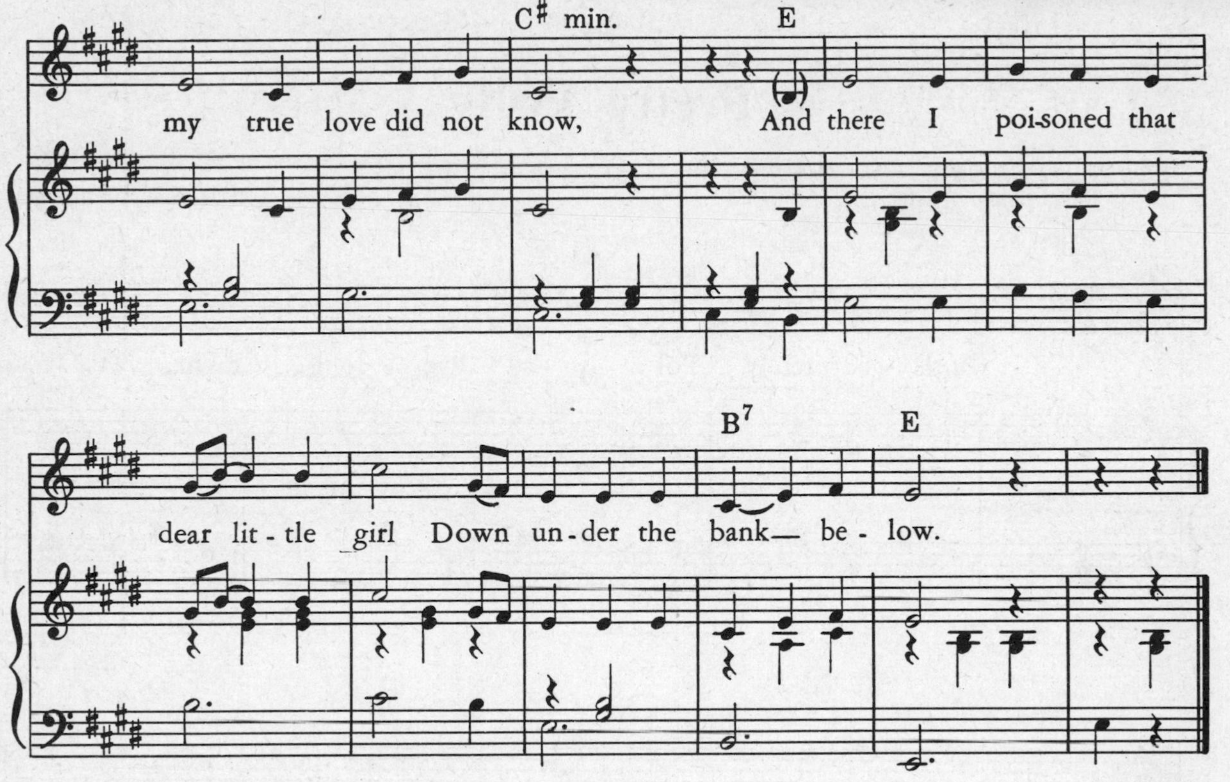

2. I stobbed her with a dagger,
Which was a bloody knife,
I threw her in the river,
Which was a dreadful sight.
My father often told me
That money would set me free,
If I would murder that dear little girl
Whose name was Rose Connelly.

3. And now he sits in his own cottage door,
A-wiping his weeping eye,
And now he waits for his own dear son,
Upon the scaffold high.
My race is run beneath the sun,
Lo, hell's now waiting for me,
For I have murdered that dear little girl I love
Whose name was Rose Connelly.

84.

Pretty Polly

Words and melody adapted and arranged by
John A. and Alan Lomax

Piano arrangement by
Charles and Ruth Seeger

1. I courted pretty Polly the livelong night,
I courted pretty Polly the livelong night,
Then left her next morning before it was light.

2. "Pretty Polly, pretty Polly, come and go along with me,
Pretty Polly, pretty Polly, come and go along with me,
Before we get married, some pleasure to see."

3. She got up behind me and away we did go,
Over the hills to the valleys below.

4. They went a little piece further and what did they spy?
A new-dug grave and a spade lying by.

5. "Willie, O Willie, I'm afraid of your way,
I'm afraid you will lead my poor body astray."

6. She fell down on her knees and she suffered no fear,
"How can you kill a poor girl that loves you so dear?"

7. "Pretty Polly, pretty Polly, you're thinking just right,
I dug on your grave the best part of last night."

8. "There's no time to talk now, there's no time to stand,"
He drew out his knife all in his right hand.

9. He stobbed her to the heart, her heart's blood it did flow,
And into the grave pretty Polly did go.

10. He threw a little dirt over her and started for home,
Leaving no one behind but the wild birds to mourn.

85.

John Hardy

Words and melody adapted and arranged by
John A. and Alan Lomax

Piano arrangement by
Charles and Ruth Seeger

2. John Hardy stood at the gamblin' table,
Didn't have no int'rest in the game,
Up stepped a yellow gal and threw a dollar down,
Said, " Deal John Hardy in the game, poor boy,
Deal John Hardy in the game."

3. John Hardy took that yellow gal's money,
And then he began to play,
Said, "The man that wins my yellow gal's dollar,
I'll lay him in his lonesome grave, poor boy,
I'll lay him in his lonesome grave."

4. John Hardy drew to a four-card straight,
And the Chinaman drew to a pair,
John failed to catch and the Chinaman won,
And he left him sitting dead in his chair, poor boy,
And he left him sitting dead in his chair,

5. John started to catch that East-bound train,
So dark he could not see,
Up stepped the police and took him by the arm,
Said, "Johnny come and go with me, poor boy,
Johnny come and go with me."

6. John Hardy's father came to him,
Come for to go his bail;
No bail was allowed for a murderin' man,
So they shoved John Hardy back in jail, poor boy,
They shoved John Hardy back in jail.

7. They took John Hardy to his hangin' ground,
They hung him there to die,
And the very last word I heard him say—
"My forty gun never told a lie, poor boy,
My forty gun never told a lie.

8. "I've been to the East, I've been to the West,
I've travelled this wide world around,
I've been to the river and I've been baptised
And now I'm on my hangin' ground, poor boy,
And now I'm on my hangin' ground."

9. John Hardy had a loving little wife,
And children she had three,
But he cared no more for his wife and his child,
Than he did for the rocks in the sea, poor boy,
Than he did for the rocks in the sea.

86.

Po' Laz'us

Words and melody adapted and arranged by
John A. and Alan Lomax

Piano arrangement by
Charles and Ruth Seeger

2. O de deputy 'gin to wonder, where in de worl' he could fin' him?
O de deputy 'gin to wonder, where in de worl' he could fin' him?
"Well, I don' know, Lawd, Lawd, I jes' don' know."

3. O dey found po' Laz'us way out between two mountains.
O dey found po' Laz'us way out between two mountains,
An' dey blowed him down, Lawd, Lawd, an' dey blowed him down.

4. Ol' Lazus tol' de deputy he had never been arrested,
Ol' Laz'us tol' de deputy he had never been arrested,
By no one man, Lawd, Lawd, by no one man.

5. So dey shot po' Laz'us, shot him wid a great big number,
Dey shot po' Laz'us, shot him wid a great big number,
Number *Forty-Five,* Lawd, Lawd, number *Forty-five.*

6. An' dey taken po' Laz'us an' dey laid him on de commissary county,**
Dey taken po' Laz'us an' dey laid him on de commissary county,
An' dey walked away, Lawd, Lawd, an' dey walked away.

7. Laz'us tol' de deputy, "Please gimme a cool drink o' water",
Laz'us tol' de deputy, "Please gimme a cool drink o' water,
Jes' befo' I die, Lawd, Lawd, jes' befo' I die."

8. Laz'us' sister run an' tol' her mother,
Laz'us' sister run an' tcl' her mother,
"Po' Laz'us dead, Lawd, Lawd, po' Laz'us dead."

9. Laz'us' mother, she laid down her sewin',
Laz'us' mother, she laid down her sewin',
She begin to cry, Lawd, Lawd, she begin to cry.

10. Laz'us' mother, she come a-screamin' an' a-cryin',
Laz'us' mother, she come a-screamin' an' a-cryin',
"Dat's my only son, Lawd, Lawd, dat's my only son!"

11. Laz'us' father, he sho' was hard-hearted,
Laz'us' father, he sho' was hard-hearted,
Didn't say a word, Lawd, Lawd, didn't say a word.

12. Laz'us' sister, she couldn't go to de funeral,
Laz'us' sister, she couldn't go to de funeral,
Didn't have no shoes, Lawd, Lawd, didn't have no shoes.

(A pause—then the gang sings:)

13. Cap'n, did you hear about— all yo' men gonna leave you?
Cap'n did you hear about— all yo' men gonna leave you?
Nex' pay-day, Lawd, Lawd, nex' pay-day.

*Sing this with the "hanhs" as a work-song, or without them as a ballad.
**Counter of the commissary store.

87.

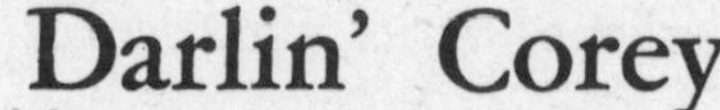

Darlin' Corey

Words and melody adapted and arranged by
John A. and Alan Lomax

Piano arrangement by
Charles and Ruth Seeger

Fast

G C

Wake — up, wake up, dar - lin' Cor - ey, ——— What makes you sleep — so — sound?

C7 F C7

The — rev - e - nue of - fi - cers is a - com - in' ——— To —— tear your still - house down.

F C

1. Wake up, wake up, darlin' Corey,
What makes you sleep so sound?
The revenue officers is a-comin'
To tear your stillhouse down.

2. The first time I saw darlin' Corey,
She was standin' in the door,
Her shoes and stockin's in her hands
And her feet all over the floor.

3. Go 'way from me darlin' Corey,
Quit hangin' around my bed,
Pretty women run me distracted,
Corn liquor's killed me dead.

4. The next time I saw darlin' Corey,
She was standing on the banks of the sea,
She had two pistols strapped around her body
And a banjo on her knee.

5. Last night as I lay on my pillow,
Last night as I lay on my bed,
Last night as I lay on my pillow,
I dreamed darlin' Corey was dead.

6. The last time I saw darlin' Corey
She had a wine glass in her hand
She was drinkin' that cold pizen liquor
With a low-down sorry man.

7. Go and dig me a hole in the meadow,
A hole in the cold, cold ground,
Go and dig me a hole in the meadow,
Just to lay darlin' Corey down.

8. Don't you hear them blue-birds singin'?
Don't you hear that mournful sound?
They're preachin' Corey's funeral
In the lonesome graveyard ground.

88.

Frankie and Albert

Words and melody adapted and arranged by
John A. and Alan Lomax

Piano arrangement by
Charles and Ruth Seeger

2. Frankie went a-walkin'
Did not go for fun,
Underneath her little red petticoat
She had Albert's forty-one.
Gonna kill her man
For doin' her wrong.

3. Frankie went to the barroom
Ordered her a glass of beer,
Says to the bartender,
"Has my lovin' man been here?
He's my man,
But he's doin' me wrong."

4. "I will not tell you no story,
I will not tell you no lie, - - -
Albert left here about an hour ago
With a gal named Alice Fly.
He's your man,
But he's doin' you wrong."

5. Frankie went by the house,
She did not give no 'larm,
She looked in through the window glass
And saw Albert in the woman's arms.
He was her man, Lawd,
Doin' her wrong.

6. When Albert, he saw Frankie,
For the backdoor, he did scoot,
Frankie drew that forty-four,
Went — *rooty-toot-toot-toot-toot!*
She shot her man,
For doin' her wrong.

7. First time she shot him, he staggered,
Next time she shot him, he fell,
Third time she shot him, O Lawdy,
There was a new man's face in hell.
She killed her man,
For doin' her wrong.

8. When Frankie, she shot Albert,
He fell all in a knot,
Cryin', "O Mrs. Johnson,
See where your son is shot.
She's killed your son,
The only one.

9. "O turn me over doctor,
Turn me over slow,
I got a bullet in my lef' han' side,
Great God, is hurtin' me so.
I was her man,
But I done her wrong."

10. Frankie went to Mrs. Johnson,
Fell down on her knees,
Cryin', "O Mrs. Johnson,
Will you forgive me please?
I kilt your son,
The onlies' one."

11. "I will forgive you Frankie,
I will forgive you not,
You shot my lovin' Albert,
The only support I'm got.
Kilt my son,
The only one."

Poor boy, poor boy,
Poor boy, poor boy.
Done gone, done gone,
Done gone, done gone.

13. Frankie went to the graveyard,
Fell down on her knees,—
"Speak one word, Albert,
And give my heart some ease.
You was my man,
But you done me wrong."

12. A rubber tir'ed buggy,
A decorated hack
Took po' Albert to the graveyard
But it didn't bring him back.
He was her man,
But he done her wrong.

Poor boy, poor boy,
Poor boy, poor boy.
Done gone, done gone,
Done gone, done gone.

14. Frankie looked down Main street,
Far as she could see,
All she could hear was a two string bow,
Playin' *Nearer My God to Thee,*
All over town,
Po' Albert's dead.

15. Frankie said to the sheriff,
"What do you think it'll be?"
The sheriff said, "It looks jest like
Murder in the first degree,
He was your man,
But you shot him down."

16. It was not murder in the first degree,
Nor murder in the third,
A woman simply dropped her man,
Like a hunter dropped a bird.
She shot her man,
For doin' her wrong.

17. Last time I saw Frankie
She was sittin' in the 'lectric chair,
Waitin' for to go and meet her God
With the sweat drippin' outa her hair.
He was her man
But he done her wrong.

Poor gal, poor gal,
Poor gal, poor gal.
Done gone, done gone,
Done gone, done gone.

89.

Take a Whiff on Me

Words and melody adapted and arranged by
John A. and Alan Lomax

Piano arrangement by
Charles and Ruth Seeger

1. Walked up Ellum and I come down Main
Tryin' to bum a nickle jes' to buy cocaine.
Ho-ho, honey, take a whiff on me.

CHORUS: Take a whiff on me, take a whiff on me,
An'-a ev'rybody take a whiff on me,
Ho-ho, honey, take a whiff on me.

2. Went to Mister Lehman's on a lope,
Sign in the window said. "No mo' coke."
Ho-ho, honey, take a whiff on me.

3. Goin' up State Street, comin' down Main,
Lookin' for the woman that use cocaine,
Ho-ho, honey, take a whiff on me.

4. I'se got a nickle and you'se got a dime,
You buy the coke and I'll buy the wine.
Ho-ho, honey, take a whiff on me.

5. The blacker the berry, the sweeter the juice,
Takes a brown-skin woman for my pertickeler use.
Ho-ho, honey, take a whiff on me.

6. I chew my terbaccer, I spit my juice,
I love my baby till it ain't no use.
Ho-ho, honey, take a whiff on me.

7. Cocaine's for hosses and not for men,
The doctors say it'll kill you, but they don't say when.
Ho-ho, baby, take a whiff on me.

8. Whiff-a-ree an' a-whiff-a-rye,
Gonna keep whiffin', boys, till I die.
Ho-ho, honey, take a whiff on me.

90.

The Durant Jail

Words and melody adapted and arranged by
John A. and Alan Lomax

Piano arrangement by
Charles and Ruth Seeger

1. The Durant jail beats no jail at all,
   If you want to catch hell, go to Wichita Falls.

Refrain: It's hard times in the Durant jay-ul,
It's hard times, poor boy.

2. It's straight from your carriage, right into your cell,
It's just like sailing from heaven to Hell.

3. There's a big bull ring in the middle of the floor,
And a damned old jailer to open the door.

4. Your pockets he'll pick,your clothes he will sell,
Your hands he will handcuff, goddamn him to hell.

5. And here's to the cook, I wish he were dead,
It's old boiled beef and old cornbread.

6. When we lay down,we are covered with fleas,
They'll eat a man's feet off slap up to his knees.

7. I wrote to my mother to send me a knife,
For the lice and the chinches had threatened my life.

8. Lice and bedbugs walkin' the j'ists,
One fell down and said, "Help me, O Christ!"

9. The bugs they swear if we don't give bail,
We're bound to git lousy in the Durant jail.

10. And here's to the lawyer, he'll come to your cell
And swear he will clear you in spite of all Hell.

11. But your money he'll get before he will rest,
Then say, "Plead guilty, for I think it is best."

12. There sits the jury, a devil of a crew,
They'll look a poor prisoner through and through.

13. And here's to the sheriff, I like to forget,
The durndest old rascal in the whole durned lot;

14. Your privileges he'll take, your clothes he will sell,
Get drunk on the money, goddamn him to hell.

15. And now I have come to the end of my song,
I'll leave it to the boys as I go along.

16. But for gambling and stealing I never shall fail,
And I don't give a damn fer lyin' in jail.

91.

The Midnight Special

1. Well, you wake up in de mornin', hear de ding-dong ring,
Go marchin' to de table, see de same damn thing.
Well, it's on-a table, knife-a, fork, an'-a pan,
An' ef you say anything about it, you're in trouble with de man.

REFRAIN: Let de Midnight Special shine its light on you:
Let de Midnight Special shine its ever-lovin' light on you.

2. Well, de biscuits on de table, jus' as hard as any rock;
Ef you try to eat 'em, break a convict's heart.
My sister wrote a letter, my mother wrote a card,
"Ef you want to come to see us, you'll have to ride de rods."

3. Now if you go to Houston, Lawd, you better walk right,
You better not stagger and you better not fight.
The sheriff will arrest you and the judge'll send you down,
You can bet your bottom dollar, — "Penitenchury bound."

4. "Well yonder comes Dr. Melton!" "How in de worl' do you know?"
"Well, dey give me a tablet de day befo'."
"Well, dey never was a doctor travel through by lan'
Dat could cure de fever on a convict man."

5. "Yonder comes li'l Rosie!" "How in de worl' do you know?"
"I can tell her by her apron an' de dress she wo',
Umbereller on her shoulder, piece o' paper in her han'
Well, I hear her tell de captain, 'I want my man.' "

6. Looky, looky yonder, what in de worl' do I see?
Well, dat brown-skin woman comin' after me.
She wore a mother hubbard, jes' like a mournin' gown;
Trimmin' on her apron, how it do hang down!

7. I'm gwine away to leave you, an' my time ain't long.
De man is gonna call me an' I'm goin' home.
Then I'll be done all my grievin', whoopin', hollerin', an' a-cryin';
Then I'll be done all my studyin' 'bout my great long time.

92.

Ain' No Mo' Cane on dis Brazis

Words and melody adapted and arranged by
John A. and Alan Lomax

Piano arrangement by
Charles and Ruth Seeger

1. It ain' no mo' cane on dis Brazis,
Oh—
Dey done, grind it all in molazzis,
Oh—.

2. Well, de captain standin' an' lookin' an' cryin',
Well, it's gittin' so col', my row's behin'.

3. Cap'n, doncha do me like you did po' Shine,
You drive dat bully till he went stone-blin'.

4. Cap'n, cap'n, you mus' be blin',
Keep on holl'in' an' I'm almos' flyin'.

5. Ninety-nine years so jumpin' long
To be here rollin' an' cain' go home.

6. Ef I had a sentence like ninety-nine years,
All de dogs on de Brazis won' keep me here.

7. B'lieve I'll do like ol' Riley,
Ol' Riley walked de big Brazis.

8. Well, de dog-sergeant got worried an' couldn' go,
Ol' Rattler went to howlin' kaze de tracks too ol',

9. Oughta come on de river in 1904,
You could fin' a dead man on every turn row.

10. Oughta come on de river in 1910,
Dey was drivin' de women jes' like de men

11. Wake up, dead man, an' help me drive my row,
Wake up, dead man, an' help me drive my row.

12. Some in de buildin' an' some on de farm,
Some in de graveyard, and some goin' home.

13. Wake up, lifetime, hold up yo' head,
Well, you may get a pardon an' you may drop dead.

14. Go down, Ol' Hannah, doncha rise no mo',
Ef you rise in the mornin' bring Judgment Day.

93.

Take this Hammer

Words and melody adapted and arranged by
John A. and Alan Lomax

Piano arrangement by
Charles and Ruth Seeger

1. Take this hammer, (huh!) carry it to the captain, (huh!)
Tell him I'm gone, tell him I'm gone. (huh!)

2. If he ask you, (huh!) was I runnin'? (huh!)
Tell him Ize flyin', tell him Ize flyin'. (huh!)

3. If he ask you, (huh!) was I laughin'? (huh!)
Tell him Ize cryin', tell him Ize cryin'.

4. I don't want no (huh!) cold i'on shackles, (huh!)
Around my leg, around my leg. (huh!)

5. I don't want no (huh!) peas, cornbread and molasses, (huh!)
They hurt my pride, they hurt my pride. (huh!)

6. Cap'n called me, (huh!) "a nappy headed devil", (huh!)
That ain't my name, that ain' my name. (huh!)

7. Cap'n got a big gun, (huh!) and he try to play bad, (huh!)
Go'n' take it in the mornin', if he make me mad. (huh!)

8. I'm go'n' make these (huh!) few days I started, (huh!)
Then I'm goin' home, then I'm goin' home. (huh!)

II. Rainbow Round My Shoulder

1. Ev'rywhere I, where I look this mornin'
Looks like rain, looks like rain.

2. I got a rainbow, tied all around my shoulder,**
Ain' gonna rain, ain' gonna rain.

3. I done walk till, walks till my feets gone to rollin',
Jes' like a wheel, jes' like a wheel.

4. Ev'ry mail day, I gets a letter
"My son come home, son, come home."

5. That ol' letter read about dyin',
My tears run down, my tears run down.

6. I'm gonna break right, break right pas' dat shooter,
I'm goin' home, Lawd, I'm goin' home.

*This is a work song for axe-men. Men with picks or road-workers with sledge-hammers. The men strike in unison between phrases of the song, and, as the edge of the tools bite in and the shock is felt in their bodies, their breath bursts past their lips suddenly in a violent grunt. This work-grunt is a regular and important part of the song.

**The flashing arc of the pick or the axe.

94.
Almost Done
Words and melody adapted and arranged by
John A. and Alan Lomax
Piano arrangement by
Charles and Ruth Seeger
Moderately fast
C F C
Take these stripes from, stripes from a-round my— shoul-der,— (huh!) Take these
mf
G7 C F
chains,— chains from 'round my leg, (huh!) Say these stripes,— stripes they sho don't
C G7 C CHORUS
wor ry me,— (huh!) But these chains,— chains gon-na kill— me dead(huh!)Lawd, it's all
F C G C
al - most done (huh!)Lawd, it's all al - most done, (huh!)Lawd, it's all,

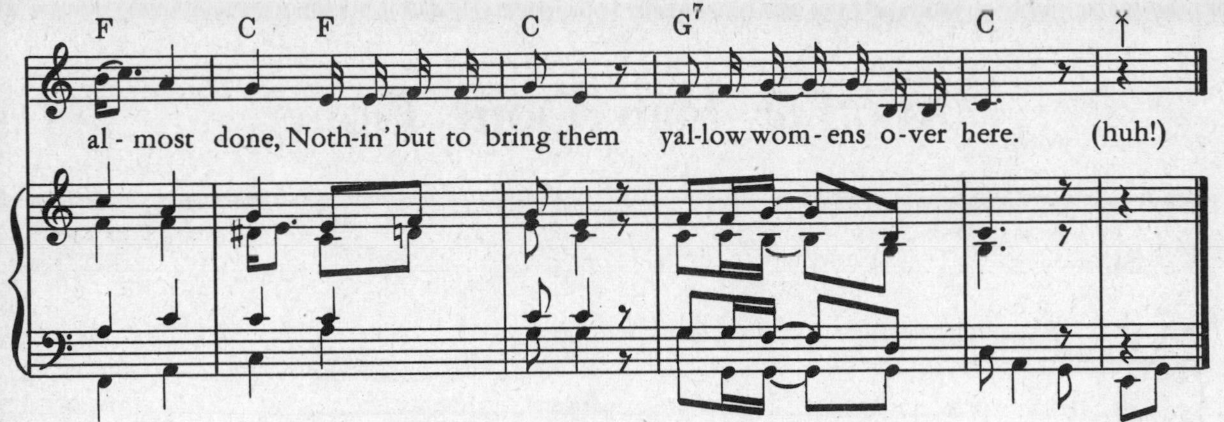

1. Take these stripes from, stripes from around my shoulder, (huh!)
Take these chains, chains from 'round my leg, (huh!)
Say, these stripes, stripes they sho don't worry me, (huh!)
But these chains, chains gonna kill me dead. (huh!)

CHORUS: Lawd, it's all, almost done, (huh!)
Lawd, it's all, almost done, (huh!)
Lawd, it's all, almost done, (huh!)
Nothin' but to bring them yallow womens over here. (huh!)

2. Says, she carried me, carried me to her parlor,
Lawd, she cooled me, cooled me with her fan,
Says, she swore by, swore by the Man that made her,
"Mother, I do love a railroad man".

CHORUS: Railroad man, *ain't* got no home,
Railroad man, *ain't* got no home,
Railroad man, *ain't* got no home,
Here, today, Lawd, tommorrow he'll be gone.

3. Well, she told me, told me that she loved me,
Jus' to give my, give my po' heart ease,
Just as soon as, soon as I got in trouble,
Well, she turned her, turned her back on me. *Chorus;* Lawd,— etc.

4. On a Friday me an' my baby was a-walkin',
On Saturday, she throwed me out of do's,
On Sunday me an' my baby was a-talkin',
On Monday she pawned all of my clothes.

5. On a Monday, Monday I was arrested,
On Tuesday locked up in jail,
On Wednesday my trial was attested,
On Thursday nobody wouldn't go my bail.

6. Says, she whispered, whispered to her mother,
"Mother I can't, can't see how he stand",
Says, "He ain't, ain't but sweet sixteen,
An' they drivin', drivin' him like a man".

7. An' if it wasn' for, wasn' for my good captain,
Lawd, I would have, would have been gone down,
By he liked, liked my hard rollin',
Then he gave me a little nahrow round.

CHORUS: *Lawd, it's all, almost done . . .*

95.

Another Man Done Gone

Words and melody adapted and arranged by
John A. and Alan Lomax

Piano arrangement by
Charles and Ruth Seeger

1. Another man done gone,
   Another man done gone,
   From the county farm
   Another man done gone.

2. I didn't know his name,
   I didn't know his name,
   I didn't know his name,
   I didn't know his name.

3. He had a long chain on,
   He had a long chain on,
   He had a long chain on,
   He had a long chain on.

4. He killed another man,
   He killed another man,
   He killed another man,
   He killed another man.

5. I don't know where he's gone,
   I don't know where he's gone,
   I don't know where he's gone,
   I don't know where he's gone.

CHAPTER XI

Deep River

Deep river,
My home is over Jordan, Lord,
Deep river,
I want to cross over into camp ground.

OVER AGAINST ALL THE SONGS IN PREVIOUS sections—the worldly songs of fleshly love and dancing and work and the carnal passions—stand these spirituals. In the minds of our singing ancestors there was a deep gulf fixed between these two families of song. On the one hand, the sinners under the guidance of Satan romped down the primrose path to a certain doom in hellfire. On the other, stood the saints and the saved, shouting glory, singing about the promised land across the Jordan river, ready for Him to call them home. Not only were the "sinful" songs banned on Sundays, but on all other days of the week as well. They were one of the "things of the world" which a convert must promise to give up, when he got religion and joined the church. This belief and this practice, once widely common among all Americans, is still a conviction among certain folk groups. The mother of a famous blues-singer told us how her son, on his death bed, put aside his guitar, renounced his "devil's tunes," and died with the words of a spiritual on his lips. Both mother and son believed that thus he, too, had some chance at heaven.

The religious folk-singer, however, has never wanted for songs to cheer him on his "rocky way." Out of the tune-stock that poured from the British Isles and out of the heritage of rhythms and song-styles welling up in the hearts of the African slaves, a deep river of song was formed that has coursed through the lives of all Americans. A deep river of melody and profoundest emotion that washed the pain and sorrow from the souls of the millions pioneering who made America strong and free. A deep river of song that caught up the best tunes from every hand and linked them with the stubborn convictions and the most poignant longings of all the people. To choose a handful of the "best" songs out of this finest flowering of religious song in the Western Hemisphere was the most difficult task in the makeup of this volume.

96. *AMAZING GRACE*

In pioneer congregations, where the people were too poor to own or too illiterate to use hymnbooks, the minister would give out the hymns line by line.

A charge to keep I have
A God to glorify—

—He'd rip out in his big voice. Then he would begin to sing the same line, using a stock melody, dragging out each syllable, decorating it with quavers and flourishes, as the congregation trailed him full chorus. While his flock wound up the last syllable, he'd line out the second verse—

A never dying soul to save
And send it to the skies—

—and then lead them as they swooped and dipped their raw, country voices through the final measures.

These so-called "surge-songs" followed the psalm singing style of New England colonial congregations. Puritan ecclesiastics believed in long sermons, heavy praying and doleful music. They led the old psalm tunes at such slow tempos and with so little feeling for the sensual in music that one contemporary compared the singing of the Puritans to the braying of a herd of asses.

During the Great Awakening of the eighteenth century, when many dissenters broke away form the established churches, this psalm singing style was somewhat enlivened and transformed by the introduction of folkier tunes and more colorful texts. Whitfield and Edwards needed hymns that carried the fire of their message of individual salvation. The lines of "Amazing Grace," written in the eighteenth century by the English divine, John Newton, are representative of the hymns of this period.

Surge-singing has never entirely died out among the folk. The white Primitive Baptist congregations still keep the style alive, singing the hymns of the Great Awakening in the old "dragged-out" fashion. With Negro folk congregations these hymns, which they call "Dr. Watts" or "long-meter," have outlived the better-known spirituals. Even though the tune is "dragged out" by Negroes to almost double the length of white performances, one is reminded not of "the braying of asses," but rather of a great organ, composed of all the most beautiful sounds in nature, breathing in a solemn choral. The singing deacon intones his lines in a rumbling voice that pulls the whole congregation up into mellow cadences, and, although here, too, each singer is decorating the melodic line with his own turns and quavers, he feels the texture of the whole sound and, without reflection or intent, his individual voice blends with that of his fellow-worshipers to produce a rich tower of sound. With the Negroes there is a sense of singing together, of blend—perhaps this is one of the profoundest differences between all white and all Negro folk-singing. Essential to the blend of voices is the "beat," the regular pulsing rhythm that runs through the Negro surge-singing (as through all their music) and which one cannot feel in the white lining hymns. The beat is extremely slow, but it is very regular and very impressive, and it binds all the voices together and makes the ancient melody roll forward like a tremendous wave in midsea, towering up and up, cresting, then subsiding into quiet, though retaining all its strength. In the quiet one hears the gentle and insistent tap-tap-tap of a single foot upon the bare, board floor.

Thus this ancient singing style has come full cycle, from the time when it lent heart and strength to the Reformation, into death in Puritan New England, thence into an attenuated life in the Great Awakening, and finally again, into full flower with Negroes. Why did the Negroes understand these tunes so well? There are two reasons. First, many of their own songs, their oldest songs, are "dragged out," highly ornamented and rhythmically free.* Second, they feel in their hearts the profound sorrow of the outcast and the persecuted, a sorrow that the early Protestants knew.

* Turn to "Ain' No Mo' Cane on the Brazis," or better to some record of a slow work-song or a holler, and discover this for yourself.

97. *POOR WAYFARING STRANGER*

I am a poor wayfaring stranger,
Traveling through this world of woe.

The dissenters, who sang these lines, were the poor, the dispossessed, the illiterate, the socially unacceptable. Slum-dwellers and poor peasants, they had come to America to find freedom to practice their own religion in which "every man was the same in the sight of God." When their dissenting congregations (the Congregationalists, the Presbyterians, the Lutherans and the Calvinists) had, in turn, become the established churches, these same people began to break away from even these churches. The shouting Baptists and Methodist preachers who preached hellfire against the rich, the rulers, the educated, and the privileged sinners, who called for individual salvation and conversion, led the little man in the colonies to form congregations of non-conformists all through the rural areas. For this the lay Baptist ministers were jailed and persecuted and their meetings broken up by the Tories and their constabulary.

When the Revolution came, it meant for these people not merely freedom from British rule, but religious freedom. Dr. George Pullen Jackson points out in his *White and Negro Spirituals* * that the Revolution of 1776 was "the first instance in Christendom that a folk had won full liberty in the religious phase of its culture." Between 1783 and 1800 the Baptists increased their membership by four times. In Virginia there were 15,000 *Free Will* Baptists in 1784, and by 1812 there were 35,000. Out in the Western frontier in Kentucky this poor man's church grew from 7,000 to 31,000 in the same period. Where the Methodists adopted the Baptist style of worship, they also made converts by the thousand.

These people were not only religious radicals, but they were carrying out a musical revolution. They needed songs that would match their soaring emotions. The result was that they threw over the old psalms and, as had happened in every revolution in the Christian churches, brought folk tunes into the hymn books. Ballad tunes, jigs, marches, love-songs, again these were put to the service of the Lord, dressed up in appropriately solemn texts, but now with texts which spoke more directly of the woes and the problems of the individuals who sang them. Their hymnbook makers compiled these new songs into the "shaped note" hymnbooks, in which the notes were distinguished by shape as well as position. *Christian Harmony* appeared in 1805 in the Northeast; *The Christian Lyre* in New York in 1830; *Walker's Southern Harmony* in South Carolina in 1835; *White's Sacred Harp* in Georgia in 1844. These books (and I have mentioned only a few out of many) incorporated more and more folk tunes as the years went by and they sold in proportionately increasing numbers, the Walker book as many as 500,000 copies over a thirty-year period.

This Sacred Harp singing movement, so thoroughly studied by Dr. George Pullen Jackson, once involved hundreds of thousands of singers in its meetings. Today only hundreds attend its summer conventions, but these gatherings still produce some of the most remarkable American singing. The meetings are run in strict parliamentary fashion with every singer given an opportunity to lead two or three songs. The singers form themselves into a hollow square—basses, altos, tenors, and trebles on their respective sides, for the songs are arranged in four-part harmony. The leader gives the number of the hymn he prefers; there comes a great rustling of pages while each singer finds his place in the fat Sacred Harp book; the leader intones the pitch; leads the congregation through a sol-fa rendition of the tune; then off these country singers sail through all the stanzas, singing four-part harmony at the tops

* Much of the material of this chapter is based upon Dr. Jackson's studies of the white spirituals. For full references see Appendix II.

of their wonderful strident voices and with more ease than most trained choirs could manage. They produce a sound that is like nothing else we have ever heard, unless it is the folk choirs of Southern Russia, at once strident and soaring, harmony without blend, polyphony in the old Bachian sense. Some of the old folks, who cannot read "reading," can read every one of the hundreds of songs in their favorite book by sight, know every one of the parts by ear, for they wander around from side to side of the square and change their voice positions without any apparent difficulty.

When you ask one of these old singers what they intend by their songs, he'll look you square in the eye and say, "Brother, every word in every one of them five hundred and eighty songs is true, true as the gospel. That's why I've memorized them all, yes sir, and that's why I sing them with my whole heart and soul."

"The Wayfaring Stranger" falls into the category of a religious ballad, a song for solo performance at a religious meeting or for group singing only at a shaped-note singin'. The range of these religious ballads gives an excellent portrait of the interests and the prejudices of the religious revolutionists who composed them.

"The Romish Lady" tells of a convert to the Protestant faith who was condemned to torture by her mother when she refused to quit reading her Bible. There were many ballads addressed as warnings to drunkards:

Poor drunkards, poor drunkards, take warning of me,
The fruits of transgression behold now I see;
My soul is tormented, my body confined;
My friends and my children left weeping behind.

This melancholy song was set to one variant of the "When You Go A-Courtin' " tune you will find earlier in this volume. "Wicked Polly," who delighted in sin—

. . . gnawed her tongue before she died,
She yelled and screamed and moaned and cried.

The people were in love with death, the great leveler:

And let this feeble body fail,
And let it faint or die,
My soul shall quit this mournful vale,
And soar to worlds on high.
Shout glory!

The religious poets told the old Bible stories over again, but the accent was always upon individual salvation through prayer:

There was Abraham, Isaac and Jacob and David,
And Solomon, and Stephen and John,
There was Simeon, and Anna, and I don't know how many,
That prayed as they journeyed along;
Some cast among lions, some bound with rough irons,
Yet glory and praises they sung.

98. WONDROUS LOVE

The religious ballads were published in little word-books without tunes; and they served well as songs of indoctrination. Yet as the fervor of the revivals mounted, the people began to simplify their spirituals and reach out for songs with more opportunity for group participation. The evangelists needed songs which their new congregations could learn quickly and sing all together. Out of this need there developed hundreds of spirituals with a simpler melodic and poetic structure; in many cases these hymns were set to melodies taken right out of the tune-bag of the folk-singer. Of all these folk-hymns, "Wondrous Love" is perhaps the most beautiful. The words were composed by the Reverend Alex Means, a Methodist minister of Oxford, Georgia; and for a tune the reverend Doctor of Divinity chose the melody which had once moved the ballad about one of the wickedest of men, Captain Kidd.

O my name was Captain Kidd, as I sailed as
I sailed,
O my name was Captain Kidd, as I sailed,
O my name was Captain Kidd,
And much wickedness I did,
And much wickedness I did, as I sailed.

99. *BOUND FOR THE PROMISED LAND*

The people, however, were not finished with their religious and their musical revolutions. They flocked to hear the evangelists preach individual salvation and damnation by the thousands, gathering in huge holiday encampments, still known in rural areas today as "camp meetings." The most independent, individualistic, free-spirited people in the world, they had been living out in the wilderness by themselves, fighting Indians and hunting bears and never hearing anything more entertaining than a catamount scream, for years. They were hungry for entertainment and for self-expression. When the hellfire and sweet-heaven message of the revivalists really took hold, when they heard, dancing behind the solemn verse, the beloved melodies of their fiddle tunes and their love-songs, grace came down on them hard—in *Kaintuck* style. At Cane Ridge, Kentucky, in 1801, 200,000 people came together and a trembling preacher describes what he saw:

> It was at night that the most terrible scenes were witnessed . . . when the campfires blazed in a mighty circle around the vast audience of pioneers. . . . The volume of song burst all bonds of guidance and control, and broke again and again from the throats of the people while over all, at intervals, there rang out the shout of ecstasy, the sob and the groan. Men and women shouted aloud during the sermon, and shook hands all around at the close in what was termed "the singing ecstasy." The "saints" and more especially those who were out to see the show would rush from preacher to preacher, if it were whispered that it was "more lively" at some other point, swarming enthusiastically around a brother who was laughing, leaping, shouting, swooning. . . . The whole body of persons who actually fell helpless to the earth was computed . . . to be three thousand. . . . These were carried to a nearby meeting house and laid out on the floor. . . . Many lay down and rolled over and over for hours at a time. Others rushed wildly over stumps and benches and then plunged, shouting, "Lost! Lost!" into the forest.

The people walked the backs of the wooden benches. They took "the jumps" and hopped up and down for hours without stopping. They took "the jerks" and lay on the ground in writhing convulsions, so regular and so rapid that the women's braids cracked like blacksnake whips. They wiggled on their bellies like the serpent in the garden. They flapped their arms and crowed like roosters. They got down on all fours, packs of them, around oak trees and "bayed the devil" until they collapsed from exhaustion.

These phenomena of religious possession, common to the Great Revival that swept from Virginia through Kentucky and Tennessee in the early years of the nineteenth century, are so well known to us from descriptions of religious meetings, Holy Roller revivals, or camp meetings from our own backgrounds, that they have been accepted as a part of our European heritage. Students have generally assumed, because white participants played the leading role in these revivals, that the Negroes in attendance merely took over this form of worship without making any contribution to it. Anyone, however, who has seen "possession" at a vaudou ceremony in the West Indies, South America, or West Africa will be struck by the similarities between the African motor behavior and that of the convert in the Great Revival. The African type of possession is everywhere typified by violent motor activity—dancing, leaping, jerking, shouting, climbing—reminiscent of the activity of the possessed in the Great Revival. On the other hand, Davenport in his study of religious revivals suggests that in the British Isles the symptoms of possession were quite different:

> . . . the difference in type of automisms of Kentucky and Ulster [Ireland]. In Kentucky . . . the voluntary muscles in violent action were the prevailing type. On the other hand, in Ulster the automisms, trance, vision, the physical disability and the sinking of muscular energy were the prevailing type.

This indicates that the white converts in the revivals were influenced by their Negro fellow-worshipers.

The Great Revival was initiated by ministers who came from Virginia and the Carolinas to Kentucky and Tennessee. There on the frontier the Negro, according to Dr. Jackson, "found himself among real friends—among those who, by reason of their ethnic, social and economic background, harbored a minimum of racial prejudice; among those whose religious practice came nearest to what he—by nature a religious person—could understand and participate in." * Melville Herskovits points out in his *Myth of the Negro Past* the many elements of similarity the Negro of that time could find between the free-and-easy frontier religion and his own African religious practice. At any rate, by 1820 there were 40,000-odd Negro Methodists and 60,000 Negro Baptists, most of them in frontier states. These churches still account for by far the largest numbers of Negro members.

There is no question about the participation of the Negro in the Great Revival nor should there be about his musical influence upon it. We have seen how prominent a musical role Negroes played in other areas of American folklore, and we believe that here, too, he took a hand. At any rate, the story of the development of the white spiritual since the early part of the nineteenth century when Negroes were converted in large numbers is one of steady progress toward the most favored Negro song structure—simplicity of language, feeling more important than meaning in the lines, much repetition, choruses coming every four lines, choruses that wander from song to song, refrains coming every two lines, refrains coming every line—in essence, the leader-chorus form. There is no doubt that, in the beginning, Negroes took over traditional white spiritual melodies; one can find them by the score in the early collections of Negro spirituals. But, today, you find that the reverse is true; the white revival churches are adopting wholesale melodies and singing styles that have been current among Negroes for some generations. It would seem reasonable to conclude, then, that the Negro had a considerable hand in forming the shouting revivalistic spirituals that fanned the flame of the Great Revival and, for the first time in the history of white religious singing, caused hymns to "burst all bonds of guidance and control."

* p. 285, op. cit.

We shall never know the final answers to these questions until we can turn the clock of time backward and look in upon our buckskin-clad forebears thrashing around in the straw when the border country was aflame with the spirit. Hundreds of thundering, rhythmic, soul-stirring hallelujah songs were born in those times and published and circulated throughout the country. The song that traveled farthest, perhaps, of them all—north into the new states, along the trails west to California and Oregon, south into Texas, north into the Great Plains—was the one that ran—

Who shall come and go with me,
I am bound for the promised land.

It was a proper hymn for the pioneers and for the followers of the Western Star.

100. *LONESOME VALLEY*

The same people who once were "bound for the promised land," now find themselves "in a lonesome valley." The descendants of the self-reliant pioneers see their farms growing ever less productive. They go to town to take the lowest-paid jobs in textile mills and auto plants and hear themselves called "hillbillies." These are the people who sing "you've got to walk that lonesome valley" in the revivalistic tradition of their forefathers. These are the people who are creating with their "string bands" a fast-stepping, red-hot religious music, based on the resources of both Negro and white spirituals.

Every time, therefore, that a hillbilly guitar-picker begins to play in a Holy Roller store-front church, his music symbolizes the essential unity of the two races, for he is likely to be playing this or some other old Negro-white tune with a Negro-white guitar accompaniment. No one knows whether "Lonesome Valley" is of Negro or white origin. Certainly its origin is of no account compared to the fact that it is sung by the Okies in California with the same enthusiasm as by a Negro Holiness congregation in Memphis or Chicago. This song marks the final development of the white song toward group singing style. It is "all chorus," and grows, like scores of other revivalistic pieces by substituting the name of the relative as the only new material for each new stanza.

101. *PO' LI'L' JESUS*

For almost a hundred years a controversy has raged among folklorists and musicologists over the composition and origin of the most beautiful of American spirituals—the religious songs of Negro singers. One camp asserts that they are purely compositions of the Negro people with their ultimate roots in African melodism. Their opponents feel that the spirituals are mere imitations of the white spirituals we have just discussed and resolutely deny any African survivals in them. Scientifically speaking, it appears to us that the solution of this controversy lies between these two extreme positions, but from the aesthetic point of view there is no doubt about what must be asserted.

Whatever their origin, whatever their structure, whatever their components—there can be no question in the minds and hearts of those who have heard them that in the Negro spirituals American folk art reaches its highest point. Indeed, we assert that these songs form the most impressive body of music so far produced by America, ranking with the best of music anywhere on this earth. After surveying the whole field of American folk song in making this book, we found that it would be as difficult to decide upon the 111 best Negro spirituals as upon the 111 best American folk songs.

Nor can anyone seriously deny their ultimate distinction as works of art from the songs of the white man. Whether this difference, which strikes directly upon the ear and the emotions of the listener, arises from the Negro's larynx, his motor habits, his African cultural heritage, his position as a social inferior, or a combination of these factors does not affect the issue. To discover that Shakespeare found his plots here or there, imitated other poets or playwrights here or there, scarcely detracts from the uniqueness and the beauty of his plays. What matters to the readers is what the poet *did* with the material he chose to use. In the same way, no amount of scholarly analysis and discussion can ever make a Negro spiritual sound like a white spiritual. Every time a Negro folk congregation sings one of these songs, this difference is reasserted. Nor can all the scientific study in the world ever deny to the Negro spiritual that quality, ineluctable and elusive, which stamps them as noble and profound art and which moves the hearts of men as great art will ever do. The motivation of those scholars who have tried to deny the Negro credit for the creation of this art is, we feel, as ignoble as it is ultimately foolish.

"Po' Li'l' Jesus" is a case in point. With a few phrases from the Bible story, with a melody so simple it might be ascribed to many sources, Negro singers have made a carol that sums up the pathos of all birth and that epitomizes the tragedy of all tender and persecuted beings. With such songs as this did old-fashioned Negro congregations greet Christmas morning. They had watched together until the cock crew to announce that Christ was born in a manger in Bethlehem to save all men, rich or poor, white or black, free or slave.

This carol has the form of the primitive "shouting" spiritual, the type of song developed by Negro slaves in the Deep South, more or less independently of white revivals. Many plantation owners actually forbade the Christianization of the slaves on the ground that such congregations might be breeding places for slave revolts. Others permitted their Negroes a minimum of worship at the outskirts of their own meetings. The deeply religious African (and there is no part of the world where religion plays a more important role in everyday life than in Africa) was anxious to learn what he could of Christianity. He had been conquered by the white man with the help, no doubt, of a white man's God; this new God was, evidently, stronger than his own and worth bowing to. The slave, therefore, took what he could learn of this new religion to the slave quarters and worshiped this new God in his own fashion —that is, by dancing, by song and by possession. He called these dancing meetings "shouts," using the Arabic word "Saut" current on the West Coast of Africa, which means to walk or run around the Kaaba. One of these "shouts" was described in *The Nation* in 1867, as follows:

> . . . all stand up in the middle of the floor and, when the sperrchil is struck up, begin first walking and, by and by, shuffling around, one after the other, in a ring. The foot is hardly taken from the floor and the progression is due to a jerking, hitching motion which agitates the entire shouter. . . . Sometimes they dance silently, sometimes, as they shuffle, they sing the chorus of the sperrchil, and sometimes the song itself is also sung by the dancers. But more frequently a band, composed of some of the best singers, stand at the side of the room to bass the others, singing the body of the song and clapping their hands together or on their knees.

We have seen "shouts" in Louisiana, in Texas, in Georgia, and in the Bahamas; we have seen vaudou dancing in Haiti; we have read accounts of similar rites in works upon Negro life in other parts of the Western Hemisphere. All share basic similarities: (1) the song is "danced" with the whole body, with hands, feet, belly, and hips; (2) the worship is, basically, a dancing-singing phenomenon; (3) the dancers always move counter-clockwise around the ring; (4) the song has the leader-chorus form, with much repetition, with a focus on rhythm rather than on melody, that is, with a form that invites and ultimately enforces cooperative group activity; (5) the song continues to be repeated for sometimes more than an hour, steadily increasing in intensity and gradually accelerating, until a sort of mass hypnosis ensues.

This "shout pattern," which involves all or most of the aforementioned characteristics wherever encountered, is demonstrably West African in origin. It represents an approach to religious song quite different from anything known in Western Europe. James Weldon Johnson in the introduction to *The Book of the Negro Spiritual* has argued that it has molded the poetic structure of a great part of the spirituals. In all likelihood, it accounts for many of the distinctive qualities of these songs. If you wish to watch this style of singing in action, visit any Negro revival congregation and you may see one of the new cousins of the "Po' Li'l' Jesus" spiritual in the process of being born.

102. *NEVER SAID A MUMBALIN' WORD*

. . . exemplifies perfectly the aesthetic distinction of the Negro spiritual, a matter we have discussed at some length. No doubt should remain of the creative power of the Negro people as expressed in his religious songs. The spirituals are in no sense mere borrowings from white folk singers. By the same token, however, it is chauvinism in reverse to call them purely or mainly African. Like so much else in Southern life, they are the offspring of the meeting of two peoples, of two rich folk cultures. Our present understanding of this complex musical mingling might be summarized as follows:

1. The language of the spirituals is English. The symbolism is mostly out of the Bible. Many phrases and lines, many melodic ideas were learned by the Negroes from the whites; many songs, sung by Negroes as spirituals, were adaptations of white revival songs.

2. On the contrary, we have pointed out that Negroes probably had a hand in the creation of many of the white revival songs. We have also shown that, parallel to the growth of the white revival, there developed the Negro "shout" which is a basic formative element in Negro spirituals.

3. Dr. Jackson and others have shown that the melodies of many Negro spirituals are based on tunes which had their origin in the British Isles. However, these critics are unable to account for the melodic origins of most of the distinctive Negro spiritual tunes. This whole debate about melodies suffers from lack of published material on West African melodism and, until such material is available, it will be impossible to say whether these, at present untraceable melodies, conform to African or British melodic patterns.

4. All commentators agree that the Negro has always handled his poetics and his melodism in certain characteristic ways, which probably bear the stamp of his African cultural heritage. Here, too, however, we suffer from lack of knowledge of African music. Nonetheless, there is still a definite residuum of qualities which have made the Negro spirituals the moving and delightful songs they are.

We mention a few of the most important of the musical characteristics of the Negro spiritual: (1) the importance of a steady beat; (2) the complex of rhythm and counterrhythm deriving from the dance background of spirituals; (3) the extreme importance of syncopation; (4) the dominance of a descending melodic line in a great proportion of these songs; (5) the feeling for blend in group singing; (6) the horizontal concept of harmony rather than the vertical; (7) then there is the Negro's vocal style, which is quite distinct from that of the white folk-singer—a matter which has been studied, but not definitively.*

Like so many spirituals, "Never Said A Mumbalin' Word" is a dramatic ballad, or, better, a dramatic ballet. Indeed, the song could serve as the basis of a musical drama. Its dirge-like and solemn melody, with its typical descending melody line, wells with tears. The leader-chorus form, although somewhat more complex than in the preceding carol, allows for the group to sing the whole of the stanza after the first line is given. The singers may linger upon the bitter details of Christ's suffering and stamp them into the listener's heart. "Blood comes twinklin' down," "They crown him with a thorny crown," but "he never says a mumbalin' word"—in these phrases the Negro singers touch the story with the freshening and magic finger of folk-poetry. That there is real and unrestrained sorrow in this spiritual arises from the fact that the Negro could, because of his own unspoken troubles, understand the tragedy of Jesus suffering torture with never "a mumbalin' word."

103. *SOON ONE MORNIN'*

. . . has brought the folks to their feet shouting and weeping in ten thousand revivals and has filled the collection box at as many country funerals. The preacher, after he has reached the climax of terror in a hellfire and damnation sermon, pops his big hands together and rumbles out the first threatening line:

* See Metfessel, Milton, *Phonophotography in Folk Music*, Chapel Hill: The University of North Carolina Press, 1928.

Soon one mornin', death comes a-creepin' in my room.

The praying deacons and the sisters in the amen corner swing in behind him and lift the second line. Then the congregation takes hold so that the whole church rocks with the final question, the eternal question:

O my Lawd, O my Lawd, what shall I do?

These singers had sat as mourners at wakes in rickety shanties. For them death was a reality to be lived with every day, to be looked at in stark little country funerals:

Look down, look down that lonesome road
With the hacks all dead in line.

For these singers death was a person who "came tippin' in the room," "a man goin' round takin' names," "the little black train comin'," "a chariot, swingin' low." It was a time: "When Jesus gonna make up my dyin' bed"; "when, all in my room, gonna hear the angels singin' "; when "if I got my ticket, I'm gonna ride"; when "I'm gonna put on my wings and try the air."

104. *WHEN MY BLOOD RUNS CHILLY AND COL'*

For white singers, too, death was not to be feared, but to be desired and courted. For them, too, death provided a release from the burdens of this world, a chance at heaven and a release from the constant struggle against sin. Yet, death was more of an abstraction with them than with the Negroes. They sang:

O lovely appearance of death,
No sight upon earth is so fair,
Not all the gay pageants that breathe
Can with a dead body compare.
In solemn delight I survey,
A corpse when the spirit is fled,
In love with the beautiful clay
And longing to lie in its stead.

Negro singers painted a more vivid reality when they sang:

When my blood runs chilly and col',
Ize got to go.

105. *SET DOWN, SERVANT*

Not only did the Negro personalize old man death, he felt himself to be on intimate terms with "the Lawd," with "Marse Jesus" and many of the prophets. Melville Herskovits has shown at length in his *Myth of the Negro Past* that one of the outstanding characteristics of West African religion is its everyday quality, the feeling of the African that his ancestral gods are all around him every day all through the day. He constantly addresses himself to them, in song and prayer and conversation. He tricks them, rebukes them, placates them—in a word, lives with them.

In the same way the folk Negro began to live with the God of the white man, to play with him and laugh heartily over religious matters. There is an old Negro rhyme which runs:

When you go to the white folks church,
You won't never see a smile;
But when you go to the colored church
You can hear them laugh for a mile.

This was the folk singer who made stanzas such as:

I'm a Baptist bred and a Baptist born,
Jine de heavens with the angels;
And when I die, dey's a Baptist gone,
Jine de heaven with the angels.

Methodist preacher you are dead,
You poured water on the baby's head;
Baptist preacher you are right,
'Cause you take them candidates out of sight. . . .

I'm gwine ride on the whistlin' chariot,
Some of these days;
I'm gonna walk and talk with the angels,

Some of these days;
I'm gonna tell my Jesus "howdy,"
Some of these days.

I chattered with the Father and argered with the Son,
And I told 'em 'bout the world I just come from.

When I get to heaven I'm gonna take my stand,
Gonna wrastle with my Lord like a nachul man.

In heaven, the folk Negro not only hopes to meet his Lawd on equal terms, and to receive all the glittering things which had been denied him on this earth—golden crowns, silver waistbands, shoes (for *all* God's chillun get shoes in heaven), milk-white robes, wine (you oughta been there ten thousand years drinking of the wine); but, above all, the Negro hopes to sit down and rest, just rest.

When I gets to heaven, gonna be at ease,
Me an' my God gonna do as we please.

Here is the kind of poetry which sets the Negro spiritual apart from most white religious song. Here is bubbling naturalness, powerful and simple imagery, and, above all, a friendliness and humor, which, with the Negro, reaches beyond the earth even into the realms of the Great Beyond. Turn now to the song "Set Down, Servant," and listen to the conversation between the Lord and one of his good and faithful servants who has labored long in the vineyard and now has come home to rest. There is nothing more charming, more gay, more tender, more appealing, or more dramatic in all folk-song literature.

106. *GREAT GITTIN' UP MORNIN'*

Beneath the apparent hysteria of a Negro revival service, there is spine and structure as stable and formal as that of a sonata. The whole service hangs upon the beat, a steady and powerful beat, very slow at the beginning and gradually increasing in tempo throughout the service. The exclamations of "Amen" and "Preach, brother," and "That's right" from the deacons, the moans and shouts of the mourners come in on this beat like so many voices in a jazz orchestra; the handclapping, the feet-slapping-and-tapping from the congregation make the rhythm section of the orchestra; but all is background for the extemporizing, improvising voice of the preacher, who composes his poem (again on the beat), coloring his chanted poem with snatches of melody, with shouts, with whispers, with moans, with driving rhythms, with growls, with crooning, and with every trick of the orator-singer. A great folk preacher reaches down between the covers of the Bible and weaves an epic poem out of what he discovers there, causing the Biblical heroes to walk the earth again "like natural men," talk again, suffer again, and triumph again. A good folk preacher has to snort like the horses of the Apocalypse, bellow like the beast of John the Revelator, leap high into the air to punctuate his purple periods, and sing like a brass-voiced angel Gabriel. He is familiar with all the devices of the Southern orators of the old school; he uses them like an African vaudou priest; and he is always on the beat. This art, which has been developed by generations of these folk ministers, is the epic phase of American folk poetry and certainly the high point of American folk theatre. It is only hinted at in a sentimentalized fashion in Bradford's *Green Pastures.*

"Great Gittin' Up Mornin'" represents in song the apocalyptic visions that compose a great part of Negro folk sermons. It is the kind of a song that could well have originated at a service. Some old sister takes from the preacher a line—

In that great gittin' up mornin', fare thee well.

The congregation makes a chorus of this. Then the preacher weaves his vision of the end of this ugly world where so much misery falls upon the poor man, as the congregation intones the response:

Fare thee well, fare thee well.

In this way the people can take their revenge in fantasy on a life that bears too hard upon them. In this way many of the great songs of mankind have been improvised. The chorus is one of the stirring and blood-tingling things in American folk music.

107. *SOMETIMES I FEEL LIKE A MOTHERLESS CHILD*

Certain commentators on the Negro spiritual have agreed among themselves that these songs do not, as their Abolitionist discoverers originally supposed, express resentment against slavery and longing for freedom. This position has been stated as follows:

> The subjects treated in the spirituals are so much the same as those in white songs as to only need passing comment. Heaven, hell, the judgment, appeals to the sinner, Biblical characters, Satan, the jubilee, the gospel trumpet, the gospel ship, the chariot, the river Jordan, the union band, etc., are the leading subjects in both the Negro and the white songs.
>
> Most of the early collectors of Negro spirituals, being ignorant of their history, read meanings into them which were not there originally. The desire for freedom expressed in many songs might have come to represent physical freedom to the slave in time, but these songs were either white songs which had reference to freedom from sin, or songs written for him by abolitionists.

The above passage exhibits an appalling ignorance of the history of slavery in the West, a history in fact punctuated by slave revolts and keyed to the slow pace of the "lazy" (i.e., unwilling and uncooperative) Negro worker. It arbitrarily assumes that enslaved Negroes and freeborn whites would find the same significance in Christianity and in the spirituals. It neglects the all-important element of concealment and double entendre in Negro folk culture, a characteristic summed up in the familiar Negro saying—"De white man talks wid de back of his head (shows you his whole mind), but de nigger just talks wid de front of his head (shows you only the surface of his thought)." Finally, this passage gives the quite inaccurate impression that Negro and white spirituals are, to all intents and purposes, identical in content and point of view.

Negro and white spirituals share similar Biblical symbolism, it is true, but, in examining the now extensive collections of white spirituals we have yet to find *any* songs with the explicit sorrow over the actual woes of this world, with the explicit anger against oppression, and with the ringing cries for freedom to be discovered in the Negro songs. In the white songs it is made abundantly clear that the "fight" is against sin and the singer's mind is fixed upon release from the struggle against Satan.

Ye little Sampson's, up and fight,
Put the Philistian host to flight;
The troops of Hell are mustering round,
But Zion's sons, maintain your ground.
CHORUS: *Shout, shout, we're gaining ground,*
Halle, hallelujah!
Satan's kingdom is tumbling down,
Halle, hallelujah!

When Israel came to Jericho,
Began to pray and shout and blow,
The tottering walls come tumbling down,
The noise like thunder shook the ground,

The Hebrews in a dreadful flame
Found Zion's King was still the same;
Young David's weapon seem'd but dull,
Yet broke Goliath's brazen skull.

In comparable Negro spirituals there is a *direct reliving of the battles* and the *physical conflict* of the prophets, not against sin, but against real enemies.

You may read in the Bible an' you understand,
Samson was the stronges' man,
Samson went out at-a one time,
An' he killed about a thousand of the Philistine
Samson was a witness for my Lord, etc.

Up to the walls of Jericho, he marched with spear in hand,
"Go blow them ram horns," Joshua cried, " 'Cause the battle is in my hands."
The lamb-ram-sheep horns begin to blow, the trumpets begin to sound,
Joshua commanded the children to shout and the walls come tumblin' down.
Joshua fit the battle of Jericho, etc.

Little David was a shepherd boy,
He killed Goliath and he shouted for joy,
Little David, play on your harp,
Halleloo, halleloo!

There are few lines in white spirituals which state unequivocally and simply man's desire for freedom as do these from Negro spirituals:

Didn't my Lord deliver Daniel, Daniel, Daniel,
Didn't my Lord deliver Daniel,
And why not every man?

Great day, great day with the righteous marchin',
Great day, the Lord has set his people free.

Run, Mary, run,
I know the udder world is not like this.

Go down, Moses, way down in Egypt land,
Tell old Pharoah to let my people go.

Free at last, free at last,
Thankgodamighty, I'm free at last.

Finally, there is nothing in white spiritual song which so poignantly states mankind's earthly sorrows as such lines as:

Keep a-inchin' along, inchin' along,
Jesus will come bymbye.
Keep a-inchin' along like a po' inch worm,
Jesus will come bymbye.

Sometimes I'm up sometimes I'm down,
O yes Lord,
Sometimes I'm almost to the ground,
O yes Lord.
Nobody knows the trouble I see,
Nobody knows but Jesus.

Come on, sister, wid yo' ups and downs,
Wanta go to heaven when I die,
The angels waitin' for to give you a crown,
Wanta go to heaven when I die.
Lis'en to the lambs all a-cryin',
Lis'en to the lambs all a-cryin',
Lis'en to the lambs all a-cryin',
And I want to go to heaven when I die.

No more peck of corn for me, no more, no more,
No more driver's lash for me,
Many thousand go.

Sometimes I feel like a feather in the air,
A long ways from home.

It must now be clear that the identity of symbolism in white and Negro spirituals is not so close as it appears to be on the surface. The Negro was hardly so concerned with *sin,* as his white fellow Baptist, but more with real woes. In the same way heaven for him represented an escape from worldly troubles, rather than from stings of the flesh and the clutch of Satan, matters which occasionally troubled the white singer more than the Negro. This is not to say that white spirituals have no reference to the burdens of the workaday world or that the Negro spirituals are not occupied with Protestant concepts of sin. The difference in emphasis is nevertheless quite striking.

It is impossible of belief that the Negro slave, who often lived through or witnessed events such as are about to be related, did not experience different emotions from his white brethren when singing and composing spirituals about the comforts of heaven. Here was a human being deprived of mother and father, of human identity, and, finally, of the very slavery home which he had sweated to build. Here indeed was a "motherless child, a long ways from home!"

Who I is, how old I is and where I is born, I don't know. But Massa Buford told me how during the war a slave trader was on his way south with my folks and a lot of other slaves, taking 'em somewheres to sell. He camped by Massa Buford's plantation and asks him, "Can I leave this little fellow here till I comes back?" The trader say he'll be back in three weeks soon as he sells all the slaves. He must still be selling 'em, 'cause he never comes back so far. My folks am took on and I's too little to remember, so I never knows my pappy and mammy. The only thing I 'members bout all that is there was lots of crying when they took me 'way from my mammy. That something I never forgits. . . .

When freedom came, Old Massa called all of us to his house and he said: "You all free, we ain't got nothing to do with you no more. Go on away. We don't whup you no more, go on your way." We goes on off, then come back and stand around just looking at him and Old Miss. They give us something to eat and then say: "Go on away, you don't belong to us no more, you been freed."

We go away, but kept coming back. We didn't have no place to go and nothing to eat. It was a terrible time. A bad time. Some took sick and had no 'tention and died. Seem like it was four or five years before they got places to live. They all got scattered.

Seem like we did expect something from freedom, but the only thing old Massa did was give old Jesse a horse and a bridle and saddle. But old Massa, every time they go back, he'd say: "You all go on away. You been set free. You have to look out for yourselves now."

What did the spirituals mean to these people?

108. *FREEDOM*

Another way master had to whup us was in a stock that he had in the stables This was where he whupped you when he was real mad. He had logs fixed together with holes for your feet, hands, and head. He had a way to open these logs and fasten you in. Then he had his coachman give you so many lashes, and he would let you stay in the stock for so many days and nights. That's why he had it in the stable so it wouldn't rain on you. Every day you got that same number of lashes. You never come out able to sit down.

So the grisly reminiscences of the ex-slaves run on and on. These were people, according to some scholars, who could sing of freedom in heaven, "sittin' down beside of the lamb," with no longing for physical freedom, but only for a heavenly release from the temptations of sin and Satan! Such apologetics deny the realities of Southern slavery. No one can doubt that in spirituals the Negroes expressed in the only fashion permitted to them the great impatience with which they awaited the day of deliverance.

They did more than wait, however. They revolted. Modern students of Southern history have found records of uprisings in the United States between 1663 and 1700, fifty during the eighteenth century, and fifty-three between 1800 and 1864.* Most of these conspiracies were small and ineffectual, but they were serious enough to cause the whites to set up the patrol system. Under this system the Negroes were required to have a pass in order to be out upon the roads away from their plantations after night. Under this system there originated the well-known song:

Run, nigger, run, the patteroll'll catch you,
Run, nigger, run, it's almost day.

This patrol kept the slaves effectively in check, while in Haiti, in Jamaica, in Cuba, and elsewhere in the New World Negroes rose up and killed their masters and took hold of the land. It should surprise no one, therefore, that Negro soldiers in the Union Army so quickly adopted songs like "O Freedom."

Open revolt was not the only way that the slaves expressed their resentment against the slavery system. They played dumb and they played lazy and they ran away in such numbers that "Southern writers gravely ascribe it

* Herskovits, *The Myth of the Negro Past*, p. 97.

to a disease—a monomania to which the Negro race is peculiarly subject." Out of this running away, there grew up the greatest of all the spirituals. . . .

109. *GO DOWN, MOSES*

America had a railroad long ago that operated without rolling stock or tracks, without rates or schedules. It ran only in the darkness of night and its motive power was sheer courage and the love of humanity. They called it the "Underground Railroad," and, in the days before the Civil War, thousands of slaves moved along its hidden lines, stopping for rest and food in the secret "stations" of its Abolitionist operators, going on to freedom and refuge from slavery.

The bravest engineer on this road was Harriet Tubman, an escaped slave woman, who dared to slip back, time after time, into the South, tell her people of the underground way and lead them back to freedom. The slave states offered ten thousand dollars for Harriet Tubman, dead or alive, but the reward was never collected. She moved like a will-o'-the-wisp through the lowlands of the South; she brought hundreds of her people into Canada and she never lost a soul along the way. John Brown addressed her as General Tubman.

The Negroes felt that she was "God-driven" and they called her "Moses," the Moses of her people. Legend has it that they made their great song, "Go Down, Moses," about her. It was sung by the Negro regiments in the Civil War, and, since that time, it has become a song of the whole world.

110. *JOSHUA FIT THE BATTLE OF JERICHO*

The only people whose opinion is really worth hearing about the content of the Negro spiritual and its original message for the people who originally formed it are the ex-slaves themselves. If you want to know what they have to say about the system they lived under, read B. A. Botkin's anthology of their reminiscences,* gathered, unfortunately, when only a few toothless and purblind oldsters remained to tell the story. Whenever you sing this stirring spiritual, which the Negro recreated out of the Old Testament story, remember these paragraphs from a man who still lives in our day, but who once lived in bondage.

The end of the war, it come just like that—like you snap your fingers. . . . How did we know it? Hallelujah broke out!—

Abe Lincoln freed the nigger
With the gun and trigger;
And I ain't going to get whipped any more.
I got my ticket,
Leaving the thicket,
And I'm a-heading for the golden shore!

Soldiers, all of a sudden, was everywhere—coming in bunches, crossing and walking and riding. Everyone was a-singing. We was all walking on golden clouds. Hallelujah!

Union forever,
Hurrah, boys, hurrah!
Although I may be poor,
I'll never be a slave—
Shouting the battle cry of freedom.

Everybody went wild. We all felt like heroes, and nobody had made us that way but ourselves. We was free. Just like that, we was free. It didn't seem to make the whites mad, either. They went right on giving us food just the same. Nobody took our homes away, but right off colerd folks started on the move. They seemed to want to get closer to freedom, so they'd know what it was—like it was a place or a city.

What I likes best, to be slave or free? Well, it's this way. In slavery I owns nothing. In freedom I owns the home and raise the family. All that cause me worriment, and in slavery I has no worriment, but I takes the freedom. . . . Better be loose than tied. I know, 'cause I seen both sides.

* See Bibliography.

III. *KEEP YOUR HAND ON THE PLOW*

The people made these songs on their long, slow march between the eastern and western oceans. Some of them came here free, some in chains. Some came to find freedom of worship, some to better themselves, some to escape a world of debtors' prisons and caste distinctions. Some came here speaking the English tongue. Many more had to learn it. In the years between their coming and this time, they have made a home for themselves out of three thousand miles of wilderness, have grown to be a mighty and homogeneous people, have fought several wars, run through many elections and, along the way, have sung. In their songs one may see the troubles and the neuroses, the crimes and the follies, the dreams and the crazy humor, the quiet strength and the noble simplicity, the cruelty and the fear, and above all, the deep yearning love of the people for the land that they caught up in its cradle, rocked, cared for, and brought into blossom. In their songs one may sense the true nature of this process of growing—an experiment in the mixing of blood, the mingling of dreams, the compromise of taste and custom, the improvising of new ideas and the discard of old. Here one comes close to the intimate emotional life of the people to whom the politicians addressed their speeches. Limned in these casual, yet extremely intense songs one can feel the heart of this country beating slowly, painfully, strongly.

With little apparent concern for such abstractions as national destiny, these small songs yet provide some index to the future of this country. With their story of frustrated sexuality, strictured gaiety, morbid concern with death and delight in savage violence, they hint at frightening potentialities in our people and a terrible destiny for America. On the positive side, the people have recorded in their songs their scorn for sham and caste, their affection for truth, their admiration for honesty and good workmanship, their healing and irreverent humor, their abiding faith in equalitarian principles and their deep, almost fanatic, devotion to liberty and individual freedom. At any rate, there is no conscious lying here. The people sing with pioneer candor. Folk Song: USA is the creation of all the people, carved out of the hard rock of stubborn courage, belonging equally to us all, reflecting shame or glory equally upon us all.

"Keep Your Hand on the Plow" is such a collaboration, a joint product of Negro and white singing. It is a spiritual for sodbusters (now and in the past), for the breakers of new ground, for the pioneers (black and white—made by both and sung by both). It is a song for men who know how to hold a turning plow steady and drive a straight, black, fertile furrow in against the broad horizon of a new world.

96.

Amazing Grace

Melody transcribed by
George Pullen Jackson

Piano arrangement by
Charles and Ruth Seeger

1. Amazing grace, how sweet the sound
That saved a wretch like me.
I once was lost, but now am found,
Was blind, but now I see.

2. 'Twas grace that taught my heart to fear,
And grace my fears relieved;
How precious did that grace appear
The hour I first believed.

3. Thro' many dangers, toils and snares,
I have already come;
'Tis grace hath bro't me safe thus far,
And grace will lead me home.

4. How sweet the name of Jesus sounds
In a believer's ear.
It soothes his sorrows, heals his wounds,
And drives away his fear.

5. Must Jesus bear the cross alone
And all the world go free?
No, there's a cross for ev'ry one
And there's a cross for me.

97.

Wayfaring Stranger

Piano arrangement by
Charles and Ruth Seeger

1. I'm just a poor wayfaring stranger,
A-traveling through this world of woe;
But there's no sickness, toil nor danger
In that bright world to which I go.
I'm going there to meet my father,
I'm going there no more to roam,
I'm just a-going over Jordan,
I'm just a-going over home.

2. I know dark clouds will gather round me
I know my way is steep and rough,
But beauteous fields lie just beyond me
Where souls redeemed their vigil keep.
I'm going there to meet my mother,
She said she'd meet me when I come;
I'm only going over Jordan,
I'm only going over home.

3. I want to wear a crown of glory
When I get home to that bright land;
I want to shout Salvation's story,
In concert with that bloodwashed band.
I'm going there to meet my saviour,
To sing his praise forever more;
I'm only going over Jordan,
I'm only going over home.

98.

Wondrous Love

Piano arrangement by
Charles and Ruth Seeger

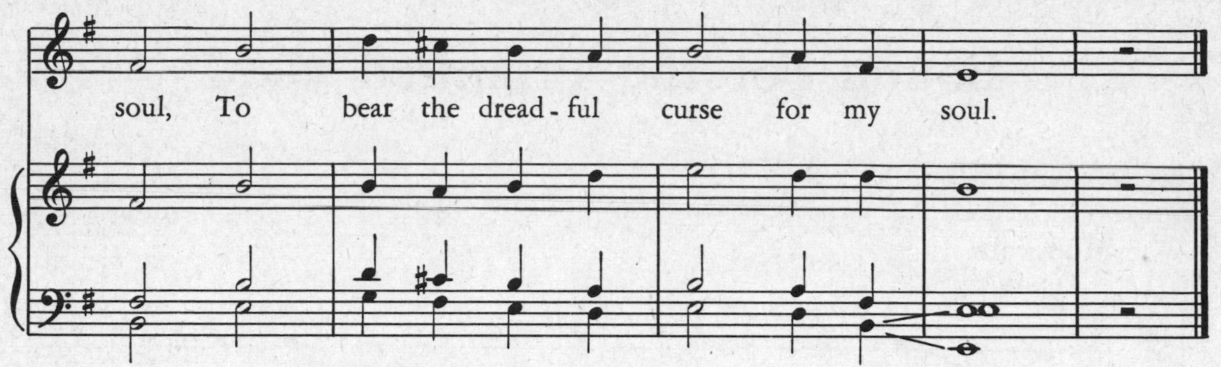

1. What wondrous love is this, oh my soul, oh my soul,
What wondrous love is this, oh my soul,
What wondrous love is this that caused the Lord of bliss
To bear the dreadful curse for my soul, for my soul,
To bear the dreadful curse for my soul.

2. When I was sinking down, sinking down, sinking down,
When I was sinking down, sinking down,
When I was sinking down beneath God's righteous frown
Christ laid aside his crown for my soul, for my soul,
Christ laid aside his crown for my soul.

3. To God and to the Lamb I will sing, I will sing,
To God and to the Lamb I will sing,
To God and to the Lamb,who is the great I AM
While millions join the theme, I will sing, I will sing,
While millions join the theme I will sing.

4. And when from death I'm free, I'll sing on, I'll sing on,
And when from death I'm free, I'll sing on,
And when from death I'm free, I'll sing and joyful be,
And through eternity I'll sing on, I'll sing on,
And thrcugh eternity I'll sing on.

The piano setting of this hymn is a condensation of the three-part score found in John McCurry's "The Social Harp", published by S. C. Collins in Philadelphia, 1868, except that, in keeping with present-day practice, a C-sharp has been added in measures 5 and 17. The original key is a minor third higher. By tradition, the bass and tenor parts may be doubled in the octave above by altos and tenors, and the treble in the octave below by tenors. Thus the three-part score may be given a three-, four-, five, or even six-part performance.

99.

Bound For the Promised Land

Melody transcribed by
George Pullen Jackson

Piano arrangement by
Charles and Ruth Seeger

1. On Jordan's stormy banks I stand
And cast a wishful eye,
To Canaan's fair and happy land
Where my possessions lie.

2. O the transporting rapt'rous scene
That rises to my sight,
Sweet fields arrayed in living green
And rivers of delight.

3. There generous fruits that never fail
On trees immortal grow;
There rocks and hills and brooks and vales
With milk and honey flow.

4. Soon will the Lord my soul prepare
For joys beyond the skies,
Where never-ceasing pleasures roll,
And praises never die.

CHORUS: I am bound for the promised land,
I'm bound for the promised land;
O who will come and go with me,
I am bound for the promised land.

100.

Lonesome Valley

Words and melody adapted and arranged by
John A. and Alan Lomax

Piano arrangement by
Charles and Ruth Seeger

1. You got to walk that lonesome valley,
You got to go there by yourself,
Ain't nobody here can go there for you,
You got to go there by yourself.

2. If you cannot preach like Peter,
If you cannot pray like Paul,
You can tell the love of Jesus,
You can say he died for all.

3. Your mother's got to walk that lonesome valley,
She's got to go there by herself,
Ain't nobody else can go there for her,
She's got to go there by herself.

4. Your father's got to walk that lonesome valley . . .

5. Your brother's got to walk that lonesome valley . . .

101.

Po' Lil Jesus

Words and melody adapted and arranged by
John A. and Alan Lomax

Piano arrangement by
Charles and Ruth Seeger

2. Po' little Jesus,
Yes, yes,
Child of Mary,
Yes, yes,
Didn't have no cradle,
Yes, yes,
Wasn' that a pity an' a shame?
Lawd, Lawd,
Wasn' that a pity an' a shame?

3. Po' little Jesus,
Yes, yes,
They tuck him from a manger,
Yes, yes,
They tuck him from his mother,
Yes, yes,
Wasn' that a pity an' a shame?
Lawd, Lawd,
Wasn' that a pity an' a shame?

4. Po' little Jesus,
Yes, yes,
They boun' him wid a halter,
Yes, yes,
An' whipped him up de mountain,
Yes, yes,
Wasn' that a pity an' a shame?
Lawd, Lawd,
Wasn' that a pity an' a shame?

5. Po' little Jesus,
Yes, yes,
They nailed him to the cross, Lawd,
Yes, yes,
They hung him wid a robber,
Yes, yes,
Wasn' that a pity an' a shame?
Lawd, Lawd,
Wasn' that a pity an' a shame?

6. Po' little Jesus,
Yes, yes,
He's risen from darkness,
Yes, yes,
He's 'scended into glory,
Yes, yes,
Now, ain't dat a pity an' a shame?
Lawd, Lawd,
Ain't dat a pity an' a shame?

7. He was po' little Jesus,
Yes, yes,
Born on Friday,
Yes, yes,
Born on Christmas,
Yes, yes,
Wasn' that a pity an' a shame?
Lawd, Lawd,
Wasn' that a pity an' a shame?

102.

Never Said a Mumblin' Word

Words and melody adapted and arranged by
John A. and Alan Lomax

Piano arrangement by
Charles and Ruth Seeger

2. Oh, dey crowned him wid a thorny crown, thorny crown, crown o' thorns,
Oh, dey crowned him wid a thorny crown, an' he never said a mumbalin' word,
Oh, dey crowned him wid a thorny crown, an' he never said a mumbalin' word,
He jes' hung down his head an' he cried.

3. Well, dey nailed him to de cross, to de cross, to de cross,
Well, dey nailed him to de cross, an' he never said a mumbalin' word,
Well, dey nailed him to de cross, an' he never said a mumbalin' word,
He jes' hung down his head an' he cried.

4. Well, dey pierced him in de side, in de side, in de side,
Well, dey pierced him in de side, an' he never said a mumbalin' word,
Well, dey pierced him in de side, an' he never said a mumbalin' word,
Den he hung down his head an' he cried.

5. Well, de blood came twinklin' down, twinklin' down, twinklin down,
Well, de blood came twinklin' down, an' he never said a mumbalin' word,
Well, de blood came twinklin' down, an' he never said a mumbalin' word,
Den he hung down his head an' he died.

103.

Soon One Mornin'

Words and melody adapted and arranged by
John A. and Alan Lomax

Piano arrangement by
Charles and Ruth Seeger

1. Soon one mornin' death come creepin' in my room, (3)
O my Lord, O my Lord, what shall I do to be saved?

2. Death done been here, tuck my mother an gone, (3)
O my Lord, O my Lord, what shall I do to be saved?

3. Death done been here, left me a motherless child, (3)
O my Lord, O my Lord, what shall I do to be saved?

4. Don't move my pillow 'til my Jesus comes, (3)
O my Lord, O my Lord, what shall I do to be saved?

5. When Jesus comes, you can turn my bed around, (3)
O my Lord, O my Lord, what shall I do to be saved?

6. I'm so glad I got religion in time, (3)
O my Lord, O my Lord, what shall I do to be saved?

104.

When My Blood Runs Chilly an' Col'

Words and melody adapted and arranged by
John A. and Alan Lomax

Piano arrangement by
Charles and Ruth Seeger

1. Oh, when-a my blood runs chilly an' col', Ize got to go,
Ize got to go, Ize got to go;
Oh, when-a my blood runs chilly an' col', Ize got to go,
Way beyond de moon.

CHORUS: Do, Lord, do, Lord, do remember me,
Oh, do, Lord, do, Lord, do remember me,
Oh, do, Lord, do, Lord, do remember me,
Do, Lord, remember me.

2. Ef you cain' bear no crosses, you cain' wear no crown,
Ef you cain' bear no crosses, you cain' wear no crown,
Ef you cain' bear no crosses, you cain' wear no crown,
Way beyond de moon.

3. De harder yo' crosses, de brighter yo' crown,
De harder yo' crosses, de brighter yo' crown,
De harder yo' crosses, de brighter yo' crown,
Way beyond de moon.

4. Ize got a mother* in de Beulah land, she's callin' me,
She's callin' me, she's callin' me,
Ize got a mother in de Beulah land, she's callin' me,
Way beyond de sun.

*Sung also for father, brother, sister, auntie, deacon, elder, etc.

105.

Set Down, Servant

Words and melody adapted and arranged by
John A. and Alan Lomax

Piano arrangement by
Charles and Ruth Seeger

2. "My Lawd, you know
That you promise me,
Promise me a long white robe
An' a starry crown."
"Go yonder angel,
Fetch me a starry crown,
Place it on-a my servant's head . . .
Now, servant, please set down."

3. "My Lawd, you know
That you promise me,
Promise me a long white robe
An' a golden waistband."
"Go yonder angel,
Fetch me a golden waistband,
Place it 'round my servant's waist . . .
Now, servant, please set down."

106.

Great Gittin' Up Mornin'

Words and melody adapted and arranged by
John A. and Alan Lomax

Piano arrangement by
Charles and Ruth Seeger

STANZA 1
LEADER
D
B min.
Stop and lem-me tell you 'bout the com-ing of the Sa - viour,
GROUP
D
B min.
D
LEADER
Fare thee well,— fare thee well,— Stop and lem-me tell you 'bout the
GROUP
B min.
D
B min.
A7
D
com-in' of the Sa - viour, Fare thee well.— fare thee well.—

STANZA 2
LEADER
D7
God's gon - na up and speak to Ga - briel,
GROUP
D
B min.
D
Fare thee well, fare thee well,
LEADER
D7
Run and look be -
hind the al - tar,
GROUP
D
B min.
A7
D
Fare thee well, fare thee well.

CHORUS: In that great gittin' up mornin',
Fare thee well, fare thee well,
In that great gittin' up mornin',
Fare thee well, fare thee well. (repeat)

1. LEADER: Stop and lemme tell you 'bout the comin' of the Saviour,
GROUP: Fare thee well, fare thee well,
LEADER: Stop and lemme tell you 'bout the comin' of the Saviour,
GROUP: Fare thee well, fare thee well. (Chorus)

2. LEADER: God's gonna up an' speak to Gabriel,
GROUP: Fare thee well, fare thee well,
LEADER: Run and look behind the altar,
GROUP: Fare thee well, fare thee well,*
LEADER: Now pick up your silver trumpet,
GROUP: Fare thee well, fare thee well,
LEADER: Blow your trumpet, Gabriel,
GROUP: Fare thee well, fare thee well.
LEADER: "Lord, How loud shall I blow it?"
GROUP: Fare thee well, fare thee well,
LEADER: "Blow it so my people will know it.
GROUP: Fare thee well, fare thee well,
LEADER: Blow one blast right calm and easy,
GROUP: Fare thee well, fare thee well,
LEADER: To wake my children that are sleeping,
GROUP: Fare thee well, fare thee well." (Chorus)

3. You will see de coffins bustin',
You will see po' sinners creepin',
Den you'll hear de hell-hounds barkin',
With the rumblin' of the thunder,
Then you see the moon a-bleedin',
See the stars a-fallin'
See the elements a-meltin',
And time will be no longer.

4. Preacher, lay aside yo' Bible,
'Kaze there's a better day a-comin',
And the righteous will be marchin',
When the Christians will be risin'
Marchin' to their home in heaven,
Marchin' home to live with Jesus,
Then you'll cry out for cold water,
While the Christians shout in glory.

*The remaining lines of the song can be sung to the melody of either Stanza I or II. The chorus may be inserted at any point in the song. The refrain is repeated after every line.

107.

Sometimes I Feel Like a Motherless Child

Words and melody adapted and arranged by
John A. and Alan Lomax

Piano arrangement by
Charles and Ruth Seeger

1. Sometimes I feel like a motherless child,
Sometimes I feel like a motherless child,
Sometimes I feel like a motherless child,
A long ways from home, a long ways from home,
O— Lawdy, a long ways from home.

2. Sometimes I feel like I has no friend,
Sometimes I feel like I has no friend,
Sometimes I feel like I has no friend,
And a long ways from home, a long ways from home,
O—Lawdy, a long ways from home.

3. Sometimes I feel like I never been borned,
Sometimes I feel like I never been borned,
Sometimes I feel like I never been borned,
I know my time ain't long, I know my time ain't long,
O—Lawdy, I know my time ain't long.

4. Sometimes I feel like a feather in the air,
Sometimes I feel like a feather in the air,
Sometimes I feel like a feather in the air,
A long ways from home, a long ways from home,
O—Lawdy, a long ways from home.

5. Sometimes I feel like I'm almost gone,
Sometimes I feel like I'm almost gone,
Sometimes I feel like I'm almost gone,
And a long ways from home, a long ways from home,
O—Lawdy, a long ways from home.

O Freedom

Words and melody adapted and arranged by
John A. and Alan Lomax

Piano arrangement by
Charles and Ruth Seeger

1. O freedom, O freedom,
O freedom after a while,
And before I'd be a slave, I'd be buried in my grave,
And go home to my Lord and be free.

2. There'll be no more moaning, no more moaning,
No more moaning after a while,
And before I'd be a slave, I'd be buried in my grave,
And go home to my Lord and be free.

3. No more weeping, no more crying,
No more weeping after a while,
And before I'd be a slave, I'd be buried in my grave,
And go home to my Lord and be free.

4. There'll be no more kneeling, no more bowing,
No more kneeling after a while,
And before I'd be a slave, I'd be buried in my grave,
And go home to my Lord and be free.

5. There'll be shouting, there'll be shouting,
There'll be shouting after a while,
And before I'd be a slave, I'd be buried in my grave,
And go home to my Lord and be free.

109.

Go Down, Moses

Piano arrangement by
Charles and Ruth Seeger

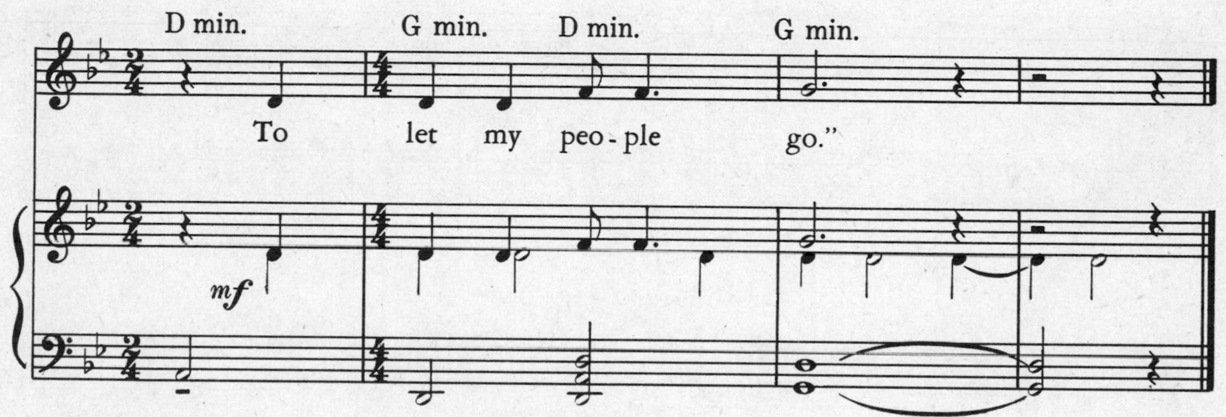

1. When Israel was in Egypt land,
   Let my people go,
   Oppressed so hard, she could not stand,
   Let my people go.

CHORUS: "Go down, Moses,
Way down in Egypt land,
Tell old Pharoah
To let my people go."

2. "Thus spoke the Lord," bold Moses said,
   Let my people go,
   "If not, I'll strike your first born dead,"
   Let my people go. (Chorus)

3. "Your foes shall not before you stand,"
   Let my people go,
   "And you'll possess fair Canaan's land,"
   Let my people go. (Chorus)

4. "You'll not get lost in the wildnerness,"
   Let my people go,
   "With a lighted candle in your breas',"
   Let my people go.

110.

Joshua Fit the Battle of Jericho

Piano arrangement by
Charles and Ruth Seeger

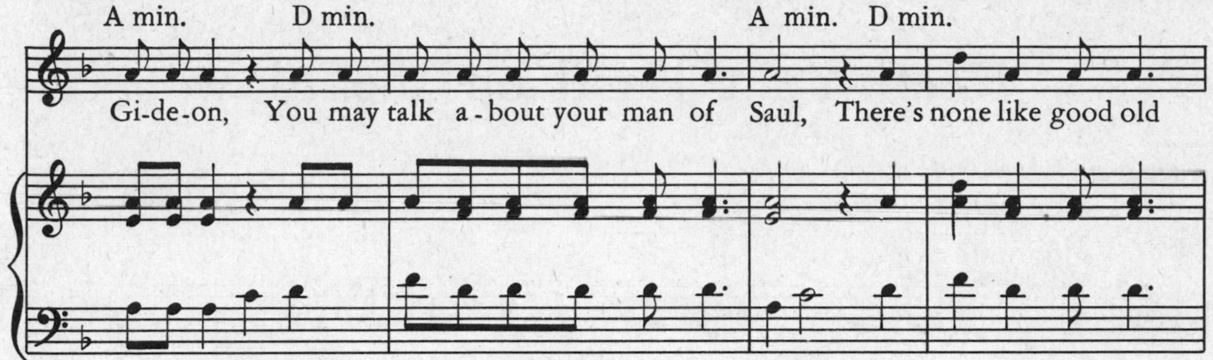

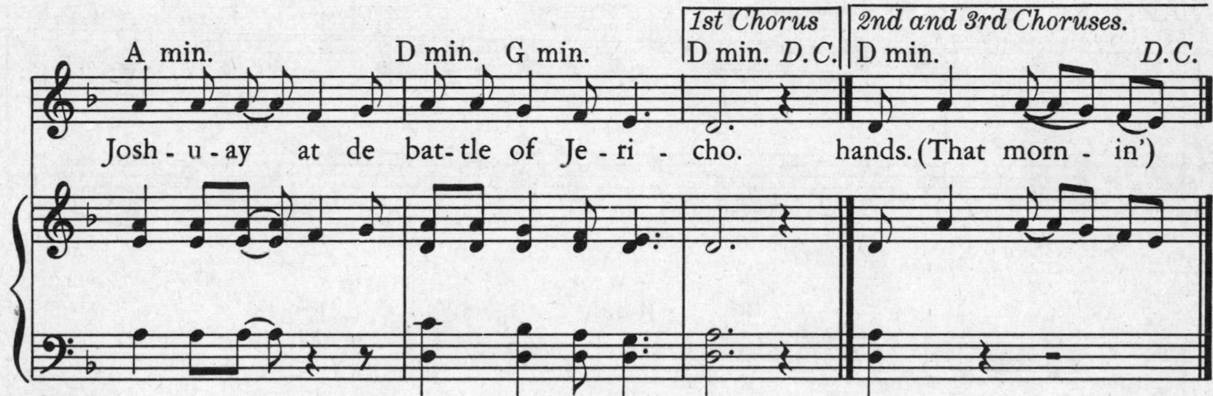

1. You may talk about your man of Gideon,
   You may talk about your man of Saul,
   There's none like good old Joshuay
   At de battle of Jericho.

CHORUS: Joshua fit the battle of Jericho,
Jericho, Jericho,
Joshua fit the battle of Jericho
And the walls come tumblin' down.

2. Up to the walls of Jericho
   He marched with a spear in his hand,
   "Go blow them ram-horns," Joshuay cried,
   " 'Cause the battle is in my hands."

CHORUS: That mornin' —,
Joshua fit the battle of Jericho, etc.

3. Then de lamb-ram-sheep-horns begin to blow
   And the trumpet begin to sound,
   Joshua commanded the children to shout
   And the walls come tumblin' down.

CHORUS: That mornin' —, etc.

111.

Keep Your Hand on the Plow

Words and melody adapted and arranged by
John A. and Alan Lomax

Piano arrangement by
Charles and Ruth Seeger

Version I

1. Mary wo' three links of chain,
Ev'ry link was Jesus name.
Keep your hand on the plow,
Hold on.

CHORUS: Hold on,
Hold on,
Keep your hand on the plow,
Hold on.

2. Paul and Silas bound in jail,
Had nobody for to go their bail,
Keep your hands on the plow,
Hold on.

3. Paul and Silas begin to shout,
Jail doors opened and they walked out,
Keep your hands on the plow,
Hold on.

4. Peter was so nice and neat,
Wouldn't let Jesus wash his feet,
Keep your hand on the plow,
Hold on.

5. Jesus said, "If I wash them not,
You'll have no father in this lot."
Keep your hands on the plow,
Hold on.

6. Peter got anxious and he said,
"Wash my feet, my hands and head."
Keep your hands on the plow,
Hold on.

7. Got my hands on the gospel plow,
Wouldn't take nothin' for my journey now,
Keep your hands on the plow,
Hold on.

Version II

1. United Nations make a chain,
Every link is freedom's name,
Keep your hand on the plow,
Hold on.

2. Now the war is over and done
Let's keep the peace that we have won,
Keep your hand on the plow,
Hold on.

3. Freedom's name is mighty sweet,
All this world is gonna meet.
Keep your hand on the plow,
Hold on.

4. Many men have fought and died
So we could sing here side by side.
Keep your hand on the plow,
Hold on.

Appendix I

THIS SECTION of FOLK SONG: USA contains the sources for tunes, song texts and continuity, as well as references to other volumes in which the songs have been published. The material is arranged serially, following the 1-111 sequence to which both the songs and the continuity conform.

In each note under SOURCES . . . we acknowledge fully the sources for the melody, the stanzas or continuity material of every song, *unless the song and the note came from our personal collections.* In a great number of instances, the reader will find no SOURCES listed, which means that the material for that unit of the book was our own.

The second half of each note consists of key REFERENCES. These references will lead you to other published versions of each ballad, and, when we could discover one, to a source in which an extensive bibliography of the ballad appeared. With the aid of these key references and a pocket-sized folk-song library, the student will be able to do some comparative study of most of the songs. We saw no point in reprinting long head-notes in this volume, however.

A considerable amount of abbreviation occurs in REFERENCES, but we trust this will not confuse you. The reference books are designated by a number, in bold face type, the same number under which they appear in the *Selected List of Books,* Appendix II. For instance the first reference under *All the Pretty Little Horses* reads—p. 341, Vol. II, *53.* Turn to No. *53* in Appendix II and you will find Cecil Sharp's "English Folk Songs of the Southern Appalachians"; and on page three hundred and forty-one of volume two of this work you will find another version of *All the Pretty Little Horses.* . . . For recorded version of songs, look through Appendix III.

2. ALL THE PRETTY LITTLE HORSES.
   REFERENCES . . . p. 341, Vol. II, *53;* p. 250, *80.*

3. GO TELL AUNT NANCY.
   REFERENCE . . . p. 245, Vol. II, *53.*

4. LEATHERWING BAT.
   SOURCES AND REFERENCES . . . Learned from Burl Ives; additional stanzas, p. 304, Vol. II, *53.* Source for story of the talking fowls: p. 24, B. A. Botkin, *Lay My Burden Down,* University of Chicago Press, Chicago, 1945.

5. GREY GOOSE.
   SOURCES . . . The story of Old Sis Goose; Publications of the Texas Folk-Lore Society, No. II, p. 50-51.
   REFERENCES . . . p. 242, *14;* p. 108, *71.*

6. MISTER RABBIT.
SOURCES . . . Song from Dorothy Scarborough, *On the Trail of Negro Folk Songs,* Harvard University Press, Cambridge, 1925. Tale from Zora Neale Hurston, *Mules and Men,* J. B. Lippincott, Philadelphia, 1935. Used by permission.

7. OLD BLUE.
SOURCES . . . Stanzas from Arthur Palmer Hudson, *Folksongs of Mississippi and Their Background,* University of North Carolina Press, 1936. Tales from many sources.
REFERENCES . . . p. 111, *15;* p. 201, *44.*

8. GROUND HOG.
SOURCES . . . Tune, Sharp, Cecil J., *English Folk Songs from the Southern Appalachians,* Oxford University Press, London, 1932, p. 340, Volume II. Text, Josiah Combs, *Chansons Populaire du Midi des États Unis,* Libraire J. Gambier, Paris, 1925. Used by permission.
REFERENCES . . . See above and: p. 340, Vol. II, *53;* p. 498, *42.*

9. SPRINGFIELD MOUNTAIN.
SOURCES . . . Song from p. 248, Mary O. Eddy's *Ballads & Songs of Ohio,* J. J. Augustin, New York, 1939, used by permission.
REFERENCES . . . p. 299; *39;* Phillips Barry's articles on *Springfield Mountain* in Nos. 11 & 12 of the Journal of the Folk Song Society of the Northeast, *3.*

10. I WAS BORN ABOUT TEN THOUSAND YEARS AGO.
SOURCES . . . Tale of Davy Crockett and the sun used by permission from Richard Dorson's *Davy Crockett, American Comic Legend,* Rockland Editions, Rockland, N. Y., 1939.
REFERENCES . . . p. 351; *14;* p. 230, *18.*

11. WHEN YOU GO A-COURTIN'.
SOURCES . . . Tale from p. 274, Thomas Clark's *Rampaging Frontier,* Bobbs-Merrill, Indianapolis, 1929; quoted there from the Nettle Bottom Ball in J. S. Robb's *Streaks of a Squatter's Life.*
REFERENCES . . . p. 6, Vol. II, *53;* p. 426, *39;* p. 128-9, *18.*

12. LOLLY-TOO-DUM.
SOURCES . . . Two stories, pp. 286 & 298, Thomas D. Clark's *The Rampaging Frontier,* Bobbs-Merrill, Indianapolis, 1929; used by permission. Note from Franklin J. Meine, *Tall Tales of the Southwest,* Knopf, New York, 1930.
REFERENCES . . . p. 126, *15;* p. 159, Vol. II, *53.*

13. WHEN I WAS SINGLE, I.
SOURCES . . . Tune from Peter Seeger, who learned it from an old lady in Alabama.
REFERENCES . . . p. 32, Vol. II, *53;* p. 437, *39;* p. 47, *18.*

WHEN I WAS SINGLE, II.
SOURCES . . . Note from p. 287, Thomas D. Clark, *The Rampaging Frontier,* Bobbs-Merrill, Indianapolis, 1929; used by permission: quoted there from *The Argus of the West,* May 24, 1826.
REFERENCES . . . p. 163, *74.*

14. THE SPORTING BACHELORS.
SOURCES . . . Story reprinted by permission from *God Bless the Devil* by the Tennessee Writers' Project, copyright 1940 by the University of North Carolina Press.
REFERENCES . . . p. 122, Vol. II, *53.*

15. JENNIE JENKINS.
REFERENCES . . . p. 129, *15;* p. 371, Vol. II, *53.*

16. BLACK, BLACK.
SOURCES . . . From *More Songs of the Hill Folk* by J. J. Niles, New York, G. Schirmer, Inc., 1936, used by permission.
REFERENCES . . . p. 31, Vol. II, *53;* also note variations of *Sweet William,* p. 84, Vol. II, op. cit.; p. 296, *51.1.*

17. COME ALL YOU FAIR AND TENDER LADIES.
SOURCES . . . Note from p. 130, Lomax, *Our Singing Country,* The Macmillan Company, New York, 1941.
REFERENCES . . . p. 128, Vol. II, *53;* p. 419, *42;* p. 477, *39.*

18. OLD SMOKY.
SOURCES . . . From the singing of the Gant family, Austin, Texas, with additional stanzas from p. 123, Sharp, Vol. II, *English Folk Songs from the Southern Appalachians,* Oxford University Press, London, 1932.
REFERENCES . . . p. 123, Vol. II, *53.*

19. DOWN IN THE VALLEY.
REFERENCES . . . p. 488, *39;* p. 228, *71;* pp. 148 & 213, *18.*

20. CARELESS LOVE.
REFERENCES . . . p. 218, *71;* p. 21, *18;* p. 40, *45.*

21. DINK'S SONG.
SOURCES . . . Song, p. 195, American Ballads and Folk Songs, The Macmillan Company, New York, 1934.
REFERENCES . . . See *Careless Love;* also p. 326-7, *79.*

22. SEE, SEE, RIDER.
SOURCES . . . Story used by permission from Howard Odum's *Rainbow Round My Shoulder*, Bobbs-Merrill, Indianapolis, 1938.
REFERENCES . . . p. 137, *71;* for background on blues see p. 17ff., *74.*

23. SHORTY GEORGE.
REFERENCES . . . p. 142, *71;* p. 199, *14.*

Introduction to Chapter III.
Balaam Foster's Fiddle, used by permission of J. Chapman Milling, Columbia, South Carolina, folklorist: Verses from *The Cowboy's Christmas Ball*, by Larry Chittenden.

24. SOURWOOD MOUNTAIN.
REFERENCES . . . p. 305, Vol. II, *53;* p. 125, p. 320, *18;* pp. 24 & 26, *45.*

25. OLD JOE CLARK.
SOURCES . . . Stanzas used by permission from Botkin, *American Play-Party Song,* University of Nebraska Press, Lincoln, 1937, and from Lomax, *American Ballads and Folk Songs* (see bibliography). "The Knob Dance," from Franklin J. Meine, *Tall Tales of the Southwest*, Knopf, New York, 1930. *Round and Round Hitler's Grave*, copyright 1942 by Bob Miller, Inc., written by the Almanacs, used by permission of the publishers.
REFERENCES . . . p. 259, Vol. II, *53;* p. 277, *14.*

26. RAISE A RUKUS.
SOURCES . . . Song from p. 253, Lomax, *American Ballads and Folk Songs* (see bibliography). Text from p. 450, *The Negro Caravan* by Sterling Brown, The Dryden Press, New York, 1941. Ex-slave stories from B. A. Botkin, *Lay My Burden Down,* University of Chicago Press, Chicago, 1945.
REFERENCES . . . p. 73-4, *74.*

27. OLD DAN TUCKER.
SOURCES . . . For note on Jim Crow see p. 162, White, *79.*
REFERENCES . . . See index under this title, *95.*

28. CINDY.
REFERENCES . . . p. 42, *45;* p. 361, Vol. II, *53.*

29. BLACKEYED SUSIE.
SOURCES . . . Song from p. 286, Lomax, *American Ballads and Folk Songs* (see bibliography).

30. SKIP TO MY LOU.
SOURCES . . . Song from p. 294, Lomax, *American Ballads and Folk Songs, 14.* Note: Owens, *Swing and Turn,* Tardy Publishing Company, Dallas, 1936; and Botkin, *The American Play-Party Song, 95.*
REFERENCES . . . see index, *95.*

31. COFFEE GROWS ON WHITE OAK TREES.
SOURCES . . . Song used by permission from Botkin, *The American Play-Party Song,* University of Nebraska Press, Lincoln, 1937. Note based on Botkin, op. cit., and Owens, *Swing and Turn,* Tardy Publishing Company, Dallas, 1936. Directions from Owens, op. cit.
REFERENCES . . . p. 164, *95;* also see index, *95.*

32. SHOOT THE BUFFALO.
SOURCES . . . p. 296, Lomax, *American Ballads and Folk Songs, 14.*
REFERENCES . . . see index, *95.*

33. BUFFALO GALS.
SOURCES . . . p. 288, Lomax, *American Ballads and Folk Songs, 14.*
REFERENCES . . . see index, *95.*

34. SWEET THING.
SOURCES . . . Tune, p. 298, Lomax, *Our Singing Country, 15.* Three stanzas learned from Josh White.
REFERENCES . . . p. 298, *15;* p. 275 and p. 357, Vol. II, *53;* p. 18, *18;* p. 241 and p. 246, *80;* p. 140, *74.*

35. JOHNNY HAS GONE FOR A SOLDIER.
REFERENCES . . . p. 281, *39;* p. 50, Vol. II, *53.*

36. BRAVE WOLFE.

Sources . . . Learned from Frank Warner, ballad singer.

References . . . p. 324, *37*.

37. JOHN BROWN'S BODY.

Sources . . . Note based on Ehrlich, *God's Angry Man, New York,* Simon & Schuster, 1932. See also p. 155, Kobbé Gustav, *Famous American Songs,* New York, Crowell Publishing Co., 1905.

References . . . p. 206, *110*; No. 46, *111*; see index, *120*.

38. MADEMOISELLE FROM ARMENTIÈRES.

References . . . p. 110, *118;* see index, *120*.

Introduction for Chapter V; material quoted from *Songs of American Sailormen,* collected and edited by Joanna Colcord, Searsport, Maine. Published by W. W. Norton, New York, 1938.

40. SANTY ANNO.

Sources . . . p. 206, Lomax, *Our Singing Country, 15*.

References . . . p. 89, *118;* p. 206, *75*.

41. SHENANDOAH.

Sources . . . Last two stanzas, Colcord, op. cit.

References . . . p. 83, *118*.

42. SACRAMENTO.

Sources . . . p. 105, Colcord, *Songs of American Sailormen,* W. W. Norton, New York, 1938, used by permission.

References . . . p. 110 and p. 112, *18*.

43. LOWLANDS.

Sources . . . p. 101, Colcord, op. cit. used by permission.

References . . . p. 101, *118;* p. 350, Vol. II, *53*.

44. BLOW YE WINDS IN THE MORNING.

Sources . . . From Colcord, op. cit., used by permission.

References . . . see index, *118*.

45. THE E-RI-E.

Sources . . . Note based on Chapter X of Harold Thompson's *Body, Boots and Britches,* J. B. Lippincott, Philadelphia, 1940. By permission.

References . . . p. 220, *37;* p. 455, *14;* pp. 178 through 180, *18*.

46. THE BIGLER.

Sources . . . Note: paper by Ivan Walton, University of Michigan, entitled *Michigan Marine Lore;* and H. Hatcher, *The Great Lakes, New York,* Oxford University Press, 1944.

References . . . p. 200, *118;* p. 168, *35;* p. 220, *15;* p. 174, *18*.

47. ROCK ABOUT MY SARO JANE.

Sources . . . *Listen to Our Story,* Brunswick Album B1024, pub. by Decca Records, Inc.

References . . . For background, see 116.

48. ONCE MORE A-LUMB'RING GO.

Sources . . . A somewhat revised version of the song of the same title in E. C. Beck's *Songs of the Michigan Lumberjacks,* p. 18, University of Michigan Press, Ann Arbor, 1942, used by permission; Paul Bunyan story from Esther Shepard, *Paul Bunyan,* Harcourt, Brace & Co., used by permission.

References . . . No. 3, *23;* see above, *114*.

49. BLUE MOUNTAIN LAKE.

Sources . . . Frank Warner, *Hudson Valley Songs, see Record List.* Verses in note from E. C. Beck, op. cit. The "Crumb" story from Botkin, *A Treasury of American Folklore,* Crown Publishers, New York, 1944, used by permission.

50. THE JAM ON GERRY'S ROCKS.

Sources . . . Song from Franz L. Rickaby's *Ballads and Songs of the Shanty-Boy,* Harvard University Press, Cambridge, 1926.

References . . . No. 25, 23; No. 2, 35.

51. A LUMBERMAN IN TOWN.

Sources . . . Song from Barry, *The Maine Woods Songster,* Powell Printing Co., Cambridge, Mass., 1939, used by permission. For background on note see Holbrook, *Holy Old Mackinaw,* The Macmillan Company, New York, 1938.

References . . . p. 61, *23*.

52. THE BUFFALO SKINNERS.

Sources . . . Lomax, *Cowboy Songs and other Frontier Ballads,* The Macmillan Company, New York, revised and enlarged, 1938.

References . . . For Canada-I-O, see No. 8, *35;* Michigan-I-O, No. 40, *23;* p. 335, *91*.

53. SWEET BETSY FROM PIKE.

Sources . . . Note from pp. 1-6, Hulbert, *Forty-Niners*, Little, Brown & Co., Boston, 1932, used by permission.

References . . . p. 343, *39* and *147*; p. 10, *84*; p. 107, *18*.

54. THE DAYS OF 49.

Sources . . . Tune and portion of text from Frank Warner, who learned it from Yankee John Galusha, New York State. Remainder of text from Lomax, op. cit.

References . . . p. 53, *84*.

55. THE OLD SETTLERS' SONG.

Sources . . . Stanzas quoted from Black, Eleanora, and Robertson, Sidney, *The Gold Rush Song Book*, The Colt Press, San Francisco, 1940. Melody, "Rosin the Bow," p. 255, *39*.

56. DOWN, DOWN, DOWN.

Sources . . . Song and note reprinted from *Minstrels of the Mine Patch* by George Korson, copyright, 1938, by University of Pennsylvania Press. Used by permission.

References . . . p. 273, *15*; p. 176, *18*.

57. THE OLD CHISHOLM TRAIL.

References . . . pp. 28-37, *91*; p. 1 and p. 5, *90*.

58. GIT ALONG LITTLE DOGIES.

Sources . . . Note quoted from Lomax, John A., *Adventures of a Ballad Hunter*, The Macmillan Company, 1947.

References . . . pp. 4-7, *91*; p. 237, *15*; p. 91 and p. 95, *90*.

59. THE STREETS OF LAREDO.

References . . . p. 13, *90*; p. 392, *39*; p. 242, *42*; p. 164, Vol. II, *53*.

60. BURY ME NOT ON THE LONE PRAIRIE.

References . . . p. 387, *39*; pp. 48-51, *91*; p. 21, *90*; p. 20, *18*; p. 236, Vol. II, *53*.

61. THE COWBOY'S DREAM.

References . . . pp. 44-48, *91*; p. 99, *90*.

62. HOME ON THE RANGE.

Sources . . . Song, Lomax, *Cowboy Songs and Other Frontier Ballads*, op. cit.

References . . . pp. 424-428, *91*; p. 171, *90*; Chap. 21, Homer Croy, *Corn Country*, Duell, Sloan and Pearce, 1947.

63. GOODBY, OLD PAINT, I.

References . . . pp. 12-14, *91*; p. 175, *90*.

GOODBY, OLD PAINT, II.

References . . . p. 17, *90*; p. 12, *18*.

64. RYE WHISKEY.

References . . . p. 163 and p. 253, *91*; also *Old Smoky*, this volume.

65. THE RED RIVER VALLEY.

References . . . p. 298, *91*; p. 196, *16*; p. 130, *18*.

Introduction to Chapter VIII.

Sources . . . Quotation from Martha Smith, *Goin' to God's Country*, Christopher Publishing House, 1941, used by permission.

66. THE YOUNG MAN WHO WOULDN'T HOE CORN.

Sources . . . Tune from Resettlement Song Sheets (edited by Charles Seeger), Special Skills Division of the Resettlement Administration, (1936-37). Stanzas from same source; from p. 286, Lomax, *Our Singing Country*, op. cit.; from p. 440, Belden, *Ballads and Songs Collected by the Missouri Folk-Lore Society*, op. cit. Tall tale from Hurston's *Mules and Men*, J. B. Lippincott, Philadelphia, 1935. Used by permission.

References . . . p. 440, *39*; p. 258, Vol. II, *53*.

67. WHOA, BUCK!

Sources . . . Talking Mule story from Hurston's, *Mules and Men*, op. cit., pp. 217-18. Used by permission.

References . . . p. 85, *71*.

68. PICK A BALE O' COTTON.

Reference . . . p. 92, *71*.

69. THE BOLL WEEVIL.

References . . . p. 352, *79*; p. 122, *14*; p. 8, *18*; p. 184, *71*.

70. STARVING TO DEATH ON A GOVERNMENT CLAIM.

Sources . . . Background for note from Evelyn Dick, *The Sod House Frontier*, D. Appleton-Century, 1937, by permission.

71. THE STATE OF ARKANSAS.

Sources . . . Note from p. 255ff. of *Tall Tales of Arkansas*, James R. Masterson, Chapman & Grimes, Boston, 1942. Used by permission.

REFERENCES . . . p. 424, *39*; p. 238, Vol. II, *53*.

72. GOIN' DOWN THE ROAD FEELIN' BAD.
SOURCES . . . Two anecdotes from Hurston, op. cit., and Russell Lord's *Behold Our Land*, Houghton Mifflin Co. Used by permission. Verses in note quoted by permission of Woody Guthrie, copyright owner.
REFERENCES . . . p. 293, *15*; p. 248, *74*.

73. 900 MILES.
SOURCES . . . From the singing of Woody Guthrie.
REFERENCES . . . pp. 244-5, *80*; p. 278, Vol. II, *53*.

74. JOHN HENRY, I.
SOURCES . . . Note based on Chappel, Louis W., *John Henry: A Folk-Lore Study*, Walter Biedermann, Jena, Germany, 1933, by permission.
REFERENCES . . . p. 233 and p. 242, *80*; p. 24, *18*; *60*; reference for "Who Will Shoe Your Feet," p. 480, *39*.

JOHN HENRY, II.
SOURCES . . . Song from Lomax, *Our Singing Country*, op. cit.
REFERENCES . . . p. 258, *15*; Record 15b, Library of Congress Series, see Record List.

75. CASEY JONES, I.
SOURCES . . . Material for note from Erie Railroad Magazine, Vol. 24, April, 1928, No. 2.
REFERENCES . . . pp. 241-245, *9*; p. 366, *18*; p. 4 and p. 14, *115*; also see index, *14*.

CASEY JONES, II.
SOURCES . . . Song, copyright MCMIX by Newton and Seibert. Copyright renewed MCMXXXVI by Charles E. Seibert and Dorothy Elizabeth Newton. By permission of Shapiro, Bernstein and Co., Inc., New York, copyright owners.

76. PADDY WORKS ON THE ERIE.
REFERENCE . . . p. 28, *115*.

77. O LULA.
SOURCES . . . Words from p. 319, Hurston, *Mules and Men*, Lippincott, 1935, used by permission.

78. CAN'CHA LINE 'EM.
REFERENCES . . . pp. 262-4, *15*; p. 14, *14*; see Hurston, *Mules and Men*, op. cit.

79. THE BIG ROCK CANDY MOUNTAIN.
SOURCES . . . Tune and words, Geo. Milburn, *The Hobo's Horn Book*, Ives Washburn, New York, 1930, used by permission.
REFERENCES . . . p. 884, *9*.

80. JESSE JAMES.
SOURCES . . . From p. 161, Lomax, *Cowboy Songs and Other Frontier Ballads*, op. cit. Note based on Robertiss Love, *The Rise and Fall of Jesse James*, New York, G. P. Putnam, 1926, by permission.
REFERENCES . . . p. 401, *39*; p. 155, *90*.

81. SAM BASS.
REFERENCES . . . p. 399, *39*; p. 161, *90*; p. 269, *15*.

82. TOM DOOLEY.
SOURCES . . . Used by permission of Frank Warner.

83. DOWN IN THE WILLOW GARDEN.
SOURCES . . . Stanzas in note quoted from Mary O. Eddy's *Ballads and Songs from Ohio*, J. J. Augustin, New York, 1939.
REFERENCES . . . p. 314, *42*; p. 256, *27*.

84. PRETTY POLLY.
SOURCES . . . Tune from p. 171, Lomax, *Our Singing Country*, op. cit. Text in note from Cecil J. Sharp and Rev. Charles Marson, *Folk Songs from Somerset*, Schott & Co., London, 1904-9, Vol. IV, p. 8.
REFERENCES . . . p. 308, *42*; p. 172, *15*; p. 60, *18*.

85. JOHN HARDY.
SOURCES . . . Portion of text and note from J. H. Cox, *Folk-Songs of the South*, Harvard University Press, Cambridge, 1925, used by permission.
REFERENCES . . . p. 175, *42*; p. 35, Vol. II, *53*.

86. PO' LAZ'US.
REFERENCES . . . p. 91, *14*; p. 342, *15*; p. 239, *80*; p. 50, *74*.

87. DARLIN' COREY.
SOURCES . . . Song from p. 302, Lomax, *Our Singing Country*, op. cit. Material for note from Richard Dorson's *Davy Crockett, American Comic Legend*, Rockland Editions, Rockland, N. Y., 1939, by permission.
REFERENCES . . . p. 302, *15*; p. 204, Vol. II, *53*.

88. FRANKIE AND ALBERT.
REFERENCES . . . p. 230, *39*; pp. 75-86, *18*.

89. TAKE A WHIFF ON ME.
REFERENCES . . . p. 6 and p. 204, *18*; p. 216, *71*.

90. HARD TIMES, PO' BOY.
REFERENCES . . . p. 214, *18*; p. 142, *14*.

91. THE MIDNIGHT SPECIAL.
REFERENCES . . . p. 71, *14*; p. 26, p. 217, *18*; p. 221, *71*; p. 18, *115*.

92. AIN'T NO MO' CANE ON DE BRAZIS.
REFERENCES . . . p. 123, *71*; pp. 58-9, *14*; see Album III of the Library of Congress Series, the Record List.

93. TAKE THIS HAMMER.
SOURCES . . . Version I from p. 380, Lomax, *Our Singing Country*, op. cit. Version II from Lomax, *American Ballads and Folk Songs*, op. cit.
REFERENCES . . . p. 250ff., *79*; pp. 233-4, *80*; pp. 90, 111, 113, and 249, *74*.

94. ALMOST DONE.
SOURCES . . . Song from p. 386, Lomax, *Our Singing Country*, op. cit. Chain gang story from Odum, *Rainbow Round My Shoulder*, The Bobbs-Merrill Company, Indianapolis, 1928, used by permission.
REFERENCES . . . p. 258, *74*.

95. ANOTHER MAN DONE GONE.
REFERENCES . . . See Album IV of the Library of Congress Series, the Record List.

Introduction to Chapter XI.
On the introduction and headnotes for white spirituals, we have leaned heavily upon the work of Dr. George Pullen Jackson, especially his volume, *White and Negro Spirituals. The Myth of the Negro Past*, by Melville Herskovits, was used as a reference throughout. For the full references see Appendix II, *111* and 65.

96. AMAZING GRACE.
SOURCES . . . Tune, used by permission, is No. 135b, Jackson, *Spiritual Folk Songs of Early America*, J. J. Augustin, New York, 1937.
REFERENCES . . . No. 38, *111*; No. 127, *109*.

97. WAYFARING STRANGER.
SOURCES . . . Final three stanzas from No. 40, Jackson, op. cit.
REFERENCES . . . p. 191, *61*; No. 40, *110*; p. 37, *15*.

98. WONDROUS LOVE.
SOURCES . . . For source see footnote under music.
REFERENCES . . . No. 88, *110*; No. 43, *111*.

99. BOUND FOR THE PROMISED LAND.
SOURCES . . . Tune and arrangement, William Walker, *Southern Harmony*, New Haven, Conn., 1835. Text, op. cit.
REFERENCES . . . pp. 80-1, *111*; see p. 238, *110*.

100. LONESOME VALLEY.
REFERENCES . . . p. 108, *80*; No. 54, *111*; No. 214, *110*.

101. PO' LIL JESUS.
REFERENCE . . . p. 124, Vol. II, *68*.

102. SOON ONE MORNIN'.
REFERENCES . . . p. 30, *15*; p. 78, *79*; p. 174, Vol. II, *68*.

103. NEVER SAID A MUMBALIN' WORD.
REFERENCES . . . p. 103, *80*; p. 174, Vol. I, *68*; p. 165, *75*.

104. WHEN MY BLOOD RUNS CHILLY AND COL'.
REFERENCES . . . p. 82, *80*; No. 27, *111*.

105. SET DOWN, SERVANT.
REFERENCE . . . p. 65, *80*.

106. GREAT GITTIN' UP MORNIN'.
REFERENCES . . . p. 40, Vol. II, *68*; p. 154, *61*; No. 126, *111*.

107. SOMETIMES I FEEL LIKE A MOTHERLESS CHILD.
SOURCES . . . Quotation from p. 86, G. P. Johnson, *Folk Culture on St. Helena Island, South Carolina*, University of North Carolina Press, Chapel Hill, 1930. White spiritual stanzas from Jackson, *Down East Spirituals*, J. J. Augustin, New York, 1941, No. 240. Slave stories from p. 156 and p. 230, Botkin's, *Lay My Burden Down*, University of Chicago Press, Chicago, 1945, by permission.
REFERENCES . . . p. 30, Vol. II, *68*; p. 146, *80*.

108. O FREEDOM.

SOURCES . . . Version from Hally Wood.

REFERENCES . . . No. 1, *111*; p. 110, *61*; p. 51, *79*.

109. GO DOWN, MOSES.

REFERENCES . . . p. 51, Vol. I, *68*; p. 165, *80*; p. 32ff., *The New Yorker*, Dec. 13, 1947, for portrait of Harriet Tubman and references to her singing.

110. JOSHUA FIT THE BATTLE OF JERICHO.

SOURCES . . . Slave stories from p. 223 and p. 267 of Botkin's *Lay My Burden Down*, University of Chicago Press, Chicago, 1945, by permission.

REFERENCE . . . p. 56, Vol. I, 68.

111. KEEP YOUR HAND ON THE PLOW.

SOURCES . . . Version II reprinted by permission of People's Songs, Inc., copyright owners, New York City.

REFERENCES . . . p. 115, *79*; p. 292, Vol. II, *53*; p. 44, *15*.

Appendix II

Selected List of Books

THERE ARE now hundreds of books and valuable articles about American folklore. To list them all would require a volume as large as this one. We have, therefore, put together a selected list of the books that the general reader might find the most helpful for extending his knowledge of the field. They are arranged by subject and each one is briefly described so that the reader can go more quickly to the material of his interest. This list is quoted in part from *American Folk Song and Folk Lore, a Regional Bibliography,* No. 7 in the list. Books marked with a single star have tunes and those marked with a double star have piano accompaniment as well.

I. BIBLIOGRAPHIES AND PERIODICALS

1. **Journal of American Folk-Lore.* Various editors, American Folk-Lore Society, 450 Ahnaip Street, Menasha, Wisconsin, 1888——.

   Source material for all regions in the United States: ballads, songs, games, customs, superstitions, tales, etc., from the entire country, much of which is not available elsewhere. Indian folk lore. *American Folk-Lore Society Memoirs,* same source.

   **New York Folklore Quarterly,* Louis Jones, 124 Roberts Place, Ithaca, New York, 1945——.

   Harold Thompson has been the guiding spirit of this society and its journal. The publication reflects his robust spirit, his catholic interest, and his sense for salty folklore.

2. **Publications of the Texas Folk-Lore Society,* Dobie and others, ed., Texas Folk-Lore Society, Austin, Texas, 1916——.

   Started by John A. Lomax and L. W. Payne, this society has done, under J. Frank Dobie, a superlative job of bringing local lore to life on the printed page. The best regional publication in the United States.

3. **Bulletin of the Folk Song Society of the Northeast,* Phillips Barry, ed., Powell Publishing Company, Cambridge, Mass., 1930-37.

   The only bulletin consistently to concern itself with folk song to the exclusion of other aspects of folk lore.

4. *Southern Folklore Quarterly,* Alton C. Morris, ed., University of Florida with Southeastern Folklore Society, Gainesville, Fla., 1937——.

   A varied coverage, with much attention to folk song; articles by most of the important collectors throughout the United States appear here from time to time, reporting on contemporary work.

   Western Folklore (formerly *California Folklore Quarterly*), Archer Taylor, Univ. of Cal. Press, Berkeley 4, Cal., 1942——.

   A handsome, scholarly, and progressive journal dealing especially with Western material.

5. Boggs, Ralph S., *Folklore Bibliography,* South-

ern Folklore Quarterly, Gainesville, Fla., Vol. 2, No. 1, March, 1938; Vol. 3, No. 1, March 1939; Vol. 4, March, 1940, and subsequently.

There appears annually in the March issue year a complete annotated bibliography which includes material appearing in current journals.

6. Herzog, George, *Research in primitive and Folk Music in the U. S.*, Bulletin No. 24, American Council of Learned Societies, Washington, D. C., 1936.

A survey of collections of folk and primitive music in America, with index of regional collectors, lists of written and recorded collections and a bibliography. Penetrating commentary on and suggestions for both fields.

7. Lomax, Alan, and Cowell, Sidney, *American Folk Song and Folk Lore, a Regional Bibliography*, Progressive Education Assn. Service Center Pamphlet #8, Progressive Education Association, 221 W. 57th St., New York City.

This is the handiest available bibliography.

Note: For information on American Folklore societies, see p. 161ff, Vol. 56; p. 477, Vol. 59, 1.

II. General Collections—Books which include folklore from a wide area and of many social groups

8. Blair, Walter, *Native American Humor*. American Book Company, New York, 1937.

Good general approach to the American newspaper folk-humorists; the open door, bibliographically, to Davy Crockett, Mike Fink and the others. Pungent selections from the field.

9. *Botkin, B. A. *A Treasury of American Folklore*. Crown Publishers, New York, 1944.

A magnificent encyclopedic collection of all kinds of folklore, from the whole country, including many songs with their tunes.

10. American Guide Series.

Guides to the states, prepared by the W.P.A. Writers Project, published in various ways. Invaluable compendia of local history, points of interest, etc., linked with folklore.

11. American Folkways, Erskine Caldwell, ed., Duell, Sloan and Pearce, 1941——.

McWilliams, Carey, *Southern California Country*
Corle, Edwin, *Desert Country*
Kane, Harnett T., *Deep Delta Country*
Kennedy, Stetson, *Palmetto Country* *
Long, Haniel, *Piñon Country*
Rayburn, Otto Ernest, *Ozark Country*
Stegner, Wallace, *Mormon Country*
Thane, Eric, *High Border Country*
Thomas, Jean, *Blue Ridge Country* *
Vestal, Stanley, *Short Grass Country*
Williamson, Thames, *Far North Country*
Webster, Clarence M., *Town Meeting Country*
Atherton, Gertrude, *Golden Gate Country*
Le Sueur, Meridel, *North Star Country* *

Regional portraits, all containing folklore. Starred volumes have high folklore content.

12. Berrey, Lester V., and Van Den Bark, Melvin, *The American Thesaurus of Slang*, Crowell Company, New York, 1947.

The folklore of the American language. A fat and rewarding volume.

13. Blesh, Rudi, *Shining Trumpets*, Knopf, New York, 1946.

The best of the theoretical books on jazz. Has a fine list of selected hot records.

14. *Lomax, John A. and Alan. *American Ballads and Folk Songs*. The Macmillan Company, New York, 1934.

Widely ranging collection; many of the songs come from rceordings made by the editors and deposited in the Archive of American Folk Song of the Library of Congress. Heavy accent on indigenous songs of all types, particularly Negro secular songs. More than 250 texts and tunes.

15. *Lomax, John A. and Alan, and Seeger, Ruth Crawford. *Our Singing Country*. The Macmillan Company, New York, 1941.

Two hundred texts and tunes, chosen entirely from field recordings. Transcriptions of the tunes were made from these recordings by Ruth Crawford Seeger. The commentary is almost entirely supplied by the singers.

16. **Luther, Frank, *Americans and Their Songs*, Harper & Bros., New York, 1942.

A compendium of folk and popular songs, arranged roughly by period.

17. Meine, Franklin J., ed., *Tall Tales of the Southwest*, Knopf, New York, 1930.

A fine anthology of "literary" tall tales. Simon Suggs and his friends.

18. **Sandburg, Carl, *The American Songbag.* Harcourt, Brace, New York, 1927.

280 songs, ballads and ditties from all over the country, woven together with sure instinct and Sandburgian insight. An American classic. The accompaniments were experiments by a group of young American composers, and the book reads better than it sings.

19. **Smith, Reed, and Rufty, Hillton, *American Anthology of Old-World Ballads.* J. Fischer and Brother, New York, 1937.

Reed Smith's 25 favorites of the 807 British ballad versions traditionally current in the United States; arranged rather elaborately for piano by Hilton Rufty.

20. **Zanzig, Augustus D., *Singing America.* C. C. Birchard, Boston, 1940.

More folk songs than any other inexpensive community songbook. 128 songs with their tunes, many arranged for part singing; available with or without accompaniment, well edited.

21. Mackenzie, W. Roy. *The Quest of the Ballad.* Princeton University Press, Princeton, N.J., 1919.

Delightful reading about ballads by a distinguished collector.

21A. Mezzrow, Milton and Bernard Wolfe, *Really the Blues,* Random House, New York, 1946.

A Chicago jazzman's story in true jive lingo. The inside of jazz and the blues, with a proper appreciation of Negro influence on same.

22. Ramsey, Frederic, and Smith, Charles E., *Jazzmen.* Harcourt, Brace & Company, New York, 1939.

A "folk-history" of jazz and jazz-musicians; New Orleans and Chicago backgrounds. Articles on various jazz styles by authorities. Excellent reading.

III. The North

23. *Barry, Phillips, *The Maine Woods Songster.* Powell Printing Co., Cambridge, Mass., 1939.

A finely edited singing compendium of the best of the Northern come-all-ye tradition. 50 grand songs in a handy volume.

24. *Bayard, Samuel Preston, *Hill Country Tunes,* Philadelphia: American Folklore Society, 1944.

A study of the fiddle tunes of Southwestern Pennsylvania. The only scholarly works in this field.

Botkin, B. A., *A Treasury of New England Folklore,* Crown Publishers, New York, 1947.

The Yankee in all his salty humor, 934 pages of him, including many songs. Definitive.

25. Dorson, Richard M., *Jonathan Draws the Long Bow,* Harvard University Press, Cambridge, Mass., 1946.

A fine selection of tall tales from New England.

26. Eckstrom, Fannie H., with Smyth, Mary W., *Minstrelsy of Maine,* Houghton Mifflin Company, Boston, 1927.

Texts of 150 traditional songs from the Maine woods; fine documentation of ballad singing, ballad making and ballad collecting in the Northeast; woods songs, sea songs and local history.

27. *Eddy, Mary O., *Ballads and Songs from Ohio,* J. J. Augustin, New York, 1939.

Lots of fine tunes acccurately noted, in a volume of wide range. About 250 texts, 150 tunes. One of the best regional collections.

28. **Flanders, Helen H., and Norfleet, Helen, *Country Songs of Vermont,* New York: G. Schirmer, 1937.

An inexpensive but representative collection; well-edited songs for schools. Melodies transcribed from recordings.

29. Hatcher, Harlan H., *The Great Lakes,* New York: Oxford University Press, 1944.

Good background for Great Lakes folklore.

30. Holbrook, Stewart, *Holy Old Mackinaw,* The Macmillan Company, New York, 1938.

A blowzy, breezy history of lumbering from Maine to Washington. 4 song texts plus a few fragments.

31. *Korson, George G., *Coal Dust on the Fiddle,* Philadelphia: University of Pennsylvania Press, 1943.

An important collection of miners' ballads, mostly Southern. Fine documentation.

32. *——, *Minstrels of the Mine Patch,* Philadelphia: University of Pennsylvania Press, 1938.

Good biographical sketches of 13 traditional ballad makers of the Pennsylvania mines; 80

song texts with 12 tunes; 25 stories and legends. An excellent regional ballad study.

33. *Lochlainn, Colm O., *Irish Street Ballads*, Constable & Co., London, 1939.

Come-all-ye's collected from Irish street singers; 102 songs with their tunes, many of which are now current in the northern United States. Some of the songs have an American locale.

34. *O'Neill, Captain Francis, *Irish Folk Music*, The Regan Printing House, Chicago, 1910.

The story of how an Irish police captain in Chicago put together one of the important collections of traditional Irish folk music. Included are a treatise on the Irish or Union pipes and hints to amateur pipers. Stories of tunes of pipers and of fiddlers.

35. *Rickaby, Franz L., *Ballads and Songs of the Shantyboy*. Harvard University Press, Cambridge, 1926.

Still one of the best collections of lumberjack songs anywhere; lake sailor ballads included. Collection made in Wisconsin and Minnesota. 51 texts with variants; 55 tunes.

36. *Shoemaker, Henry W., *Mountain Minstrelsy of Pennsylvania*. N. F. McGirr, Philadelphia, 1931.

175 texts and notes, with 4 tunes. Miscellaneous songs sung in Pennsylvania; a third edition of *North Pennsylvania Minstrelsy*, revised and enlarged. A rich ragbag of backwoods songs; some rare local items, but so casually edited that it is hard to use.

37. Thompson, Harold W., *Body, Boots and Britches*, J. B. Lippincott, Philadelphia, 1940.

Delightfully written folk-history of New York State: the whole thing. Injun fighters, tricksters, whalers, rafters, murderers, canallers and others, complete with their ballads. No tunes.

IV. The White South

38. Aswell, James R., and others. *God Bless the Devil*. University of North Carolina Press, Chapel Hill, 1940. Compiled by the staff of the Tennessee Writers' and Art Projects, Work Projects Administration.

"Liar's bench tales from Tennessee," some rare and juicy local anecdotes, transcribed and recreated with good literary feeling. "Fiddler's Dram," "Little Eight John" and "Fool-killin' Shep Goins" are American classics.

39. *Belden, Henry M., ed., *Ballads and Songs Collected by the Missouri Folk-Lore Society*. University of Missouri Studies, Vol. XV, No. 1. University of Missouri, Columbia, 1940.

A ballad accumulation of decades by one of America's leading ballad scholars; most of the material was contributed by the editor's students. Notes, lively and catholic. New songs. 285 texts and 70 tunes.

40. Chase, Richard, *The Jack Tales*, Houghton Mifflin Company, The Riverside Press, Cambridge, 1943.

The fairy tales of Grimm and Anderson in their Southern mountain versions. One of the most delightful and rewarding books of genuine American folklore.

41. *Chase, Richard, *Old Songs and Singing Games*. University of North Carolina Press, Chapel Hill, 1938.

A selection for use in schools and recreation centers, chosen from the author's collection and elsewhere.

42. *Cox, John Harrington, *Folk-Songs of the South*, Harvard University Press, Cambridge, 1925.

Another broad and catholic regional collection mostly from West Virginia. Useful for amateurs and scholars. A candid account of professorial collecting. 185 songs with 26 tunes.

43. *Davis, Arthur Kyle, Jr., *Traditional Ballads of Virginia*, Harvard University Press, Cambridge, 1929.

Ballads on Child's list only. A good account of a thorough investigation of the archaic ballad tradition in Virginia; scholarly. No American ballads, no Negro ballads; 51 titles, with variants; 148 tunes.

44. Hudson, Arthur Palmer, *Folksongs of Mississippi and Their Background*. University of North Carolina Press, Chapel Hill, 1936.

Mississippi regional folk song with no Negro material, with a competent, although conservative, presentation of their historical and social background.

45. **Lunsford, Bascom Lamar, and Stringfield, Lamar, *30 and 1 Folk Songs from the South-*

ern Mountains, Carl Fischer, Inc., New York, 1929.

One of the best inexpensive collections, with accompaniments that do the tunes no violence.

46. **Niles, John J., *Ballads, Carols and Tragic Legends,* G. Schirmer, New York, 1938.

10 serious songs from the southern Appalachians, with fine simple accompaniments. All the Niles volumes are in inexpensive pamphlet form.

47. **——, *Seven Kentucky Mountain Songs,* G. Schirmer, New York, 1929.

Lyric mountain songs with simple accompaniments.

48. **——, *Songs of the Hill Folk,* G. Schirmer, New York, 1934.

49. **——, *More Songs of the Hill Folk,* G. Schirmer, New York, 1936.

Ballads and sorrowful songs from Kentucky, Virginia, Tennessee, North Carolina and Georgia. The Niles collections have unpretentious accompaniments.

50. **——, *Ten Christmas Carols from the Southern Appalachian Mountains,* G. Schirmer, New York, 1935.

Fine songs. *Songs of the Hill Folk* contains two more American carols.

51. *Randolph, Vance, *The Ozarks: An American Survival of Primitive Society.* Vanguard Press, New York, 1931.

Throughout America the mountains have preserved more of the archaic and pioneer traits than other sections. Randolph authoritatively discusses these survivals in the Ozarks. About 40 songs with tunes: play party songs, Child ballads, and others. Rich documentation.

51. 1. *Randolph, Vance, *Ozark Folksongs,* Vol. I, published by the State Historical Society of Missouri, Columbia, Missouri, 1946.

The first volume of the great Randolph collection. Songs and ballads of British origin with tunes. Elaborate reference notes.

Peattie, Roderick, *The Great Smokies and the Blue Ridge,* Vanguard Press, New York, 1943.

A sensitive portrait of the most fertile of Folk-song regions—history, folkways, fauna and flora, geology, etc.,—well written.

52. *Scarborough, Dorothy, *A Song Catcher in Southern Mountains,* Columbia University Press, New York, 1937.

The story of a summer's collecting trip in the Southern mountains, engagingly if superficially written; 208 texts and 133 tunes, transcribed from cylinders.

53. *Sharp, Cecil J., *English Folk Songs from the Southern Appalachians,* Oxford University Press, London, 1932. Two volumes.

The most important collection of white folksongs in America. More than 1000 songs with tunes, from Child ballads to game songs.

54. *Thomas, Jean, *Ballad Makin' in the Mountains of Kentucky,* Henry Holt & Company, New York, 1939.

Where the songs came from and how they were made, as told to Jean Thomas by singers in northeastern Kentucky, and retold in feature-story style by this able newswoman collector. Some extremely interesting local and contemporary songs. 120 texts and 23 tunes.

55. Wilson, Charles Morrow, *Backwoods America,* University of North Carolina Press, Chapel Hill, 1934.

The Ozarks Mountains of Arkansas and Missouri. Chapters on backwoods language, rural humor, religious gatherings, peasant morality, folk-beliefs, fun-making, the country doctor and country storekeeper, old trades, buried treasure and so on. 8 mountain ballad texts.

V. The Negro South

56. *Allen, W. F., Ware, C. P., and Garrison, L. McK., *Slave Songs of the United States,* A. Simpson & Company, New York, 1867; Peter Smith, New York, 1929.

136 songs with their tunes. Almost all are spirituals; a few work songs and Creole songs. This is the earliest extended collection and contains many historically important songs not to be found elsewhere.

57. *Ballanta (-Taylor), N. G. J., *St. Helena Island Spirituals,* G. Schirmer, New York, 1925.

113 spirituals very carefully written out, with discusion of their characteristic musical elements. One of the best books in the field of Negro music.

58. *Bolton, Dorthy G., and Burleigh, Harry T.,

Old Songs Hymnal, The Century Company, New York, 1929.

Words and melodies of Negro spirituals from Georgia, many not to be found elsewhere.

59. Botkin, B. A., *Lay My Burden Down,* University of Chicago Press, 1945.

The reminiscenses of Negro ex-slaves, gathered by W.P.A. Writers Project under John A Lomax's direction, edited and sifted by B. A. Botkin. A people's history of slavery. One of the great American books.

59A. Brown Sterling, *Negro Caravan,* Dryden Press, New York, 1941.

The best anthology of Negro literature, including folk songs, tales, and historical material necessary to understanding of Negro folklore.

60. Chappell, Louis W., *John Henry: A Folk-Lore Study,* Walter Biedermann, Jena, Germany, 1933.

The most penetrating and well-conceived critical study of one ballad in English. The social and psychological background of John Henry. Many texts, no tunes.

61. *Dett, Nathaniel, *Religious Folk Songs of the Negro as Sung at Hampton Institute,* G. Schirmer, New York, 1927.

Four parts, unaccompanied; annotated, with much simplification, from singing. This is in many ways the handiest volume for singing groups. 165 songs.

62. Ehrlich, Leonard, *God's Angry Man,* New York: Simon & Schuster, 1932.

A novelized biography of John Brown.

63. **Gellert, Lawrence, and Siegmeister, Ellie, *Negro Songs of Protest,* Carl Fischer, New York, 1936.

This volume contains 24 chain-gang and other Negro songs of protest, collected in the South.

64. Harris, Joel Chandler, *Uncle Remus: His Songs and His Sayings,* D. Appleton-Century Company, New York, 1881.

The best book, still, of Negro animal tales.

65. Herskovits, Melville J., *The Myth of the Negro Past,* New York: Harper & Brothers, 1941.

The African background of American Negro culture ably presented by the best scholar in the field. Much material on folklore.

66. Hurston, Zora Neale, *Jonah's Gourd Vine,* J. B. Lippincott, Philadelphia, 1934.

A novel about a Negro preacher in Florida. Full of rich and accurate folk talk. Contains a magnificent Negro sermon.

67. *——, *Mules and Men,* J. B. Lippincott, Philadelphia, 1935.

The finest single book in American folklore. The rich essence of Negro folk-tale, folk talk, folk-life. A Florida small town, a turpentine camp, and the only account of "hoodoo" in America. Marvelous folk tales; some fine songs.

68. **Johnson, James Weldon, and Johnson, J. Rosamund, *The Book of American Negro Spirituals,* The Viking Press, New York, 1925.

**——, *The Second Book of American Negro Spirituals,* The Viking Press, New York, 1926.

Over 60 songs in each volume, with a fine introduction. Accompaniments are designed for solo performance in concert, in the classic European tradition. The two collections were ringbound and reissued inexpensively in a single volume by The Viking Press in 1940.

69. **Kennedy, R. Emmet, *Mellows,* Albert & Charles Boni, New York, 1925.

**——, *More Mellows,* Dodd, Mead & Company, New York, 1931.

Negro spirituals and folk songs from southern Louisiana, some with rather elaborate accompaniment, all with affectionate commentary.

70. *Krehbiel, Henry E., *Afro-American Folk Songs,* G. Schirmer, New York, 1914.

The earliest serious musical discussion in this field, by a leading American music critic. Many musical examples. A fine and stimulating study.

71. *Lomax, John A. and Alan, *Negro Folk Songs as Sung by Leadbelly,* The Macmillan Company, New York, 1936.

A study of a Negro guitar player of the Southwest—Texas and Louisiana. Many examples of recitative ballads. Folk biography.

72. Odum, Howard W., *Rainbow Round My Shoulder,* The Bobbs-Merrill Company, Indianapolis, 1928.

Black Ulysses talking to himself. Background

for blues, ballads, work songs of the Negro. An American classic.

73. ——, and Johnson, Guy B., *The Negro and His Songs,* University of North Carolina Press, Chapel Hill, 1925.

Discussion of religious and secular Negro songs in their social settings, with 205 illustrative song-texts.

74. *——, *Negro Workaday Songs,* University of North Carolina Press, Chapel Hill, 1926.

A rich compilation of Negro songs and discussion of their social backgrounds. A chapter on the commercial phonograph record of the blues. Includes a few phonophotographic graphs. 14 tunes.

75. **Parrish, Lydia, *Slave Songs of the Georgia Sea Islands,* New York: Creative Age Press, 1942.

A collection of very primitive and interesting Negro songs, with fine photographs and documentation.

76. *Scarborough, Dorothy, *On the Trail of Negro Folk Songs,* Harvard University Press, Cambridge, 1925.

Lovely stuff, like everything Dr. Scarborough touched. Includes a chapter on the Negro's part in transmitting the traditional British songs and ballads. Sections on dance songs, game songs, lullabies, animal songs, work songs, railroad songs and blues. 140 songs with tunes; many more texts.

77. Stoney, Samuel Gaillard, *Black Genesis,* The Macmillan Company, New York, 1930.

Full, rich, accurately-heard versions of Afro-American folk tales. A very beautiful book.

78. Talley, Thomas W., *Negro Folk Rhymes, Wise and Otherwise,* The Macmillan Company, New York, 1922.

The Brer Rabbit rhymes, the game songs and the juba dance lyrics of the slaves. Some written material. A companion volume for *Uncle Remus.*

79. *White, Newman I., *American Negro Folk Songs,* Harvard University Press, Cambridge, 1928.

A penetrating, critical study of the history of folk song, well documented. Good material on minstrels. About 800 fragmentary texts in all; 15 tunes.

80. *Work, John W., *American Negro Songs,* Howell, Soskin & Company, New York, 1940.

A large collection, 5/6 religious and 1/6 secular. Versions of the classic spirituals as collected by Work, previously unprinted. Some contemporary religious songs.

VI. The West

81. Abbott, Edward Charles ("Teddy Blue"), with Helena Huntington Smith, *We Pointed Them North,* Farrar & Rinehart, New York, 1939.

Folk autobiography. The open-hearted story of an old-time cowpuncher, warmly written down by H. H. Smith. A contemporary folk classic.

82. Adams, Andy, *The Log of a Cowboy,* Houghton Mifflin Company, Boston, 1903.

The puncher's story of the Chisholm trail. A full-length, slightly formal picture of the cowboy. Nevertheless, one of the best all-round accounts of cowboy life in our literature.

83. Adams, Ramon F., *Cowboy Lingo,* Houghton Mifflin Company, Boston, 1936.

The best book on the subject of the racy language of the cowboy. Accurate, rich with new material and fruitful research.

84. *Black, Eleanora, and Robertson, Sidney, *The Gold Rush Song Book,* The Colt Press, San Francisco, 1940.

25 of the best Forty-Niner songs, chosen from early California songsters and set to the tunes that belonged to them. The foreword offers lively notes on folk-singing style.

85. Clark, Thomas D., *The Rampaging Frontier,* Bobbs-Merrill Company, Indianapolis, 1939.

Backwoods varmints, fiddlin', foolin' with the gals, etc. A story each from Tennessee, Missouri, Wisconsin, Indiana, Arkansas, Iowa, Illinois and southern Ohio. Well documented and witty, a picture of life in the American West between 1800 and 1860.

85A. De Voto, Bernard, *Across the Wide Missouri,* Houghton Mifflin Co., Boston, 1947.

The story of the mountain men—the fur traders who first ventured into the Far West in the 1820's.

86. Dobie, J. Frank, *The Longhorns,* Little, Brown & Company, Boston, 1941.

Nobody knows more about the romantic

Southwest than Dobie, and nobody tells it better. This is a full-bodied portrait of one of our most romantic folk figures, the Texas longhorn.

87. ——, *Vaquero of the Brush Country,* The Southwest Press, Dallas, 1929.

Frank Dobie here acts as amanuensis and commentator for one of the great old-time Texas cowmen. Much material for a social history of cowpunching is suggested, especially for the early South Texas period.

88. Dorson, Richard M., *Davy Crockett, American Comic Legend, Rockland Editions,* Spiral Press, Rockland, N. Y., 1939.

From the old Davy Crockett almanacs comes this ripsnorting folk biography of the folk comic hero. Some of the best Americana ever written: all-fired wonderful.

89. **Hulbert, A. B., *Forty-Niners,* Little, Brown & Company, Boston, 1932.

The California trail comes to life in a series of extracts from diaries of Forty-Niners. A few songs with delightful contemporary drawings.

90. **Larkin, Margaret, and Black, Helen, *Singing Cowboy,* Alfred A. Knopf, New York, 1931.

42 fine cowboy songs with their tunes; several ballads not found elsewhere. A pleasant book, handsomely published.

91. *Lomax, John A. and Alan: Edward N. Waters, music editor. *Cowboy Songs and Other Frontier Ballads.* The Macmillan Company, New York. Revised and enlarged, 1938.

The 1938 edition has 207 texts and 116 tunes transcribed from early recordings. Rangers, Indian fighters, buffalo hunters, outlaws, Forty-Niners, stage-coach drivers, bronchobusters and cowboys of every sort. All the songs.

92. Lomax, John A., *Songs of the Cattle Trails and Cow Camp,* The Macmillan Company, New York, 1919.

Cowboy and western verse. An important literary supplement to the traditional material in *Cowboy Songs and Other Frontier Ballads.*

93. Shepard, Esther, *Paul Bunyan,* The McNeil Press, Seattle, 1924.

A large number of stories, some northwestern: simply edited and perhaps the most authentic of the books on Paul Bunyan. Has recently been re-issued (Harcourt, Brace) with magnificent illustrations by Rockwell Kent.

94. Siringo, Charles, *A Texas Cowboy,* Rand, McNally and Company, Chicago, 1885.

The saltiest of the cowboy autobiographies, written with clarity and humor. Required reading.

VII. Dances and Games

95. *Botkin, B. A., *The American Play-Party Song,* University of Nebraska Press, Lincoln, 1937.

A scholarly volume, unique in the thoroughness with which variants are considered. Gives tunes for half of its 127 titles, and many variants for each title. A penetrating discussion of the whole history of game songs and of their important place in frontier society.

96. **Burchenal, Elizabeth, *American Country Dances,* G. Schirmer, New York, 1918.

50 dances, with very precise directions and music. Useful when the leader's personal experience of dancing in rural America provides an understanding of the nonchalance which belongs to this kind of dancing.

97. *Collins, Fletcher, Jr., *Alamance Play Party Songs and Singing Games.* Elon College, North Carolina, 1940. Obtainable from the office of the County Superintendent of Public Schools.

45: with directions. This volume resulted from song collecting by a group of teachers whose purpose was to intensify circulation of traditional music in a North Carolina county. The music included was chosen for its living values today, not for its interest to collectors. Such an enterprise should be possible in every county in America.

98. Greggerson, Herb, *Herb's Blue Bonnet Calls,* H. Greggerson, Box 3061, Station A, El Paso, Texas, 1940.

Breezy directions and rhymed calls for western square dances, with pictures. 53 figures, with trimmings.

99. ***Harding's Collection of 200 Jigs, Reels and Country Dances,* Richmond-Robbins, Inc., New York, 1929.

For piano, violin, flute or mandolin.

100. *McDowell, L. L., *Folk Dances of Tennessee,* Edwards Bros., Ann Arbor, Mich., 1938.

Includes 28 play party games with tunes and

directions, and a few country dances. Perhaps the most useable of the play party collections.

101. *Newell, W. W., *Songs and Games of American Children,* Harper & Brothers, New York, 1884-1911.

Early collection of British game song survivals among American children. 190 in all, with 37 tunes.

102. *Owens, William A., *Swing and Turn,* Tardy Publishing Company, Dallas, 1936.

64 Texas play party games, ring games, children's games and longways dances, with 58 tunes.

103. *Ryan, Grace L., *Dances of Our Pioneers,* A. S. Barnes, New York, 1939.

Gives music, directions, calls, with stimulating illustrations of many figures. Quadrilles, contra, circle and couple dances. 26 tunes.

104. Shaw, Lloyd, *Cowboy Dances,* Caxton Press, Caldwell, Idaho, 1939. Available from The Methodist Book Concern, New York.

Lots of pictures; fine background materials, lists of old fiddlers' favorite tunes and directions. No music. Explains and describes the widest variety of American country dance types.

105. **Snyder, Jack, *Jack Snyder's Collection of 200 Favorite Jigs, Reels, Country and Folk Dances, Jack Snyder Publishing Company,* New York, 1925.

106. *Tolman, Beth, and Page, Ralph, *The Country Dance Book,* E. C. Schirmer, Boston, 1937.

"Complete and joyful instructions," with directions and 6 tunes from New England.

VIII. White Spirituals

107. **Buchanan, Annabel Morris, *Folk Hymns of America,* J. Fischer & Brother, New York, 1938.

The settings of these authentic folk hymns exemplify one school of thought about modal harmonization of folk melodies. 50 folk hymns from 17 states, with discussion.

108. *Fisher, William Arms, *Ye Olde New England Psalm-Tunes: 1620-1820,* Oliver Ditson, Boston, 1930.

42 hymns as sung by the Pilgrims, fuguing tunes by Billings and others, in the original versions as published in early hymn books in the north.

109. *Jackson, George Pullen, *Down East Spirituals,* J. J. Augustin, New York, 1941.

300 religious folk songs. Early New England, represented here by more than 100 titles, is now considered by this eminent authority to have been the source from which the white spirituals spread through the south.

110. *——, *Spiritual Folk Songs of Early America,* J. J. Augustin, New York, 1937.

Texts and melodies of 250 traditional religious songs, chiefly from the South, edited by the outstanding scholar in the field. Folk hymns, revival spirituals and religious ballads from the shaped-note song books of early America.

111. *——, *White and Negro Spirituals,* J. J. Augustin, New York, 1943.

Dr. Jackson here completes his monumental work on the white spiritual, presenting his conclusions. A most important and controversial book.

112. *Walker, William, *The Southern Harmony and Musical Companion,* E. W. Miller, Philadelphia, 1847-54. Reproduced in facsimile by the Federal Writers' Project of Kentucky, Works Progress Administration. Obtainable from Hastings House, New York, 1939.

Another large collection of folk hymns in 3 and 4 parts, in the 4-shape notation which has become rare in use. Excellent introductory notes have been added to the 1939 edition.

IX. Occupational Ballads

Canallers

See The North: Thompson.

Cowboys

See The West: Dobie, Lomax.

Frontier

For early Alabama and Georgia, Arkansas and the Ozarks, see The White South. For the Mississippi River from its source to Arkansas, see The North. For the Far West, the Southwest, the Pacific Northwest, the Pacific Coast, see The West.

Hoboes

113. Milburn, George, *The Hobo's Horn Book,* I. Washburn, New York, 1930.

The song-lore of the railroad jungles and roadside camps. Some rowdy ballads.

Lumberjacks

See The North: Barry, Eckstrom and Smyth, Holbrook, Rickaby, Thompson, Shoemaker.

114. Beck, E. C., *Songs of the Michigan Lumberjacks,* Ann Arbor: University of Michigan Press, 1942.

Miners

See The North: Korson; The White South: Belden, Cox, Thomas; The West: Black and Robertson, Lomax.

Outlaws and Bad Men

See The North: Shoemaker, Thompson; The West: Finger, Lomax, etc.

Railroad Men

See The Negro South: Hurston, Chappell, Work, Johnson, Odum, Lomax.

115. **Sherwin, Sterling and McClintock, Harry K., *Railroad Songs of Yesterday,* Shapiro, Bernstein & Co., New York, 1943.

Most of the important railroad ballads with handsome, documentary photographs.

Roustabouts

116. **Wheeler, Mary, *Roustabout Songs,* New York: Remick Music Corporation, 1939.

The only collection of the singing of Negro roustabouts. Extremely interesting songs, from the Ohio River area, with good documentation.

Seamen

117. *Bone, D. W., *Capstan Bars,* Harcourt, Brace & Company, New York, 1932.

This book tells the living story of sailor songs, shanties and their relationship to life on the sea. Metronomic indications carefully established for each shanty.

118. *Colcord, Joanna C., *Songs of American Sailormen,* W. W. Norton & Company, New York, 1938.

The most complete and authoritative American collection. More than 100 texts and tunes, including some fo'c'sle ballads.

119. Dana, Richard Henry, Jr., *Two Years before the Mast,* Houghton Mifflin Company, New York, 1911.

A picture of the hard life that produced the shanties and a description of shanty singing; texts of a few shanties heard during an early voyage to California.

Soldiers

120. **Dolph, E. A., *Sound Off,* Farrar & Rinehart, New York, 1942.

The soldiers' omnibus: songs from each war the United States has fought; regimental songs and West Point ditties; more than 150 of them.

121. **Niles, John J., and Moore, Douglas S., and Wallgreen, A. A., *The Songs My Mother Never Taught Me,* The Macaulay Company, New York, 1929.

About 50 soldiers' and sailors' songs of World War I, collected from the men who sang them; highly seasoned.

Whaling

See The North: Thompson, Colcord; Seamen: Colcord.

Workers' Songs

**Gellert, Lawrence, and Siegmeister, Elie, *Negro Songs of Protest,* see The Negro South. *Korson, George, Minstrels of the Mine Patch,* see The North. Contains 16 strikers' songs.

122. ***Songs for America,* Workers' Library Publication, Box 148, Sta. D, New York, 1935.

33 songs of protest.

123. ***The People's Songbook,* various editors, People's Songs, Boni and Gaer, 1948, New York City.

The best available collection of progressive, union, topical songs, together with many fine pieces by folk composers. A section of folk ballads. Guitar chords. Forewords by A. Lomax and B. Betkin. 96 songs.

124. *People's Songs Wordbook, No. 1,* People's Songs Inc., 126 W. 21st, New York City, 1947.

The words of the best of contemporary progressive songs.

125. ***UAW-CIO Sings,* UAW-CIO Education Dept., 28 West Warren St., Detroit 1, Mich.

The unions are now going in for ballad singing and ballad publishing. Ninety songs, some with melodies, some with piano accompaniment.

126. *Sing Out Brother,* Highlander Folk School, Monteagle, Tennessee.

A collection of the songs used by Southern labor organizers in their work in the mill towns and farmers' unions in the South. 60 songs with melodies.

Appendix III

Selected List of Record Albums

THE BEST WAY to learn folk singing is to listen to folk singers themselves, or, failing that, to recordings of such singers. We have, therefore, assembled a selected list of *albums,* commercially available, indicating in our comments which of these are the most desirable. We have not included single records in this list, since that would have made this appendix too cumbersome. We suggest, however, that, if you are interested in building, a collection of folk records, you listen to all the "hill-billy" and "race" recordings you can find; they are full of folklore material.

Put yourself on the mailing lists of: The Library of Congress, Washington, D. C.; Decca Recording Company (50 West 57th Street, New York City); Disc Record Company (117 West 46th Street, New York City); and you will be notified of most of the new albums as they are published. These are the three main sources. If there is no large store in your vicinity, you may order the commercial albums by mail through The Gramaphone Shop (18 East 48th Street, New York City) or the Liberty Music Shop (50th and Madison Avenue, New York City). This list of albums was published in part in the Christmas issue of *Vogue,* 1946, and is reprinted here by permission.

A good many of the songs included in this volume may be found in the following list.

1. Almanac Singers—*Sod-Buster Ballads*—General Album #21. Ground Hog; State of Arkansas; I Ride an Old Paint.*

   An old album of the Almanac Singers with some of the best recorded versions of cowboy and farmer songs from the Middle West. It should be in every folk song collector's library.
2. ———*Deep Sea Shanties — General* — Album #20. Blow Ye Winds Hi Ho: Santy Anna.

   The Almanac singers turn shanteymen with surprisingly good results. The songs are not sung just the way they were aboard ship, but the results are salty, anyway.
3. ———*Talking Union*—Keynote—#K 106.

   A group of contemporary topical ballads, composed and arranged by the Almanacers, that have now become part of the repertoires of all good union men up and down the land.
4. Archive of American Folk Song, Library of Congress—*Folk Music of the United States* series. Eleven Albums.**

   This is the best. If you want to know American folk song, buy all these albums.

   Album 1—*Anglo-American Ballads.*

   Pretty Polly.

   Singers from the Virginia Mountains, from Oklahoma, Texas, and Wisconsin, give a good sample of the American ballad tradition, especially sides 2a, 4a, 4b (the fine recordings from Mrs. Texas Gladden, who is possibly America's finest living traditional singer).***

   Songs, Dance Tunes, and Spirituals.

   Jenny Jenkins; Cindy; Old Joe Clark.

   Album III—*Afro-American Spirituals—Work Songs and Ballads.*

   Ain't No Mo' Cane on this Brazos; The Grey Goose; John Henry.

   Unaccompanied spirituals by Negro singers

* We mention only the titles of songs contained in this volume. Albums 1 and 2, reissued Decca-Commodore.

** Price list obtainable on request from the Library of Congress, Washington, D. C.

*** A new album of Mrs. Gladden is now available, Disc #737.

from Alabama and Virginia, work songs and prison songs recorded on the job in southern penitentiaries from Texas to Florida. These unique recordings, full of passion, melancholy, and the rhythmic drive of labour, will give you a new slant on life in the South. Every collection should have them.

Album IV—*Afro-American Blues and Game Songs.*

Another Man Done Gone; The Boll Weevil; Shorty George Blues.

Primitive Negro blues, songs and ballads performed by country singers; delightful Negro children's game songs and ante-bellum reels. Unique among available records.

Album V—*French Ballads, Dance Tunes, Spanish Religious Songs, and Game Songs.*

Dance songs and work songs from the Bahama Negroes; Norman French ballads and dance tunes from Cajun country in southwestern Louisiana; Spanish-American ballads and children's songs from Texas and Arizona. This album is for the specialist in folk lore.

Album VI—*Songs from the Iroquois Long House.*

A definite collection of drum-accompanied Iroquois chants from upstate New York, accompanied by a fine explanatory booklet by William Fenton, a collector. This album is for specialist.

Album VII—*Anglo-American Ballads.*

Sanford Barnes (The State of Arkansas).

This album is an extension of the materials in Album I.

Album VIII—*Negro Work Songs and Calls.*

Negro Railroad Work Songs; Track Lining Song.

More Negro Work Songs recorded on the job, including especially interesting songs from railroad gangs, sounding calls from the Mississippi River steamboats. Side 36b shows you where Mark Twain got his name.

Album IX—*Play and Dance Songs and Tunes.*

A lively album of square dance sides with calls, Negro game songs and other country dance tunes from the South. Side 43a, a recording of a Negro washboard band, is a stand-out.

Album X—*Negro Religious Songs and Services.*

See this album for a fine example of the folk Negro sermon.

Album XI—*Sacred Harp Singing.*

Wondrous Love.

The songs in this album were recorded at a convention of white spiritual singers who used the shape-note hymn book called The Sacred Harp.

5. Bill Bender—*Frontier Ballads*—Stinson*—Vol. 1. Sweet Betsy from Pike; Buffalo Skinner; Jack O'Diamonds.

   Bill Bender comes from Texas and he sings this good selection of traditional cowboy songs, authentic both in text and tune, the way many Texans like to hear them.
6. Al Brundage — caller, *County Fair Square Dances,* Folkcraft Album F I, with Peter Seeger, leader.
7. Dan Burleigh—*South Side Shake*—Circle #S3.

   With Brownie McGhee and Pops Foster, Dan Burleigh has cut the most exciting album of honky-tonk music ever recorded.
8. Calypso—Vol. 1 (Modern), Lord Invader and Lord Beginner with Felix and His Internationals. Disc #614.

   Vol. II (Standard), Lord Invader, Duke of Iron, and Macbeth with Felix and His Internationals. Disc #628.
9. Richard Dyer-Bennet—*Ballads*—Asch—#461. John Henry.

   Richard Dyer-Bennet learned to sing folk songs in Sweden, studying under the master minstrel singers of the type who have kept the art of ballad singing alive since the middle ages.
10. ——— *Ballads by the 20th Century Minstrel*—Stinson S-364.

    More ballads in the minstrel style. A new Decca album of Mr. Bennet is to appear shortly.
11. ——— —*Elizabethan Love Songs,* Disc #609.
12. Ed Durlacher—*Country Dances*—Sonora MS-

479—Good New England square dances.

13. Cousin Emmy—*Kentucky Mountain Ballads* —Decca #A-574. Lonesome Road Blues.

A banjo queen from the hills makes the best available commercial album of spirited mountain music.

14. Tom Glazer—*Olden Songs*—Keynote #K-131.

*All Asch and Stinson albums obtainable from Stinson Trading Co., Union Square, New York City.

A good collection of Americana by a sincere and skillful "city-billy."

15. Woody Cuthrie—*Ballads from the Dust Bowl* —Disc #610.

Woody Guthrie has seen some hard traveling on the long, dusty road of the Okies. Out of the hard rock of their lives, Woody has carved some hard hitting and memorable ballads. He sings them with ferocity and colour. Woody is our great contemporary folk poet. You must have this album.

16. ——— *Songs to Grow On*—Disc #605.

Woody Guthrie made these songs for his own little daughter. He sings them as an Oklahoma truck driver might sing them to his child on his day off. The best recorded album available for children from two to six.

17. ——— —Stinson #347—Nine Hundred Miles, John Henry.

Woody, Son Terry, and Cisco Houston here record some of the wildest and most wonderful Southern music ever put on discs.

18. ——— —Stinson #347—

More of Woody's fine singing of native and topical material.

19. ——— —*Folksay, I*—Stinson #332. Nine Hundred Miles.

Fine fiddling, harmonica blowing, banjo picking, and singing by Woody, Peter Seeger, and Son Terry.

20. Paul Hunt—and Rock Candy Mountaineers, *Square Dances* (without calls), Disc #631.

21. Burl Ives—*Ballads and Folksongs*—Decca #A 407.

Dan Tucker; Erie Canal; Lolly-too-dum; Aunt Rhody.

Burl Ives, the best of contemporary ballad singers, in a group of his best songs.

22. ——— *Ballads and Folk Songs, II*—Decca #A 431.

More of Burl's best.

23. ——— *The Wayfaring Stranger* — Columbia #C103. The Streets of Laredo, Sweet Betsy from Pike, Old Smoky, Darlin' Corey, Leather Wing Bat.

Ives at his sweetest with a fine selection of songs.

24. ——— *The Wayfaring Stranger*—Asch #345. Buckeye Jim.

The best Ives singing on record.

25. Lonnie Johnson — *Blues,* John Davis at the piano—Disc #710.

Lonnie Johnson helped to bring jazz and blues from New Orleans. His style is fine and these records, especially with the piano work of Davis, satisfying.

26. Tony Kraber—*The Old Chisholm Trail*—Keynote #104. Boll Weevil, Rye Whiskey, The Old Chisholm Trail, Kansas Boys.

Tony Kraber of Montana sings these songs with the enthusiasm and fresh style of a real Westerner.

27. Leadbelly — *Negro Folk Song* — Disc #660.

Leadbelly has been playing his twelve-string guitar and singing for his people in Texas for longer than most of us can remember. In this album, you find stirring work songs, gay and rhythmic square dance tunes, haunting blues, and bad men ballads. Leadbelly plays piano, guitar, and concertina. An excellent buy.

28. ——— *Negro Sinful Songs* — Musicraft #31. Frankie, Boll Weevil.

A fine sampling of Leadbelly's songstock, recorded in 1937.

29. Leadbelly, Cisco Houston, and Woody Guthrie — *Midnight Special* — Disc #726. Grey Goose, Midnight Special.

These are Negro prisoner songs from Texas, sung by some of the best balladeers in the country. Leadbelly learned his songs in the penitentiary and sings them with complete authenticity. This same album, once available with the Golden Gate Quartet as sponsoring artists under the Victor label, is a collector's item.

30. Bess Lomax, Pete Seeger, Butch Hawes, Tom Glazer — *America's Favorite Songs* — Disc #607.
    Down in the Valley; Casey Jones; Go Tell Aunt Nancy; Cowboy's Lament; Buffalo Gals; Careless Love.
    A group of the best-loved American country songs sung with charm and honest feeling by a group of city kids. Pete Seeger's performance, as usual, is a stand-out.
31. Alan Lomax, ed.—*Listen to our Story*—Brunswick No. B-1024, American Folk Music Series.
    Pretty Polly; The Death of John Henry; Rock About, My Saro Jane.
    An album of reissued records made in the '20's by *Brunswick* and *Vocalion.* Some of the best and most authentic singing available on discs.
32. ——— *Mountain Frolic* — Decca #B1025 — Cindy, Black-Eyed Susan, Old Joe Clark.
    A follow-up of No. 31 with words, music, and story background for 1840 square dance.
33. John A. Lomax, ed., *Smoky Mountain Ballads,* Victor P79.
    Darling Corey; Down in a Willow Garden.
    An album of reissued records selected from the Victor hill-billy catalogue. Out of print, but worth paying a stiff price to own.
34. John Jacob Niles—*Seven Joys of Mary,* Disc #732.
    Some very beautiful, antique modal melodies, done in Mr. Niles' style.
35. John Jacob Niles—*Early American Ballads*—Victor #604.
    Contains the best available recording of I Wonder as I Wander, except for Gladys Swarthout's rendition on Victor #10-1181.
36. ——— *Early American Carols and Folk Songs* —Victor #718.
    Niles with dulcimer giving his strangely appealing fine-art performance of beautiful modal tunes.
37. Ralph Page and his New England Orchestra—*Square Dances with Calls,* Disc #630.
    A representative album of New England country dances.
38. Susan Reed—*Folk Songs and Ballads*—Victor #1086. Jennie Jenkins.
    Miss Reed up to some cute and some occasionally moving tricks with a group of fine folk songs.
39. ——— *Folk Songs and Ballads, Vol. II*—Victor #1107. Black is the Color. More of the same.
40. Tex Ritter—*Tex Ritter*—Capitol #BD27.
    Boll Weevil; Chisholm Trail; Rye Whiskey.
    Tex Ritter has been singing folk songs for "westerns" for years. However, he's kept a good deal of his Texas spirit, and that makes some of the sides a lot of fun.
41. Carson Robison and his Pleasant Valley Boys —*Square Dances*—Victor P-155.
42. Earl Rogers—*Folk Songs of New England*—Musicraft—#M68.
    Canaday; The Jam on Jerry's Rock.
    Lumberjack ballads, sailor songs, local ballads, and traditional English folk songs collected in New England.
43. Earl Robinson—*Americana*—Keynote #132. Sweet Betsy.
    Earl Robinson has his own special way with a group of rare American songs.
44. Carl Sandburg — *Cowboy Songs and Negro Spirituals*—Decca No. A-356.
    I Ride an Old Paint; Whoopie-Ti-Yi-Yo; Sam Bass; Jesse James; Go Down; Moses; O Freedom.
    Great songs, greatly sung by our most intuitive folk-song singer.
45. Pete Seeger, Cisco Huston, Charity Bailey, and Leadbelly—*School Days,* Disc #604.
    Skip to My Lou; Crawdad Hole.
    Some of the best songs, fetchingly sung.
46. Peter Seeger, Lcc Hays, Dock Reese, Hally Wood, Butch Hawes, *Roll the Union On,* Disc #370.
    An album of the topical ballads produced

by *People's Songs, Inc.* Sung with great spirit: fine five-string banjo: everybody should hear it.

47. Lloyd Shaw and Alan Lomax — *Cowboy Dances*—Decca No. A-524. American Folk Music Series.

Lloyd Shaw has been studying, calling and teaching the western square dance in Colorado for many years. He and his dancers have demonstrated their polished style at folk festivals all over the country. This album contains a Sing-Along book of instructions for square-dancing with prompter's cards of the calls.

48. Montana Taylor—*Barrel House Blues*—Circle #S 2.

Montana Taylor, born in that tough town, Butte, Montana, wanderer of the hard streets and dark ways of the South and Mid-West, has made a wonderful album of the Negro folk blues for piano. This is basic, modern American folk music, haunting and cacophonous, folk music of city streets.

49. Thrasher Wonders and Two Gospel Keys—*Spirituals*—Disc #658.
Motherless Child.

The Thrasher Wonders sing in the Negro folk quartet style, sometimes awkwardly but always with verve and originality. The Gospel Keys, two Negro women who walk the streets of America spreading the word with guitar and voices of brass, sing their spirituals with even more passion and strength. This is a fine album if you like your modern folklore straight.

50. Conrad Thibault—*Roustabout Songs*—Decca #451.

The songs of this album stem from the steamboat days on the Mississippi and Ohio Rivers when the Negro roustabouts sweated the freight on board to the accompaniment of improvised work chants. These roustabout songs, which are like animal cries and are full of savage rhythm, are here performed by Mr. Thibault as concert pieces.

51. Merle Travis—*Folk Songs of the Hills*—Capitol #AD 50. John Henry.

Work songs of the East Kentucky coal camps, perfectly performed. A new album, one of the ten best.

52. Union Boys — *Songs for Victory* — Stinson #346. Hold On.

Topical pieces and progressive ballads from World War II, excitingly performed by Peter Seeger, Burl Ives, Josh White, Tom Glazer, Woody Guthrie, Son Terry, and Brownie McGhee.

53. Frank Warner—*Hudson Valley Songs*—Disc #661 (assisted by Bess Lomax, Pete Seeger, and Butch Hawes).
Blue Mountain Lake; Tom Moore in the Days of '49; Montcalm and Wolfe.

Frank Warner is one of the best ballad collectors as well as one of the outstanding ballad singers in the country. He has gone directly to the folk for his material and he sings his songs just as they do—word for word, quaver for quaver.

54. Josh White—*Folk Songs*—Asch #358.
Joshua Fit the Battle of Jericho.

Josh White learned his songs on the road when he was a little boy, as he led blind Negro minstrels from town to town. His guitar style and his songs are genuine and full of great feeling.

55. ——— *Ballads and Blues*—Decca #A 447.
John Henry; Sometime.

This is the best available album of Josh White. Another one will be released by the time this book has appeared.

56. ——— *Ballads and Blues, II*—Decca #A-611.

Josh White's repertory of Anglo-American lyric songs, plus one fine blues.

57. ——— *Strange Fruit* — Keynote #125. John Henry, Sweet Thing.

A fine album of Josh in his best period.

58. ———, Dick Bennett, Eithne Golden, George Edwards, Aino Karelia, Adolf Stark—*Ballads*—Stinson #560.

Ballads from Ireland, Finland, Spain, Portugal, New York State and the South, beautifully sung and recorded. The two by Edwards are the only available sides of traditional ballads from the North East.

Index of Explanatory Material

Index of Song Titles and First Lines

(For a listing of recorded versions of the songs in this book see Appendix III)